VOLUME 1

Scholastic LITERACY PLACE

Printed in the U.S.A.
ISBN 0-590-59261-0
3 4 5 6 7 8 9 10 24 02 01 00 99 98 97

CHAPTER BY CHAPTER

SECTION 1: READY, SET, GROW

SOURCE Novel
Class-Picture-Taking Day 10
by Pam Conrad
illustrated by Joel Spector
from *Staying Nine*

SOURCE Reference Book
The Inside Story: Science Facts About Growing Up 22
from *Big Science*

SOURCE Personal Anecdotes
Tales of a Fourth Grade Rat 24
told by Jerry Spinelli

MENTOR Author
Jerry Spinelli 30

SECTION 2: WITH A LITTLE HELP

SOURCE Picture Book
The Rag Coat 40
by Lauren Mills

SOURCE Novel
***from* The Pool Party** 54
by Gary Soto
illustrated by Tony de Luz

SOURCE Letters
***from* Penny Pollard's Guide to Modern Manners** 62
by Robin Klein

SECTION 3: A POCKETFUL OF MEMORIES

SOURCE Short Stories
The President's Wife 70
by Eleanora E. Tate
illustrated by Eric Velasquez
from *Front Porch Stories*

SOURCE News Magazine
Barbara Bush: First Lady of Literacy 82
from *Scholastic News*

SOURCE Memoirs
Under the Back Porch 84
by Virginia Hamilton
illustrated by Pat Cummings
from *Home*

SOURCE Photo Biography
***from* Cherokee Summer** 86
by Diane Hoyt-Goldsmith
photographed by Lawrence Migdale

SOURCE Personal Narrative
***from* Family Pictures** 100
by Carmen Lomas Garza

WORKSHOP 1

How to Create a Table of Contents 34

WORKSHOP 2

How to Make a Book Jacket 64

PROJECT

How to Write a Personal Narrative 106

Glossary 112
Authors & Illustrators 116
Books & Media 118

UNIT 2

What an Idea!

Section 1: New and Improved

SOURCE Time Line
Amazing Inventions & Discoveries 10

SOURCE Picture Book
A Piece of String Is a Wonderful Thing 14
by Judy Hindley
illustrated by Margaret Chamberlain

SOURCE Inventor's Handbook
The Invention of Sneakers 32
by Steven Caney
from *Steven Caney's Invention Book*

MENTOR Inventor
Julie Lewis 40

WORKSHOP 1
How to Write a Product Improvement Letter 44

Section 2: Inventors at Work

SOURCE Classic Fiction
The Doughnuts 50
by Robert McCloskey
from *Homer Price*

SOURCE Nonfiction
***from* Mistakes That Worked** 68
by Charlotte Foltz Jones
illustrated by John O'Brien

SOURCE Poetry Collection
The Inventor Thinks Up Helicopters 76
by Patricia Hubbell
illustrated by Ju-Hong Chen
from *The Tigers Brought Pink Lemonade*

WORKSHOP 2
How to Make an Invention Diagram 78

Section 3: Fast Forward

SOURCE Novel
The Star Ship 84
by Betsy Byars
illustrated by Lisa Adams
from *The Computer Nut*

SOURCE News Magazine
The First Computers 94
by Richard Chevat
illustrated by Dan Picasso
from *Scholastic News*

SOURCE Short Story Collection
Lafff 100
by Lensey Namioka
illustrated by Tim Lee
from *Within Reach*
edited by Donald R. Gallo

SOURCE Magazine
Things to Come 120
by Curtis Slepian
illustrated by Nathan Jarvis
from *3•2•1 Contact*

PROJECT
How to Market Your Invention 122

Glossary 128
Authors & Illustrators 132
Books & Media 134

DISCOVERY TEAMS

OFF TO DISCOVERY

SOURCE Picture Book
The Lost Lake 10
by Allen Say

SOURCE Magazine
Pushing the Limits 24
by Ross Bankson
from *National Geographic World*

SOURCE Novel
***from* Sarah, Plain and Tall** 30
by Patricia MacLachlan
illustrated by Marni Backer

DARING DESTINATIONS

SOURCE Biography
All the Way There 54
by Sean Dolan
from *Matthew Henson: Arctic Explorer*

SOURCE Magazine
Standing Up for Antarctica 64
from *National Geographic World*

MENTOR Astronaut
Dr. Mae Jemison 66

SOURCE Science Fiction
The Best New Thing 70
by Isaac Asimov
illustrated by Tom Leonard

SCIENCE SEARCH

SOURCE Picture Book
The Great Kapok Tree 90
by Lynne Cherry

SOURCE Science Nonfiction
***from* The Desert Beneath the Sea** 104
by Ann McGovern and Eugenie Clark
illustrated by Craig Phillips

SOURCE Article
The Jason Project: Passport to Adventure 116

WORKSHOP 1

How to Make an Exploration Map 48

WORKSHOP 2

How to Create a Team Profile 84

PROJECT

How to Create a Multimedia Presentation . 122

Glossary 128
Authors & Illustrators 132
Books & Media 134

UNIT
1

CHAPTER BY CHAPTER
CARMEN LOMAS GARZA

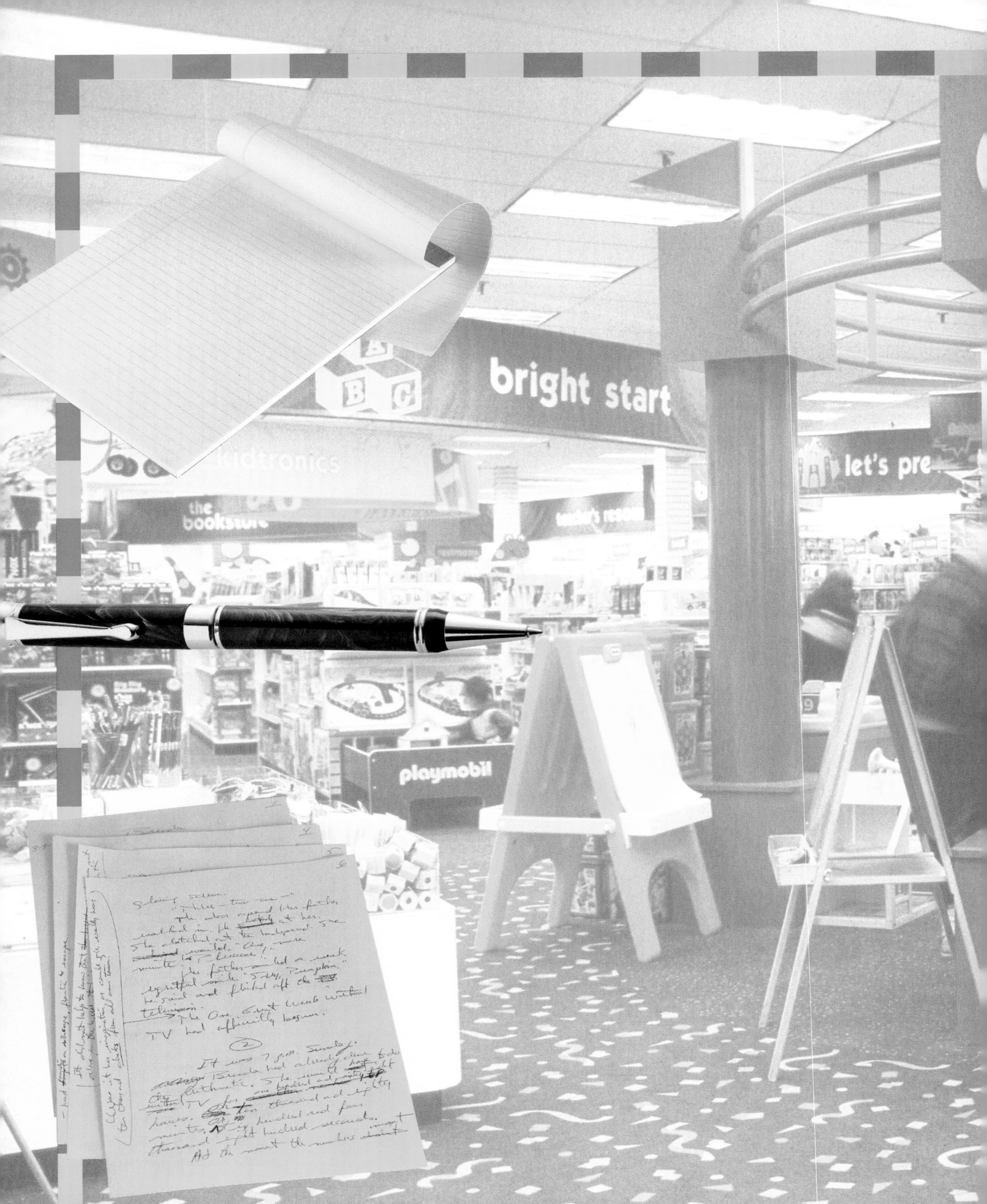
bright start
kidtronics
the bookstore
let's pre
playmobil

Browse

in a Bookstore

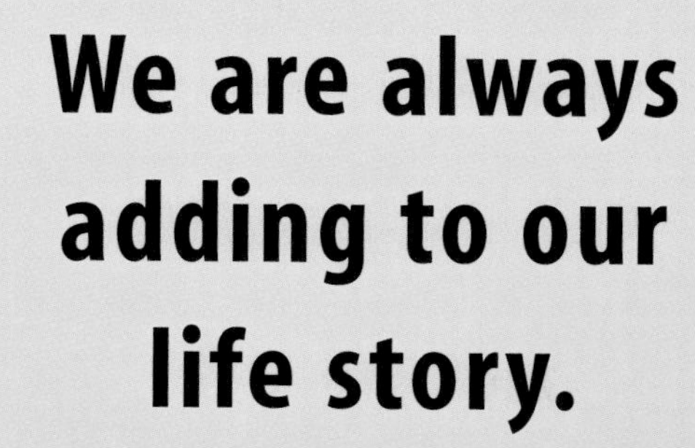

We are always adding to our life story.

Ready, Set, Grow

We have many thoughts about growing up.

SOURCE **Novel**

Class-Picture-Taking Day 10

by Pam Conrad
illustrated by Joel Spector

from *Staying Nine*

SOURCE **Reference Book**

The Inside Story: Science Facts About Growing Up 22

from *Big Science*

SOURCE **Personal Anecdotes**

Tales of a Fourth Grade Rat 24

told by Jerry Spinelli

MENTOR **Author**

Jerry Spinelli 30

WORKSHOP 1

How to Create a Table of Contents 34

Contents

Starting-point
Papa and Mama 13
Kindergarten, 1922-3 21

Llandaff Cathedral School, 1923-5 (age 7-9)
The Bicycle and the Sweet Shop ....
The Great Mouse Plot ....

With a Little Help

We can look to older people for help.

SOURCE **Picture Book**

The Rag Coat 40

by Lauren Mills

SOURCE **Novel**

from **The Pool Party** 54

by Gary Soto
illustrated by Tony De Luz

SOURCE **Letters**

from **Penny Pollard's Guide to Modern Manners** 62

by Robin Klein

WORKSHOP 2

How to Make a Book Jacket 64

When I Was Nine
by James Stevenson

A Pocketful of Memories

Families and traditions are an important part of who we are.

SOURCE **Short Stories**

The President's Wife 70
by Eleanora E. Tate
illustrated by
Eric Velasquez

from
Front Porch Stories

SOURCE **News Magazine**

Barbara Bush: First Lady of Literacy 82
from *Scholastic News*

SOURCE **Memoirs**

Under the Back Porch 84
by Virginia Hamilton
illustrated by Pat Cummings

from *Home*

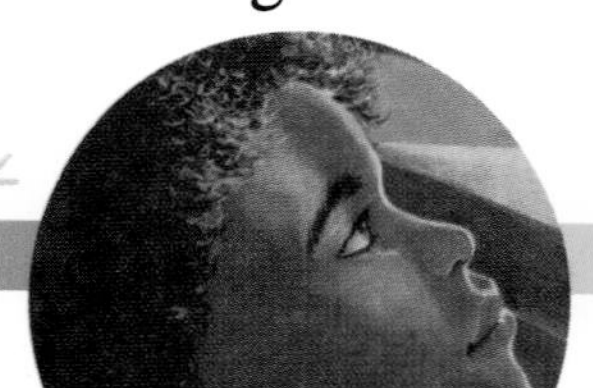

SOURCE **Photo Biography**

from **Cherokee Summer** 86
by Diane Hoyt-Goldsmith
photographed by Lawrence Migdale

SOURCE **Personal Narrative**

from **Family Pictures** 100
by Carmen Lomas Garza

PROJECT

How to Write a Personal Narrative 106

Glossary 112

Authors & Illustrators 116

Books & Media 118

Trade Books

The following books accompany this *Chapter by Chapter* SourceBook.

Humorous Fiction

Fourth Grade Rats

by Jerry Spinelli
illustrated by
Paul Casale

Biography

The Last Princess

by Fay Stanley
illustrated by
Diane Stanley

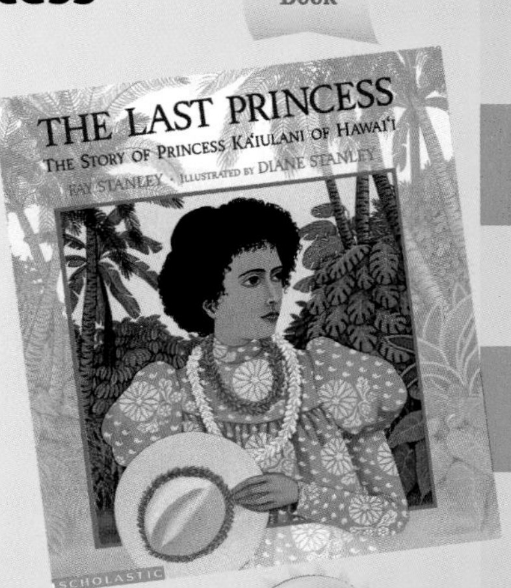

Realistic Fiction

My Name Is María Isabel

by Alma
Flor Ada
illustrated by
K. Dyble
Thompson

Realistic Fiction

Stealing Home

by Mary Stolz

Sportsmanship
Respect
Courage
Kindness
Honest
Aa Bb Cc Dd Ee Ff Gg Hh Ii Jj Kk Ll
Mm Nn Oo Pp Qq Rr Ss Tt Uu Vv Ww Xx Yy Zz
1933
APRIL
BALLOT BOX
365 ÷ 12 = 30.41
KNOWLEDGE IS THE KEY TO FULFILLMENT
KNEW - NEW
KNOW - NO
SEE - SEA
BLEW - BLUE
WE - WEE
125 ÷ 6 = 20.8
97 ÷ 3 = 32.3
834 ÷ 4 = 208.5
213 ÷ 22 = 9.68
767 ÷ 7 = 109.57

We have many thoughts about growing up.

Ready, Set, Grow

Meet a girl who wants to stay nine forever. Then learn how fast your bones can grow.

Find out what fourth grade was like for author Jerry Spinelli.

Visit Jerry Spinelli at home and meet his pet chinchilla, Chi-Chi.

Workshop 1

Create a Table of Contents for your life story.

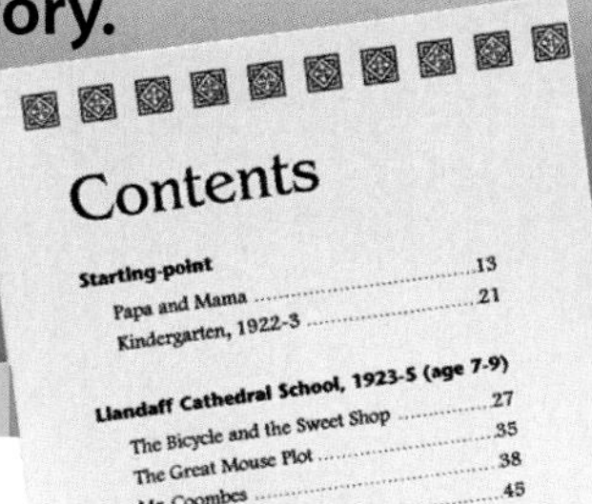

Contents

Starting-point 13
Papa and Mama 21
Kindergarten, 1922-3

Llandaff Cathedral School, 1923-5 (age 7-9) 27
The Bicycle and the Sweet Shop 35
The Great Mouse Plot 38
Mr. Coombes 45
Mrs. Pratchett's Revenge 51
Going to Norway 57

SOURCE

Pam Conrad
STAYING NINE
Illustrated By Mike Wimmer

Novel

from STAYING NINE

CLASS-PICTURE-TAKING DAY

By
Pam Conrad

Illustrated by
Joel Spector

AWARD WINNING Author

Heather likes being nine. She's worried about turning ten in another week—so worried that she wants time to stand still. Today is class-picture-taking day, and Heather has decided to wear the same clothes that she wore for last year's picture. The only problem is that she and her friend Dorelle had planned to wear identical outfits.

Heather put the chewable vitamin right on the side of her mouth, over the tooth that was loose, and she bit hard, making it pinch.

"But I thought you and Dorelle were going to wear the same outfits," her mother was saying. "Didn't you say you wanted to look like twins? Same clothes? Same hairdo?"

Heather took a mouthful of scrambled eggs. "I changed my mind," she said.

"But Heather, those clothes have been in your closet for months. I can't remember the last time you wore them. And they look all wrinkled, like you slept in them!"

"These clothes fit me just fine. I haven't worn them in a while, but I haven't grown at all since the last time. It's what I want to wear." Heather kept eating, hoping her mother wouldn't force her to change and ruin everything.

"What about Dorelle?" her mother asked, taking a different view. "Isn't she expecting you to wear—"

"Ma!" Sam looked up suddenly from her homework notes that were spread out across the breakfast table, scattering cereal onto the floor. "You have to let her wear what she feels good in," she said. "This is a sign of growing interference."

"I think you mean growing *independence*," Mrs. Fitz said, pouring herself a cup of coffee and tapping meaningfully on the dictionary that was propped up in front of Sam. Then she turned back to Heather with a puzzled expression. "Well, I guess it *is* up to you, dear. It's just I think it's silly to wear old clothes to have your picture taken, especially when you already promised somebody—"

“No, Ma, it’s growing *interference*,” Sam said, pointing to a page in the dictionary. “It says here, ‘Interference: taking part in other people’s affairs without invitation.’ ”

Heather smiled a little and kept her head down.

“Well, excuse me!” their mother said, narrowing her eyes at Sam. “If I get in the way around here, you’ll let me know, won’t you?”

“No problem,” Sam answered as she got up, stacking her books and taking a last drink of her juice. “You will be *notarized* if you get in the way.”

“Notified,” Mrs. Fitz corrected, clearing off the table brusquely. “Now both of you get out of here, or you’ll be late for the halls of academia.”

“Halls of academia?” Sam stared at her mother.

“Look it up,” Mrs. Fitz said in a clipped voice. “Not now!” she fussed, when Sam sat down again. Mrs. Fitz put the dictionary back in the pile and eased Sam toward the door. “Come on, Heather,” she added. “It’s time to pack up and leave. You don’t want to be late for the photographer.”

It was a cold, gray day, and Heather walked along quickly with her backpack over her shoulders and her hands thrust into her pockets.

She was feeling pretty good, satisfied with herself and content. In a word, she was feeling nine. She was holding on to nine without any problem at all. No problem, that is, until she got to the school yard and saw Dorelle waiting for her at the front gate.

"I thought you'd *never* get here," Dorelle called, waving her hand, and then her wave stopped in midair. Her smile vanished. "Your hair! You said you'd wear it loose today. You said you'd just let it be curly."

Heather smoothed her hand along the side of her head, pushing any stray strands back toward her ponytail. She felt a little uneasy. "I changed my mind, and it was late by the time I decided, so I couldn't call you."

"What do you mean you changed your mind?" Dorelle's face looked angry and tight. Her hair wasn't naturally curly like Heather's, and Heather could tell Dorelle's mother had probably set it the night before. It curled all over the place, framing her squinting eyes and her furious mouth.

Heather looked off into the distance, staring at the kids who were chasing each other across the school yard. She shrugged. She didn't know what to say. She didn't know how to explain it. After all, Dorelle had turned ten a few months ago. She'd had a skating party, and Dorelle had even whispered to Heather that she almost felt like a teenager now that she had two digits in her age. How do you explain staying nine and not changing to someone like that? Heather shrugged and looked back at her friend. "I don't know. I just changed my mind. I decided to wear the same thing I wore for last year's picture."

Dorelle's mouth fell open. "The same thing? You're wearing the same thing, the exact same thing as *last* year?"

Heather nodded. It still didn't sound at all stupid to her. What was the big deal?

Dorelle's face grew small and mean. "I should have been twins with Lauren," she said slowly. "I never should have been twins with you!" And at that Dorelle turned and walked away from Heather. Heather could see her dark skirt, and her white tights, the gray shoes, and the little pink barrette in her hair.

I guess I should have called, she thought with an awful sinking feeling inside; and letting the backpack slide down her arms, she grabbed the straps with her hands. The school bell rang and she headed for her classroom.

Mrs. Kleintoch was waiting at the door, and Heather had to look at her twice. Was it really Mrs. Kleintoch? She had blue eye shadow on her lids and a sparkly earring showing through her hair beneath each ear. She patted Heather's shoulder as she passed, and Heather noticed the red nail polish and the unfamiliar perfume.

"Let's hurry, people," she was saying. "We have a lot to do today, and we're the first class to be photographed, so we need to get our things in order and line up right away."

Everyone was beginning to line up, and Heather looked around. Dorelle was whispering to Lauren over by the pencil sharpener. Heather looked away. And then she saw Sonya. Sonya's desk was right next to Heather's, and she usually wore her hair kind of plain, but today she had about three hundred little braids all over her head, and at the end of each braid was a tiny bead.

"Oh, your hair is beautiful!" Heather said, delicately touching the beads with her fingers and seeing them clink against each other.

Sonya smiled broadly. "My mother said I could wear my hair like this when I was ten years old, for my ten-year-old picture. She would never do it before. Said it was too much trouble to do on someone so little, but now I'm old enough."

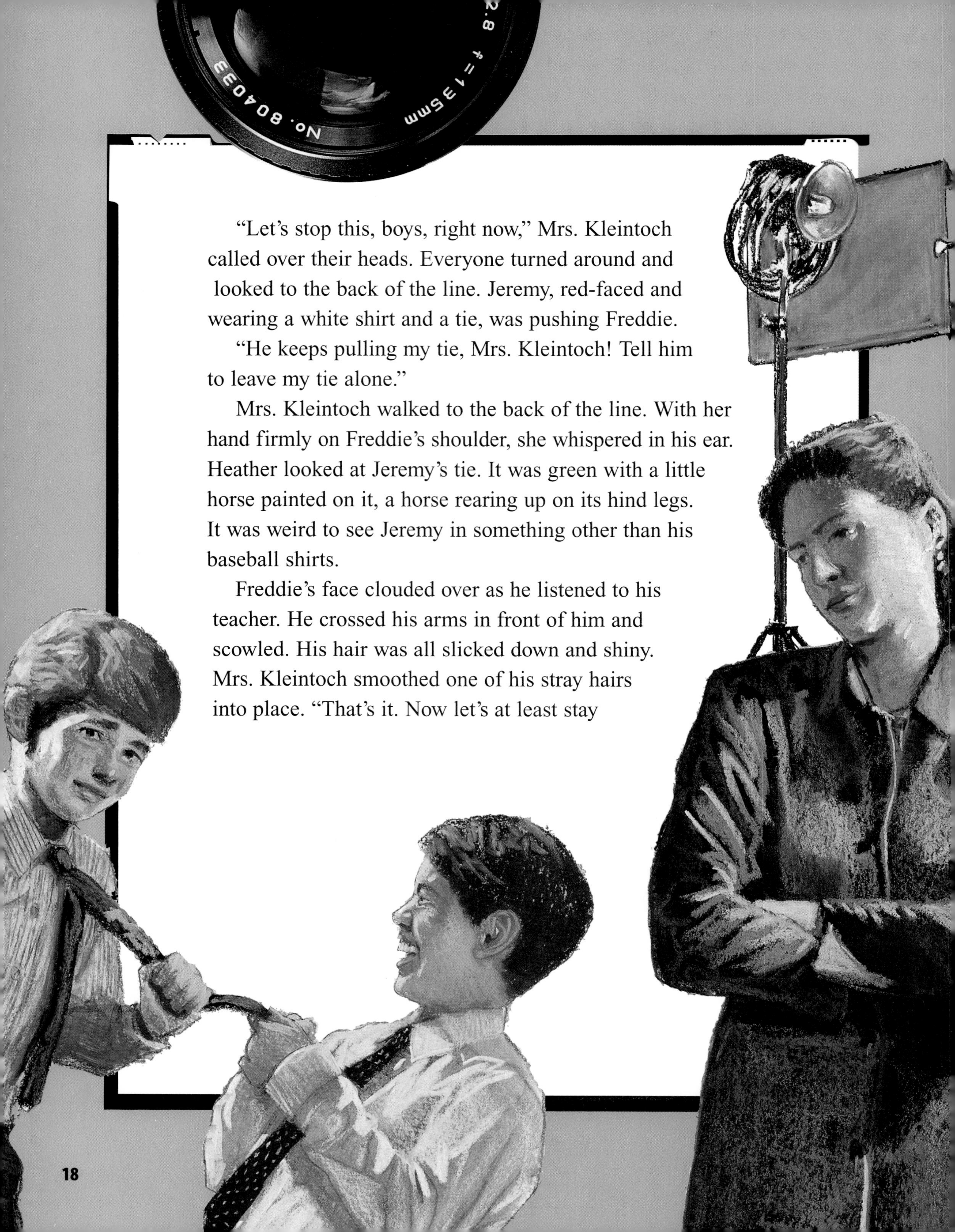

"Let's stop this, boys, right now," Mrs. Kleintoch called over their heads. Everyone turned around and looked to the back of the line. Jeremy, red-faced and wearing a white shirt and a tie, was pushing Freddie.

"He keeps pulling my tie, Mrs. Kleintoch! Tell him to leave my tie alone."

Mrs. Kleintoch walked to the back of the line. With her hand firmly on Freddie's shoulder, she whispered in his ear. Heather looked at Jeremy's tie. It was green with a little horse painted on it, a horse rearing up on its hind legs. It was weird to see Jeremy in something other than his baseball shirts.

Freddie's face clouded over as he listened to his teacher. He crossed his arms in front of him and scowled. His hair was all slicked down and shiny. Mrs. Kleintoch smoothed one of his stray hairs into place. "That's it. Now let's at least stay

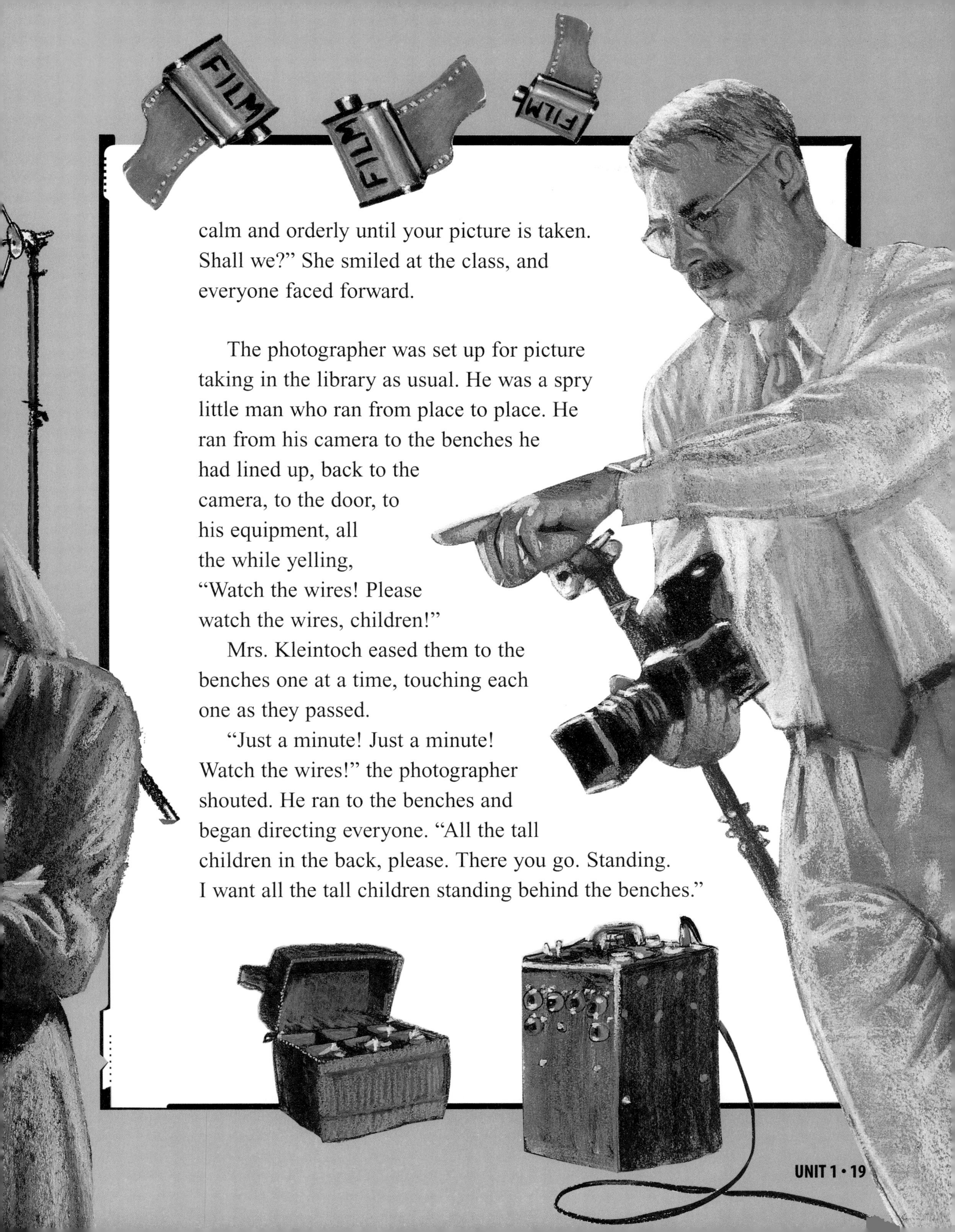

calm and orderly until your picture is taken. Shall we?" She smiled at the class, and everyone faced forward.

The photographer was set up for picture taking in the library as usual. He was a spry little man who ran from place to place. He ran from his camera to the benches he had lined up, back to the camera, to the door, to his equipment, all the while yelling, "Watch the wires! Please watch the wires, children!"

Mrs. Kleintoch eased them to the benches one at a time, touching each one as they passed.

"Just a minute! Just a minute! Watch the wires!" the photographer shouted. He ran to the benches and began directing everyone. "All the tall children in the back, please. There you go. Standing. I want all the tall children standing behind the benches."

He directed and pointed and poked until the whole class was jammed together either behind or on the benches. Heather sat on the first bench next to Sonya. With one foot she felt to make sure her one sock was down, and she pulled the other one up tight.

The photographer peered into his camera at them, and Heather smiled. "Just a minute," he said. "We need some adjustments." First he would peer in the camera and then he would look around at them. "You in the green shirt," he'd say. "Change places with the boy at the end. That's better. That's good. Now you, with the glasses, come in closer."

Heather yawned and just sat there. She glanced at Sonya's clinking beads.

"And you. You in the red sweater."

She wondered how Sonya's mother made such tiny braids like that.

"Heather!" the whole class shouted at once.

Heather was startled.

"Yes, you," the photographer said. "You in the red sweater, I want you to stand in the back next to the boy with the tie."

"But I'm short," she said.

"You're taller than everyone on the bench," he told her, motioning with his arm where to go.

Heather took her place at the end of the back row. She couldn't believe it. Standing in the back row! She wasn't tall enough for the back row, and nobody would see her socks from back here.

The photographer ran to his camera and peered inside once again. “Beautiful,” he said. “Now I want everyone to say ‘Frank Sinatra.’ ”

There was dead silence except for Mrs. Kleintoch, who sang right out. “Frank Sinatra.”

And when everyone laughed, the photographer snapped the picture.

THE INSIDE STORY:

How much taller are you this year than last year? You can thank your bones for those extra inches. You're growing taller because your bones are growing longer. These X rays show how the bones in a person's hand grow. How are the X rays different?

INFANT

At first, your tiny skeleton was made of a tough, rubbery material called *cartilage*. (Your nose and your ear are still made of cartilage.) Slowly, strong, hard bone began to replace cartilage in your skeleton. The bright white parts in this X ray show where bone has begun to grow.

2-YEAR-OLD

Just how do your bones grow? At the ends of a bone are areas called *growth plates*. These plates keep forming new cartilage which makes the bone longer. Then bone cells move in to replace the cartilage and make it harder.

SCIENCE FACTS ABOUT GROWING UP

5-YEAR-OLD

By age 5, more bones in the hand have formed. Others are still growing longer. As bones grow, things happen inside them, too. Slowly a hole forms inside the bone. *Bone marrow* fills this hole. That's where your body makes blood and stores fat.

12-YEAR-OLD

By age 12, almost all of the 30 bones in the hand are in place. The bones will keep growing longer until about age 18. Some cartilage will stay at the ends of the bones near the joints. This makes a cushion between the bones.

SOURCE

Personal Anecdotes

Jerry Spinelli's Tales of a Fourth Grade Rat

Jerry Spinelli

In *Fourth Grade Rats* Jerry Spinelli writes about a boy who isn't sure he's ready for the fourth grade. Spinelli admits he's had some growing pains of his own. Here, the author tells some tales from his own life as a fourth grade rat.

Fourth Grade Heartache

I was in fourth grade when Judy Brooks broke up with me. Judy was my neighbor. She lived up the street at 718 George Street in Norristown, Pennsylvania, where I grew up. As a matter of fact, George Street is Oriole Street in a few of my books, and Norristown is the town of Two Mills in *Maniac Magee, Dump Days,* and *The Bathwater Gang.*

Judy and I were an item for about four years. Then in the fourth grade she informed me that she hated all boys—and that included me. Well, I told her that if that was the case, then I hated all girls. For the next year or two I was into a pretty severe girl-hating stage. By the way, in *Fourth Grade Rats* the girl in the book that the boy really likes is named Judy Billings. She just happens to have the same first name and same initials as Judy Brooks!

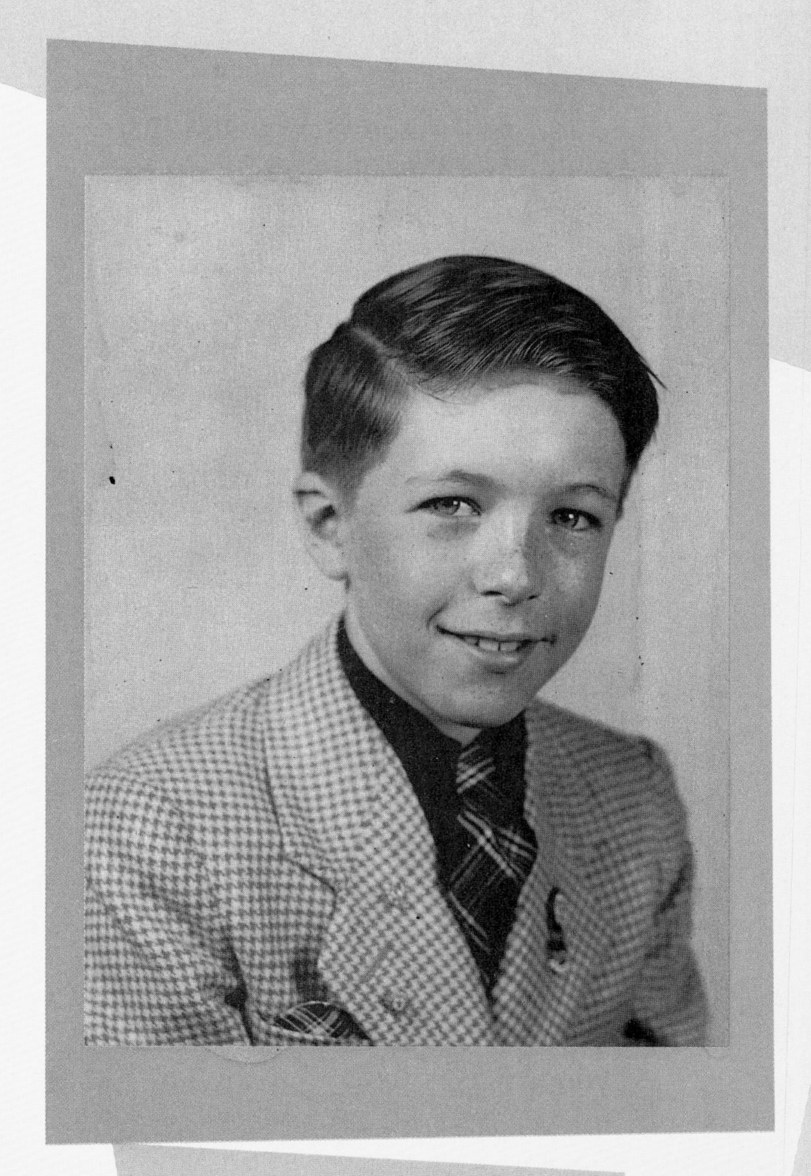

This is me in fourth grade, the year Judy Brooks broke up with me. Can you imagine any girl dumping such a cute little face?

Neighbors

On summer evenings my father and I would go out after dinner and toss a baseball because I wanted to be a Major League shortstop. The Seeton's house was perpendicular to ours—their dining room windows faced our backyard. One evening, my father and I were throwing the ball, and my aim wasn't too accurate. I threw the ball over my father's head right through the Seeton's dining room window. I was a real coward at times like that, so it was up to my father to tell the Seetons what had happened, and offer to pay for it.

After a week or so, the window was fixed. But then a couple of days later my father and I were playing catch again and I did the same thing! It's just unbelievable—same window, same baseball—and my father took care of it again. And the most amazing thing about the whole episode was that none of the Seetons ever said anything about it. Mr. Seeton may have been fuming behind the walls of his own house, but he never said anything to me. I just got off scott free—all I had to deal with was my own conscience.

Overnight Fright

I had two best friends in the fourth grade—Roger Adelman and Johnny Seeton, and I have a little story about each of those friends. My Roger Adelman story makes me cringe, even today, to think of what a baby I was. You see, I was never one to go to camp for weeks at a time or even overnight. I went to YMCA day camp, but I never stayed overnight. To me that seemed too adult. But Roger Adelman went away to Boy Scout camp for a week or two at a time.

Even though I wasn't the type to do this, somehow I ended up with a pup tent. I put it up in my yard and the next thing I knew, I was inviting Roger Adelman to come down and sleep over. So he came down and my mother, as mothers will do, had all kinds of comforts—blankets and snacks and some kind of lantern light. So we had our snacks and chatted and played cards, and then turned out the light and lay down in the pup tent. Roger went to sleep immediately like a veteran Boy Scout. But I was wide awake, nervous and spooked for about an hour or so. Finally, I shook Roger's shoulder to tell him that I had to go back in the house. My last memory is of me picking up my blanket and heading in the back door of my house while Roger trudged off the three or four blocks to his house.

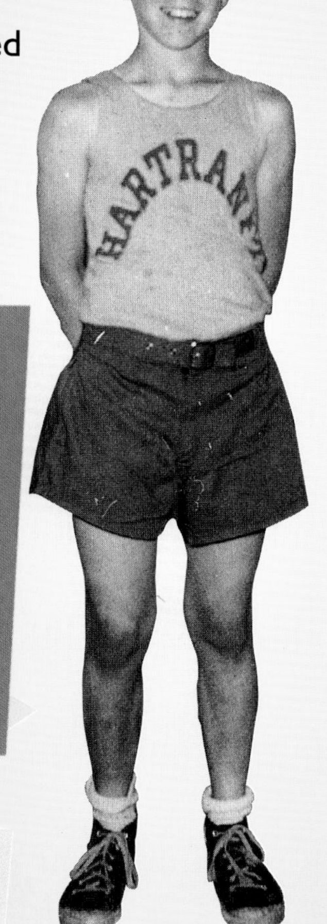

You are looking at the 1953 50-yard dash champion of the Norristown, Pennsylvania, grade schools. Wisely, I retired from track after that.

Adventure at the Creek

Another day I was down at the creek with Johnny Seeton. I had been standing in the water, which was only about a foot deep. When I came up out of the creek I saw that there were leeches—what we used to call bloodsuckers—all over my shins. Well, I knew what to do in case of rattlesnake bite from reading books and watching movies. You'd just get out your old trusty knife, make an X-shaped cut at the bite mark, and suck out the poison. So I figured, well, I guess you do something similar for leeches. I must have thought they were poisonous. So I brushed the leeches off my legs—I did not have the nerve to start making cuts—and I told Johnny to start sucking. The last thing I remember was a kid with horror in his eyes turning and running and racing up the steep bank, and that was the last of Johnny that I saw that afternoon. And I went with wet shins and bare feet to my house wondering if I was going to die in a few days because my friend wouldn't suck out the poison.

A Happy Ending

I want to end by saying that in spite of some unpleasant memories, fourth grade wasn't all bad. In fact, one of the best things I remember from that time is my teacher, Miss Coleman. As the years go by, I tend to appreciate her more and more. That's why I dedicated my book *Fourth Grade Rats* to her.

Here I am having lunch at a school I visited. As you can see, I'll do anything for a free lunch—even eat with kids.

I had <u>two</u> best friends in the fourth grade. Here's a poem I wrote about the situation.

Stuck

In fourth grade
for some reason we had
this test
and one of the questions was:
<u>Who is your best friend?</u>
I was really stuck
because I could not decide
between Roger Adelman
who was in my class
and Johnny Seeton
who was my neighbor.
Surely the one I didn't choose
would be offended.
The answer space
was still a blank
when the teacher called
for papers.
Quickly,
I wrote in both names.
I never found out
how well I did.

—Jerry Spinelli

MENTOR

Jerry Spinelli

Author

Authors are *full* of the *"write"* stuff.

As an author of children's books, Jerry Spinelli is so successful that writing is his full-time job. But he never thought much about writing when he was growing up. "My dream was to play baseball. I was going to be a shortstop in the major leagues."

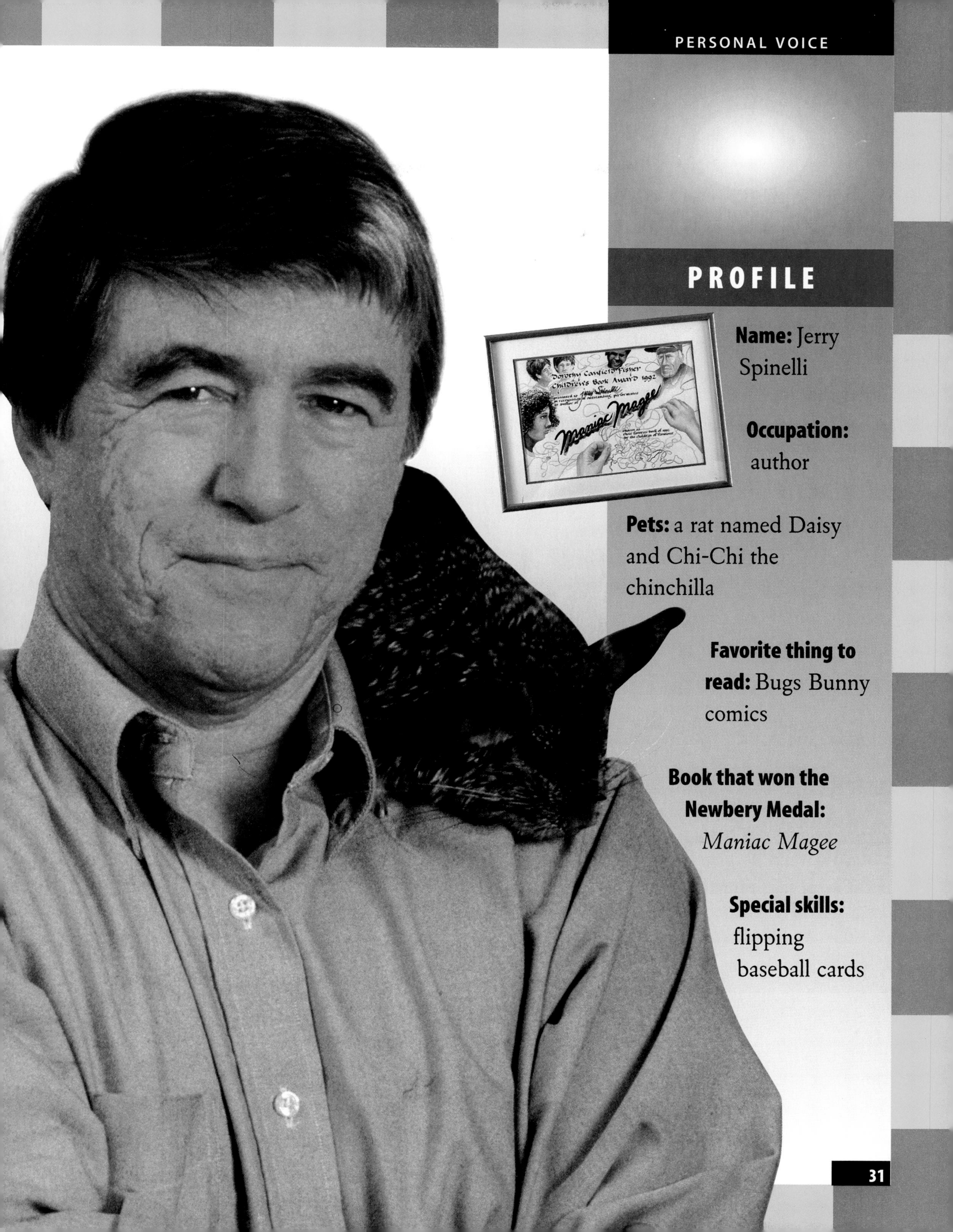

PROFILE

Name: Jerry Spinelli

Occupation: author

Pets: a rat named Daisy and Chi-Chi the chinchilla

Favorite thing to read: Bugs Bunny comics

Book that won the Newbery Medal: *Maniac Magee*

Special skills: flipping baseball cards

QUESTIONS
for Jerry Spinelli

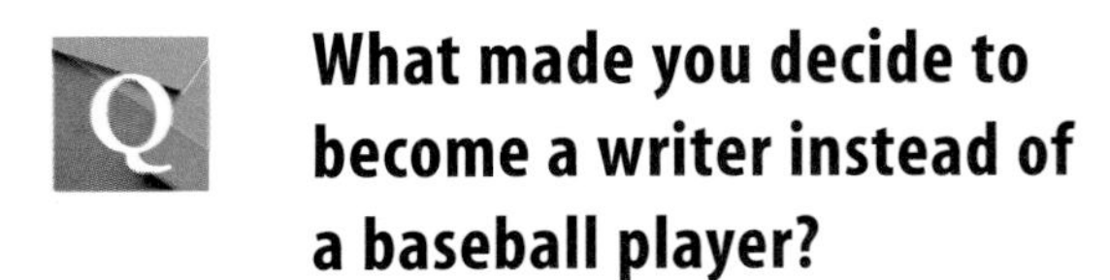

Q What made you decide to become a writer instead of a baseball player?

A When I was sixteen my high school football team won a big game. I was so excited—I wrote a poem about it. A local newspaper published the poem. That's when I decided to become a writer.

Q And how did you become a writer?

A Well, first I became a grown-up. And I thought, *Now on to the important stuff!* So I tried writing grown-up novels about important stuff. But nobody wanted to publish them.

Q What made you decide to try children's books?

A I married my wife Eileen, a writer who already had five kids. One night, one of our little angels snuck into the refrigerator and swiped a piece of fried chicken I was saving for lunch. When I discovered the chicken was gone, I wrote about it. That piece of writing became my first published novel, *Space Station Seventh Grade*. At the time I had no idea I was going to write a children's book.

Do you have a regular writing schedule?

I usually write in the morning from 10:00 to noon. Then after dinner, I write some more from 9:00 to midnight. I like working at night.

Are your childhood memories important to your writing?

When I was growing up, I didn't think my childhood was special. It was full of kid stuff: bike riding, flipping baseball cards, and catching poison ivy. It wasn't until I started writing about it that I realized what an adventure it had been!

What do you like best about your job?

A The best part is being able to make a living from what I do. I was able to quit my job as an editor of a magazine. I love writing, and the fact that I get paid for it is an added bonus.

Jerry Spinelli's Tips for Young Writers

1. **Subject Matter: See how successful authors write for themselves as well as for their audience.**
2. **Trust Your Ideas: Remember to listen to your ideas.**
3. **Keep Writing: Whether playing the piano, baseball, or writing, the more you do something, the more you will improve. Have fun with it!**

WORKSHOP 1

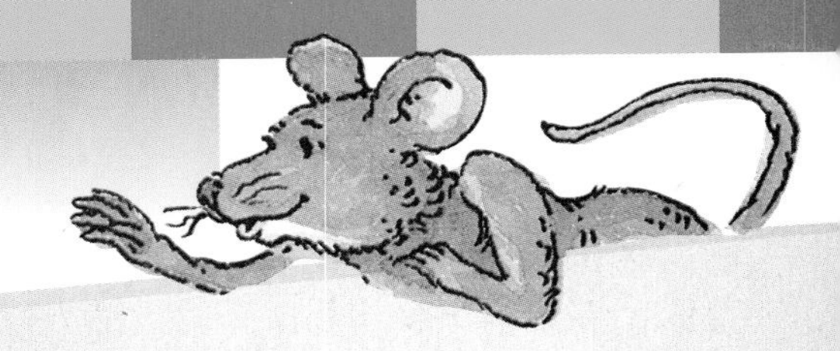

How to Create a Table of Contents

The title of the chapter describes what the chapter is about.

When you pick up a book, how can you tell what the story is about? One way is to read the Table of Contents.

What is a Table of Contents? The Table of Contents is a list of the chapter titles you will find in a book. Sometimes, you can tell if you will like a book just by reading the titles of the chapters. Chapters with interesting titles will grab the reader's attention.

Contents

The word *Contents* goes at the top of the page.

Starting-point

Papa and Mama 13
Kindergarten, 1922-3 21

Llandaff Cathedral School, 1923-5 (age 7-9)

The Bicycle and the Sweet Shop 27
The Great Mouse Plot 35
Mr. Coombes 38
Mrs. Pratchett's Revenge 45
Going to Norway 51
The Magic Island 57
A Visit to the Doctor 64

St. Peter's, 1925-9 (age 9-13)

First Day 69
Writing Home 74
The Matron 79
Homesickness 86
A Drive in the Motor-car 91

The page number gives the page on which the chapter begins.

One way to organize chapters is by putting them in the order that the events happened.

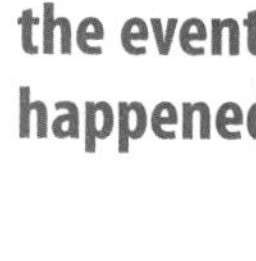
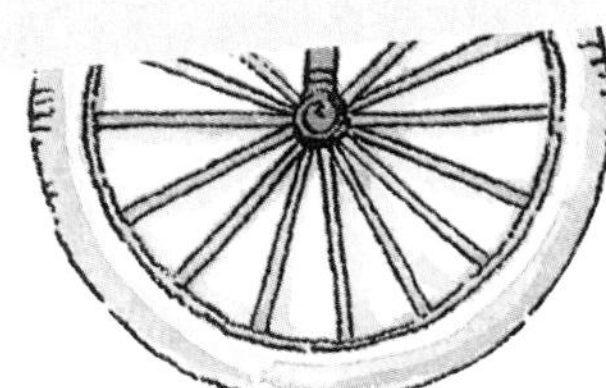

1 Choose Events From Your Life

List all the important events you can remember from your life. Here are some ideas to help get you started. Did you ever take a fun trip? make a new friend? win an award? move to another city? Are there photographs of special moments from your life? Make a list of events, and choose at least six of your favorite ones. These will be the chapters in your Table of Contents.

2 Create Chapter Titles

Once you have your list of possible chapters, the next step is to give them titles. Keep in mind that a title gives the reader an idea of what that chapter is about. Look at your list of events, and think about how each one makes you feel. If one of the events is funny, give it a funny title. Use lots of action words and descriptive details to add life to your titles.

3 Organize Your Table of Contents

After choosing your chapter titles, think about how to organize them in your Table of Contents. You could list them in chronological order, or divide them into different categories. One chapter might be about family, another about sports, and still another about school.

Tip Try reading your titles to some friends and ask them what they think the chapters will be about.

4 Put It All Together

Make up a title for your book and write it at the top of the page. Underneath the title write *Table of Contents,* then list your chapter titles. Finish your Table of Contents by adding made-up page numbers. Then share your work with your classmates.

FIRST PLACE

If You Are Using a Computer . . .

Write a short journal entry for each event that you want to include in your Table of Contents. Make up a title for each entry, and then print them out. After looking at them, decide on their order, and use the titles to write your Table of Contents.

THINK

Imagine that you are ten years older. What new chapter titles might you add to your Table of Contents?

Jerry Spinelli
Author

SECTION 2

We can look to older people for help.

With a Little Help

Meet an Appalachian girl who teaches her classmates about courage.

Laugh with Rudy as he practices party etiquette with his dad. Then read a humorous advice column.

WORKSHOP 2

Make a book jacket starring *you*.

SOURCE

Picture Book

The Rag Coat

by Lauren Mills

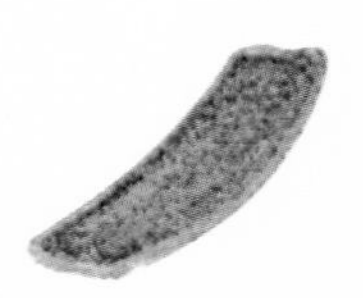

In winter, Papa carried me to church in a burlap feed sack because I didn't have a coat. Mama, Papa, Clemmie, and me—we'd all hitch a ride on Jeremy Miller's hay wagon and huddle under Mama's big quilt. I know Papa loved that quilt, because he said it had all the nice, bright colors of the day in it, and the day was something he hardly ever saw. He worked down in the black coal mines and didn't come up till the sun was gone.

I told Papa it was warmer under that quilt than if I *had* a coat. He always laughed when I said that, and told me, "Minna, you got the right way of thinking. People only need people, and nothing else. Don't you forget that."

Papa got sick with the miner's cough and couldn't work much, so Mama stitched day and night on her quilts to try to make some money.

When I was old enough to start school, I couldn't go. They needed me at home to help Mama. I would card all her quilt stuffing and keep Clemmie's dirty fingers out of all that cotton. I made a doll for myself by stitching up some of Mama's quilt scraps and stuffing cotton inside. I talked to her like she was my friend, because I didn't have any. Mama was too busy for much talk, and when Papa was home he mostly stared out the window.

The summer I was eight, Papa called me over to his rocking chair. I climbed up on his lap and he said, "You're getting big, Minna."

"Too big for laps?" I asked.

"Not too big for mine," he said softly, "but too big to still be at home. It's nearing time you went to school."

I could hardly hold back my smiling just thinking about all the friends I would have. But I didn't want to leave Mama without a helper. "Papa," I said, "I can't go to school. Mama needs me here."

Papa just looked at me real steady and said, "They have books at school, Minna. You can learn things from those books that you can't learn at home."

"But I don't have a coat, Papa," I quietly reminded him.

"Minna," he said, "don't you worry about a coat. I'll think of something." But he never got the chance. Papa died that summer.

Everyone came at once and brought us food. I couldn't figure out how so many people could squeeze into our little cabin, but somehow they managed it. They all said they knew my papa well.

I sat on a stool back by the woodstove with Clemmie on my lap, so no one would step on us.

I couldn't stand it! They all wore black, black like the coal mines that killed my papa. He didn't even like black. He liked all the bright colors of the day. So why were they wearing black, I wondered.

School started in September. Mama said I could go, but I decided not to. I still didn't have a coat to wear, and I knew it was no use starting something I'd have to quit when the weather turned cold.

Other mothers who had children in school came over to quilt with Mama. I called them the Quilting Mothers. That fall they were all working on a pattern called Joseph's Coat of Many Colors. I looked at it and said, "That Joseph sure was lucky to have such a coat. I wish I had one like that."

"Why do you say that, Minna?" Mrs. Miller asked me.

"Because then I could go to school," I said, a little embarrassed that I had mentioned it.

"Well now, Minna," said Mrs. Miller, "I don't know that any of us has a spare coat we could hand down to you, but I'm sure we have some scraps to spare. We could piece them together, and you'd have a coat like Joseph's after all." Mrs. Miller looked around the room, and the other mothers nodded.

Mama quickly protested. "You all need those rags for your own quilts. Don't go giving us things you need yourselves."

They paid no attention to Mama. Mrs. Hunter said, "And we could use feed bags for the inside of the coat."

My eyes filled with tears, but I wasn't embarrassed anymore. I said, "I have a feed sack Papa used to carry me in!" I ran and fetched it. "Will this do?"

Yes, it would do just fine, they told me. Then I thought of something important. "But you need to make quilts to *sell*. You can't take time out to quilt a coat."

"First things first," said Mrs. Miller, and they all repeated it. Mama smiled and shook her head, and I saw tears in her eyes, too.

The very next day I went to school, running most of the way to keep warm and thinking all the while of the coat I would soon have.

The schoolhouse was just one room filled with fourteen children. I had seen most of them at church but never got the chance to talk to them much.

I knew I would love school, even though I was put in the front row with the youngest ones, and Clyde Bradshaw whispered that it was because I was dumb. Then Shane Hunter pulled my braid, and Souci Miller said I asked the teacher too many questions. But our teacher, Miss Campbell, smiled at me and said, "Smart people are those who have asked a lot of questions."

My most favorite thing about school was Sharing Day. Each of us had our own day when we shared something special with the class.

Clyde Bradshaw brought in the watch his grandpa gave him. It still ticked, and he made sure we all heard it.

On her day Lottie showed us the porcelain doll her aunt from New York had sent her. We all thought it was the most beautiful thing ever and wanted to touch it, but Lottie wouldn't let anyone near it. She said, "Nope, it's mine," which made everybody mad.

I knew just what I would show when it was my Sharing Day, but I kept it a secret, and I knew the Quilting Mothers would keep it a secret, too.

Each day I hurried home to see my coat. It was looking like the colors of the fall days—the yellow-golds of the birch leaves, the silvery grays and purples of the sky, the deep greens and browns of the pines, and the rusty reds of the chimney bricks—all the colors Papa would have chosen. I decided to put a piece of his work jacket in there. It just seemed right.

The mothers worked as quickly as they could, but the cold weather was quicker. At recess Souci asked me why I didn't wear a coat. I told her I couldn't jump rope as well with one on. Jumping a lot kept me warm. I was fast becoming the best rope-jumper in the school.

Not last night but the night before
Twenty-four robbers came knocking at my door.

That was my favorite rope tune.

One night when Mama looked sad I told her things could be worse. We could have twenty-four robbers knocking at our door.

She said, "Now, what on earth would they want from *us*, Minna?"

"Oh, Mama, they would want the coat, first thing," I said.

She laughed then, but I was most serious.

Finally my coat was done. It was so beautiful, and the Quilting Mothers had finished it in time for my Sharing Day!

That morning I walked to school looking down at all the different colored pieces of cloth in my coat. All the stories the Quilting Mothers had told me about the rags and who they belonged to, I knew by heart. I had ended up choosing the most worn pieces for my coat because the best stories went with them. I was still looking down and repeating each story to myself when I bumped into Clyde outside the schoolyard.

"Hey, Rag-Coat!" he said, and all the others laughed. Before I knew it, Souci, Lottie, and Clyde were dancing around me singing, "Rag-Coat! Rag-Coat!"

Lottie said, "Look, it's even dirty with soot!" and she poked her finger into my papa's cloth!

Then Souci said, "Hey, Minna, you were better off with *no* coat than with that old, ragged thing."

"Maybe you're right!" I yelled. "If I had *no* coat, then I never would have come to school!" I broke through their circle and ran away from them, far into the woods.

I found an old log and sat on it for a long time, too angry to cry. I just stared across the fields Papa used to gaze at.

"Oh, Papa, I wish you were here," I said, and then I couldn't help but cry. I cried for Papa, and I cried for the Quilting Mothers, who had wasted their time. I was crying so hard I rocked that old log.

Then all at once I stopped because I felt something warm and familiar. The feed bag inside my coat made me feel like Papa's arms were around me again. I could almost hear him say, "Minna, people only need people, and nothing else. Don't you forget that."

I jumped off the log, wiped the tears from my cheeks, and brushed the leaves off my coat. "I won't forget it, Papa," I said, and I headed back to school.

When I walked into the schoolroom, Miss Campbell looked up, surprised. "Why, Minna," she said, "I was told you ran home sick."

Souci jumped up, her face all red. "That's not true, Miss Campbell," she blurted out. "We lied to you. Minna left because we made fun of her old coat."

"I'll tell her, Souci," I said. "It's not an *old* coat. It's a *new* coat."

"But it's just a bunch of old rags," said Lottie.

"It is not just a bunch of old rags!" I said. "My coat is full of stories, stories about everybody here."

They all looked at me, real puzzled.

"Don't you see? These are all *your* rags!" They still seemed puzzled.

So I showed them. "Look, Shane, here is that blanket of yours that your mama's sister gave her the night you were born. The midwife said you wouldn't live but three days because you were so small. But your mama wrapped you up tight in that blanket and put you in a little box by the woodstove. And your papa kept the fire all night for three weeks. Of course, you lived, all right," I said, looking up at Shane. Shane was big. "And you hung on to that blanket for years, until it was nothing but shreds."

"My blanket," he whispered. "I thought I'd *never* see it again." He looked at his old rag like he wanted to touch it.

Then the others began discovering their old, favorite things and crowded around me. They each wanted their story told, and I remembered every one.

I even showed the piece of the woolen jacket Souci had let her calf wear when it was sick. Lottie's rag was a faded piece from the fancy dress her aunt from New York had sent for her seventh birthday. And Clyde had a scrap from the pants that he always wore when he went fishing with his grandpa.

Souci said, "Minna, I sure am sorry we ever said anything bad about your coat."

"Me, too," I heard the others murmur.

"I wouldn't blame you if you didn't let us touch it," Lottie said.

"I wouldn't blame you if you didn't want to be our friend at all!" said Clyde.

"Friends share," I said, and I let them each touch their rag. Then I showed them the feed sack inside my coat and told them how it made me feel my papa's arms again.

Shane put his hand on my shoulder and said, "Minna, I bet you got the warmest coat in school."

"Well, it took a *whole lot of people* to make it warm," I told him, and we all laughed.

FROM

THE POOL PARTY

by Gary Soto

illustrated by Tony De Luz

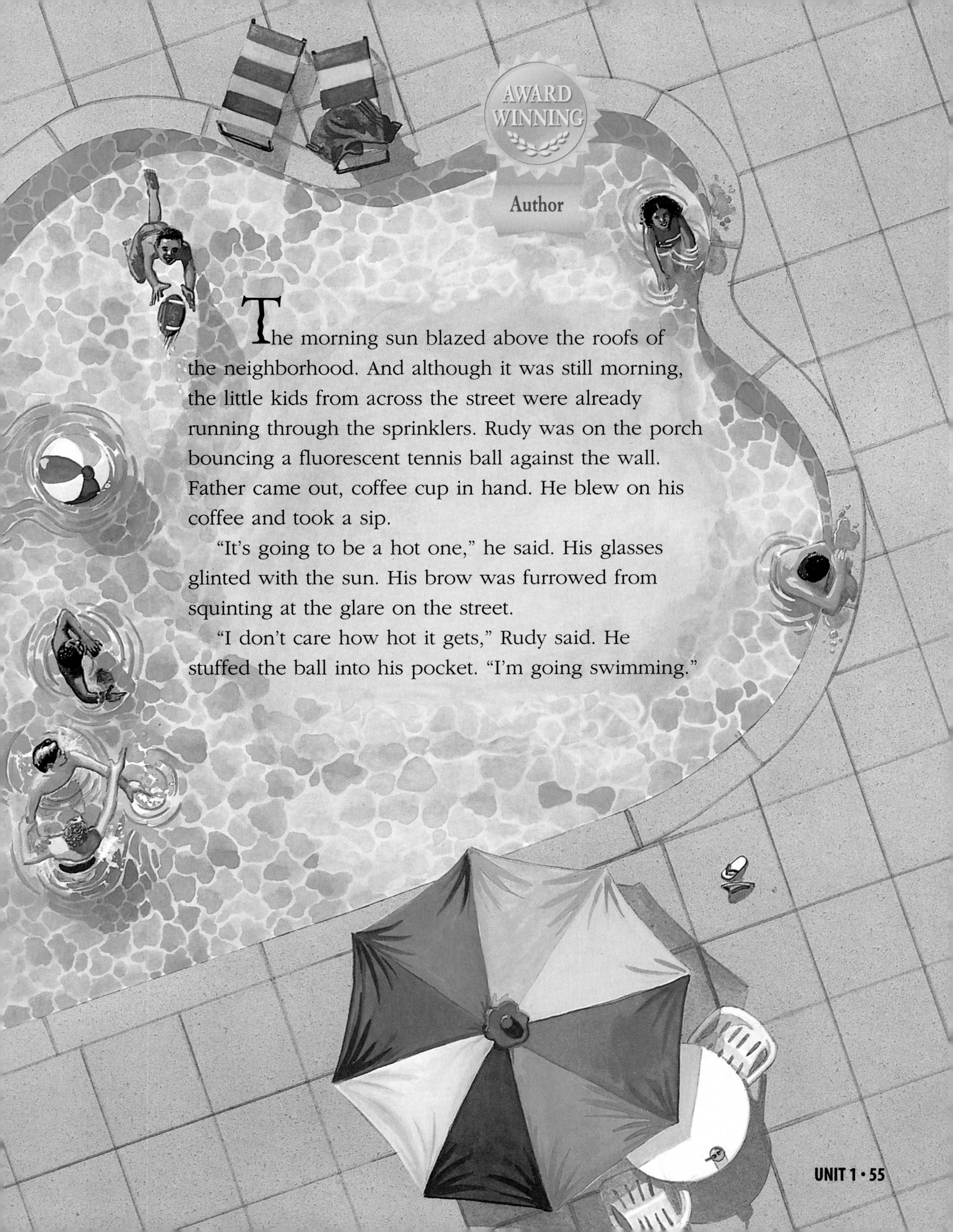

The morning sun blazed above the roofs of the neighborhood. And although it was still morning, the little kids from across the street were already running through the sprinklers. Rudy was on the porch bouncing a fluorescent tennis ball against the wall. Father came out, coffee cup in hand. He blew on his coffee and took a sip.

"It's going to be a hot one," he said. His glasses glinted with the sun. His brow was furrowed from squinting at the glare on the street.

"I don't care how hot it gets," Rudy said. He stuffed the ball into his pocket. "I'm going swimming."

Rudy had talked up a storm about the party. He had talked about his inner tube and about Tiffany Perez, the girl in his class. He talked about what he was going to wear and what kinds of dives he would do in the swimming pool. He had told Alex that he was going to try to hold his breath underwater for two minutes.

"Sit down, Little Rudy," Father said. He took a sip of coffee and looked thoughtfully at the sky. "So Tiffany is pretty rich, huh?"

"I think so."

"Well, Rudy, let me give you some advice. You can't eat with your fingers."

"Yeah, I know," Rudy said. "Estela told me already."

"And when you get there, you gotta be polite. You have to make small talk."

"Small talk?"

"Yeah, you got to talk so small that ants can understand what you're saying." He rubbed his chin and thought deeply.

"Let me help you. I'll be Mrs. Perez and you be yourself."

"You're going to be Mrs. Perez?"

"*Simón.*"

They stood up, face-to-face. Rudy pretended to knock on the door.

"How's it going, ma'am?" Rudy said as he greeted Mrs. Perez. He had a difficult time seeing Mrs. Perez in the form of his father, especially in a work shirt and thick black glasses.

"No, Rudy. You have to be polite," Father corrected him. "Say, 'Hello, Mrs. Perez. It's a swell day for a swell pool party.' Can you do that? And immediately start making conversation. You could tell her about yourself. Tell her about baseball."

Rudy tried a second time. He knocked and said, "Hello, Mrs. Perez, it's sure a hot day for a hot pool party. I adore fried chicken."

"That's it, *hombre,*" Father screamed with delight. He slapped his thighs and said, "Tell her more. *Otra vez.*"

"I adore fried chicken *con frijoles,* and *mi perro,* Chorizo, he likes tortillas with peanut butter." Rudy giggled and slapped his own thighs.

"That's it, Rudy," Father encouraged. "Tell her more. Spit it out!"

"I like *huevos con weenies y papas fritas. Me gustan café con leche y helado de coco.*" Rudy was smiling from ear to ear as he realized how funny he sounded. He reminded himself of Kid Frost, the rapper from East Los Angeles.

Father slapped his thighs a second time. He took a sip from his coffee cup and smiled broadly at his son. "Rudy, you're gonna be a hit. Bethany-Tiffany-Riffany, or whatever her name is, she's gonna crack up. You know why?"

"No. Why, Dad?"

"You mean you don't know why?"

"No, Dad. Why?"

Father became more serious. "Sit down, Little Rudy." He popped his knuckles and looked around the neighborhood. More children were playing in the sprinklers. The neighbor across the street was washing her car.

"Rudy, we're just ordinary *gente,*" Father started. "I work, and El Shorty—your gramps—works. We get by. We're honest. That's it. We get by month to month. That's why she's gonna like you. She's gonna see that you're real. *¿Entiendes?*" He stopped and waved to a neighbor driving past. "Hey, Louie, I got that jack for you. Come by later." The man in the car waved and nodded his head. Father looked at his son with understanding. "Listen, they may be rich folks, but don't worry. Just go and have fun, do some fancy dives in the pool and be nice and . . . bring me home a piece of cake. Okay?"

"Okay, Dad," Rudy said. He understood his father. He understood that while they were everyday workers, they were proud and worked as one—*la familia.* He understood that his father was a good father, serious but not too serious.

Father left with Grandfather to cut lawns. Rudy played with Chorizo and then, struck with a little guilt, he stopped to admire his grandfather's landscaping efforts. His grandfather was working on making a pool in their own backyard. "*Pobre abuelito*," thought Rudy, "I should help him." Rudy shoveled until he was hot and sweaty and it was time to go to the pool party.

He showered and then, at the foggy bathroom mirror, practiced making polite conversation. "Hello, Mrs. Perez, I adore fried chicken." He raised two splayed fingers and said, "I'll take two pieces." He splashed his father's cologne on his face. "It's a hot day for a swell pool party." He splashed on more cologne. He admired himself in the mirror. "Mrs. Perez," he continued, "I understand that you love turtle soup. I, too, adore turtle soup." He was happy with his small talk, and happy with the way he smelled.

When he came into the kitchen, where Mother was ironing his shirt, he said in a British accent, "Hello, dear mother. I must be off for the pool party."

"Oh, you look so handsome," she said. She pulled at his cheek and said, "*¡Qué bonito!*"

"Mom, I'm ten years old. I'm not a baby."

"You're my baby." She beamed. She had never seen her son so clean, and so dressed up. She sniffed the air. She studied her son with a little smile on her face.

"You smell nice, like your *papi*," she said as she handed him the ironed shirt.

"Well"—he blushed—"I put on a little bit of his cologne."

Mother smiled and asked, "You have a ride?"

"*Simón*," Rudy said, snapping his fingers. "I got my own wheels, Mom. My inner tube!"

Rudy's ride was his inner tube—taller than his father and wide as Alex. He left the house and rolled it up the street, past the neighbor kids who were once again in the sprinklers. Past his sister who was sitting on a car fender dreaming about boys. Past Louie the neighbor and his dog Charlie. Past other dogs and mothers and the lawns browning under the Fresno sun. A mile north, where the houses turned nice, he passed it all, including his father and El Shorty, whom he didn't see. Their Oldsmobile was stalled. They had run over a board with a nail and now had a flat tire. He didn't hear them scream, "Hey, Little Rudy, we need that inner tube!"

He had on sunglasses, and his headset on his ears, listening to Kid Frost. Father and El Shorty called and shouted, "Little Rudy, come back!" But Rudy rolled his inner tube toward the pool party, rehearsing inside his head, "Hello, Mrs. Perez, I adore fried chicken."

SOURCE

Letters

From
PENNY POLLARD'S GUIDE TO MODERN MANNERS

by Robin Klein

Penny Pollard's school assignment is to write a report on good manners. Penny soon becomes a pro at politeness. She even starts an advice column for kids who have questions about etiquette.

Speechless

Dear Trouble Shooter

I was asked out to lunch and the hostess served with pride and joy a totally horrible mucky mixture of squid, lima beans and onions in horse radish sauce. I just took one mouthful and gagged! How can I handle it if I get asked over there again?

Poisoned

Dear Poisoned

Unfortunately you'll have to eat a little bit (though you might be lucky enough to have an allergy to some of the ingredients and can truthfully say so).

Take small mouthfuls and sips of water. When the plates are being collected and it becomes obvious you've left most of your helping, say, 'It was really delicious, but I made the mistake of having a huge late breakfast.' Or, 'I hate not being able to finish this when you went to so much trouble, but I've got a tiny appetite and I want to leave room for that yummy-looking fermented goat's cheese dessert.' Or (looking really apologetic), 'Creative cooking is just wasted on me, I'm afraid. Mum says my idea of a gourmet meal is a tomato sandwich.' (None of this will fool the hostess for a minute, of course, but at least you're not hurting her feelings.)

Yours faithfully
Trouble Shooter

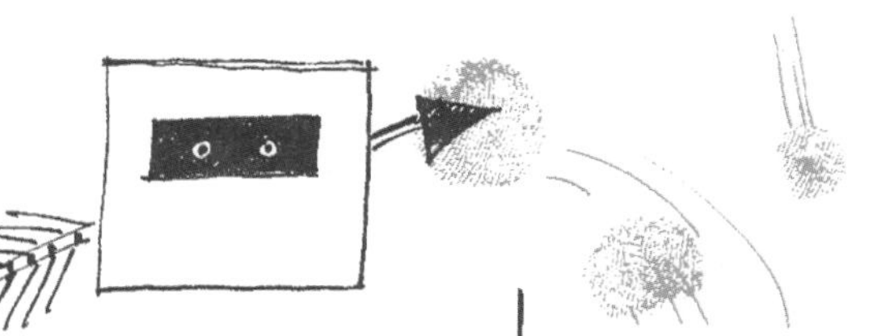

Double Ducks

Dear Trouble Shooter

On my birthday I unwrapped one of the presents, a terrific umbrella with a carved duck handle. The only trouble was that the last present I'd unwrapped was exactly the same, and both present-givers looked really embarrassed.

Ducky

Dear Ducky

You could have said something like, 'Oh, that's fantastic, getting *two*! Now I'll be able to keep one in my room, and the other one in the car for emergencies.'

Trouble Shooter

P.S. If you happen to know where they were bought, you could take one back to the shop secretly and explain to the shop assistant what happened. They might let you exchange it for something else, but be careful the present-giver doesn't ever suspect.

WORKSHOP 2

How to Make a Book Jacket

Have you ever picked up a book because you liked the way the cover looked? You can learn a lot about a book from its cover illustration and the information found on the book jacket.

What is a book jacket? A book jacket is made up of several parts. The front cover shows the title of the book, the name of the author, and artwork related to the book. The inside front flap has a paragraph about the book, while the back cover may have quotes from reviewers or a photo of the author.

The title is on the cover.
The author's name is below the title.
When I Was Nine
by James Stevenson
My own children are grown up now; that's how old I am. But sometimes I look back and I remember . . .
In that pre-World War II time, the radios were bigger, the cars larger, and the days seemed to be longer. But some things were exactly as they are now: arithmetic, older brothers, and the ecstasy of jumping into an icy mountain stream. This evocation of a summer in the 1930s is the perfect answer for every grandchild (and child) who has ever said, "Tell me about when you were little."
The inside flap gives a summary of the book.
Pictures give clues to what the book is about.

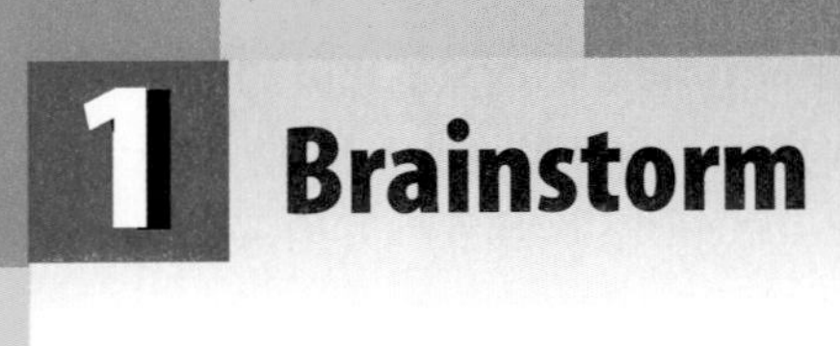

1 Brainstorm

What words and pictures tell a story about you? Get out your notebook and jot down things you like to do, places you like to go, people you know, talents you have, and all the words you can think of that tell about you.

TOOLS

- pencil and ruler
- construction paper
- colored markers
- picture of you
- glue

2 Investigate

When you've finished your list, put check marks next to your best ideas. Decide on a title for your book. Then look at some book jackets to see what pictures, titles, and designs they use. Write down some ideas for your own jacket design. Think about what colors you want to use and what pictures should go on your cover.

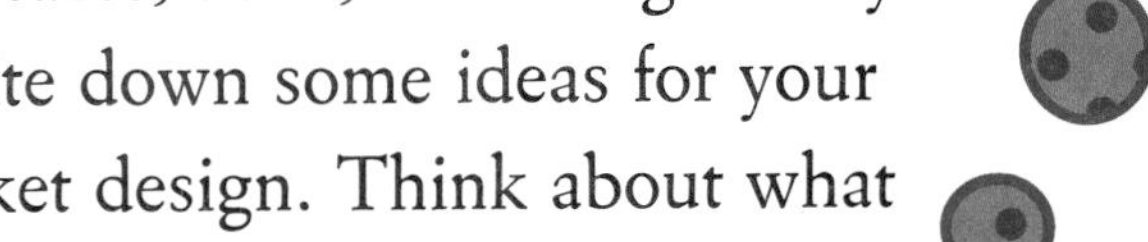

3 Write Flap Copy

After deciding on a cover design, the next step is to write a brief paragraph that describes what your book is about. This paragraph is like a short book report. It goes inside the front flap of your book cover and is called flap copy. The more interesting the flap copy, the more likely that people will read your book. Be sure to use lots of details when you write your paragraph.

Tips

- Having trouble drawing? Try using some family photos—but ask first! Or use some pictures from magazines and make a collage.
- Don't be afraid to use lots of bright colors. Remember, a book jacket has to catch your eye!

The first time I rode a bicycle

The time that the dog ate my birthday cake

4 Make Your Book Jacket

- Fold a piece of construction paper in half to make the jacket. Then fold down the inside flaps.
- Draw the design you want on the cover, and then add the title and your name.
- Put your flap copy on the inside of the front flap.
- If you want, decorate the back cover with a picture of yourself or some "quotes" from made-up book reviews.

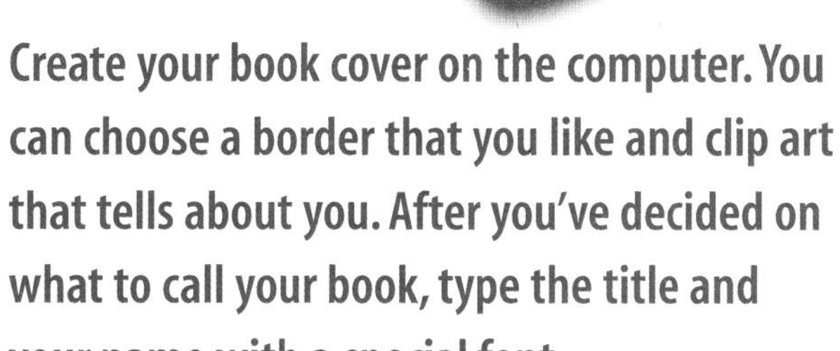

If You Are Using a Computer . . .

Create your book cover on the computer. You can choose a border that you like and clip art that tells about you. After you've decided on what to call your book, type the title and your name with a special font.

Jerry Spinelli
Author

SECTION 3

Families and traditions are an important part of who we are.

A Pocketful of Memories

Listen as a father tells how he met Eleanor Roosevelt. Afterward, meet another First Lady.

Take a tour of a young Cherokee girl's world.

Learn about an artist's childhood through her words and paintings.

PROJECT

Turn a favorite memory into a personal narrative.

SOURCE
FRONT PORCH STORIES
at the One-Room School
Eleanora E. Tate
Short Stories

From

Front Porch Stories at the One-Room School

by Eleanora E. Tate
illustrated by Eric Velasquez

The President's Wife

One hot summer night, 12-year-old Margie Carson and her cousin Ethel picnic on the old school's front porch with Margie's dad. He tells them stories about the childhood adventures he shared with his sister Stella and their twin cousins, Delmo and Elmo.

Daddy yawned. "But hey, the wife of a United States president came here one time."

"You mean, the one who has that dog that wrote a book?" asked Ethel.

"No, that's somebody else. I mean, Eleanor Roosevelt, wife of Franklin Roosevelt. She was probably the most famous of all the presidents' wives. She was a good friend to Dr. Mary McLeod Bethune, too, who was an internationally known educator and leader."

"Well, come on and tell us about when Mrs. Roosevelt came," I said.

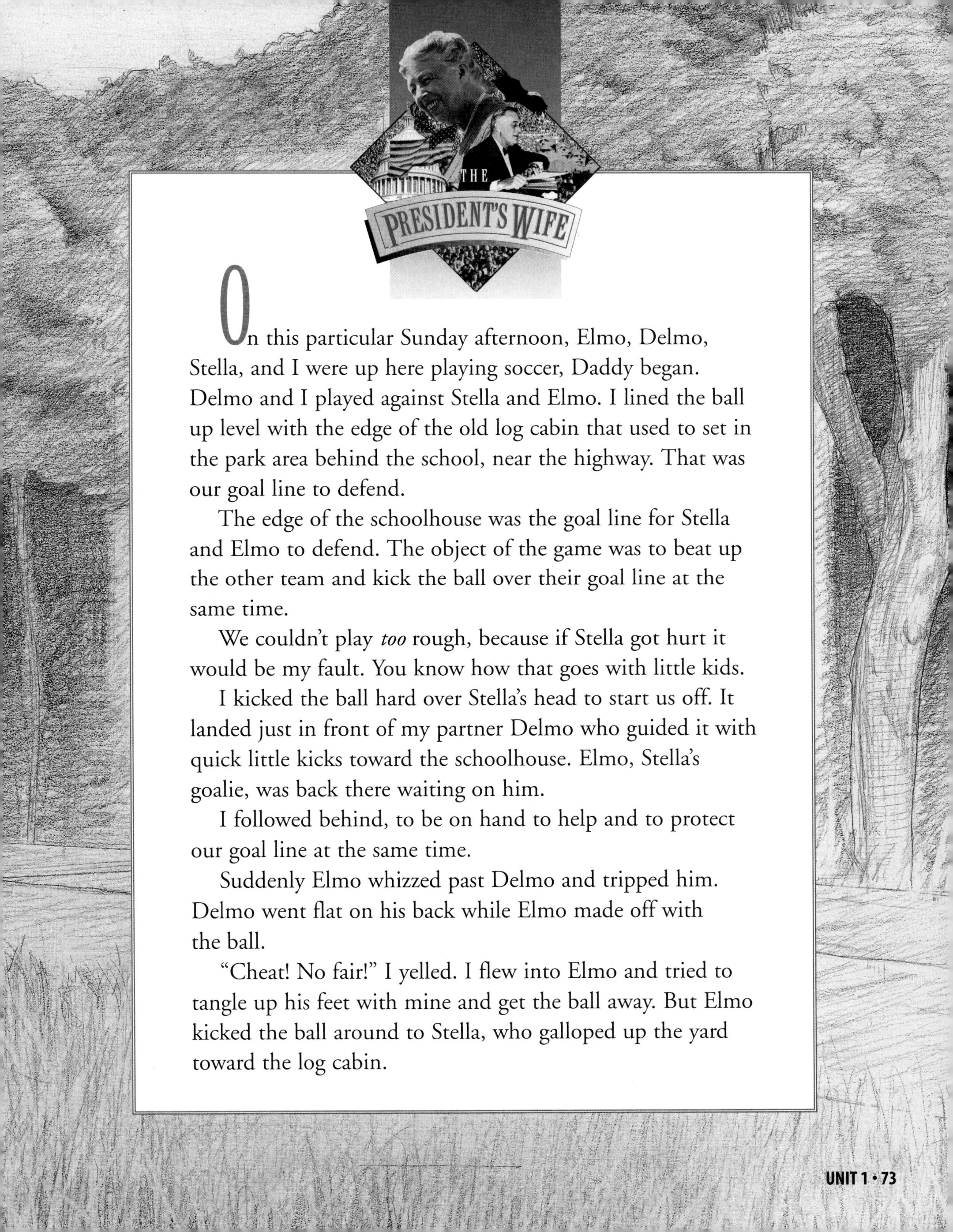

On this particular Sunday afternoon, Elmo, Delmo, Stella, and I were up here playing soccer, Daddy began. Delmo and I played against Stella and Elmo. I lined the ball up level with the edge of the old log cabin that used to set in the park area behind the school, near the highway. That was our goal line to defend.

The edge of the schoolhouse was the goal line for Stella and Elmo to defend. The object of the game was to beat up the other team and kick the ball over their goal line at the same time.

We couldn't play *too* rough, because if Stella got hurt it would be my fault. You know how that goes with little kids.

I kicked the ball hard over Stella's head to start us off. It landed just in front of my partner Delmo who guided it with quick little kicks toward the schoolhouse. Elmo, Stella's goalie, was back there waiting on him.

I followed behind, to be on hand to help and to protect our goal line at the same time.

Suddenly Elmo whizzed past Delmo and tripped him. Delmo went flat on his back while Elmo made off with the ball.

"Cheat! No fair!" I yelled. I flew into Elmo and tried to tangle up his feet with mine and get the ball away. But Elmo kicked the ball around to Stella, who galloped up the yard toward the log cabin.

I had almost caught up with her when Elmo banged into me and knocked me flat. I saw stars. By the time I got up, Delmo was hobbling after Stella. He caught up with her and stole the ball away. I raced to the log cabin. Just in time! Elmo stole the ball from Delmo and sliced it over to Stella. She cut loose with her best kick.

The ball popped up in the air and hit the roof of the cabin. I shot around to the other side. If I could catch it before it touched the ground, I could keep them from scoring. If I missed, they'd go ahead of us two to zip.

The ball rolled off the roof, hit a tree, and bounced over my head. I scrambled backwards, trying to catch it before it hit the ground.

"Stop!" everybody hollered, so I did.

And found myself in the middle of the street, with a big white car coming right at me!

Screech! The car stopped not two inches from me. I was so scared, I couldn't even breathe right. That car stopped so hard that it left tire marks on Highway 61 for a month afterwards. But better the road than on me.

"Kid?" A White man jumped out of the car and ran over to me. "Kid, are you okay?" He squatted down in front of me and patted me all over. "Didn't you see me?"

Sanity started to return to my brain. I managed to nod and shake my head.

4K7113

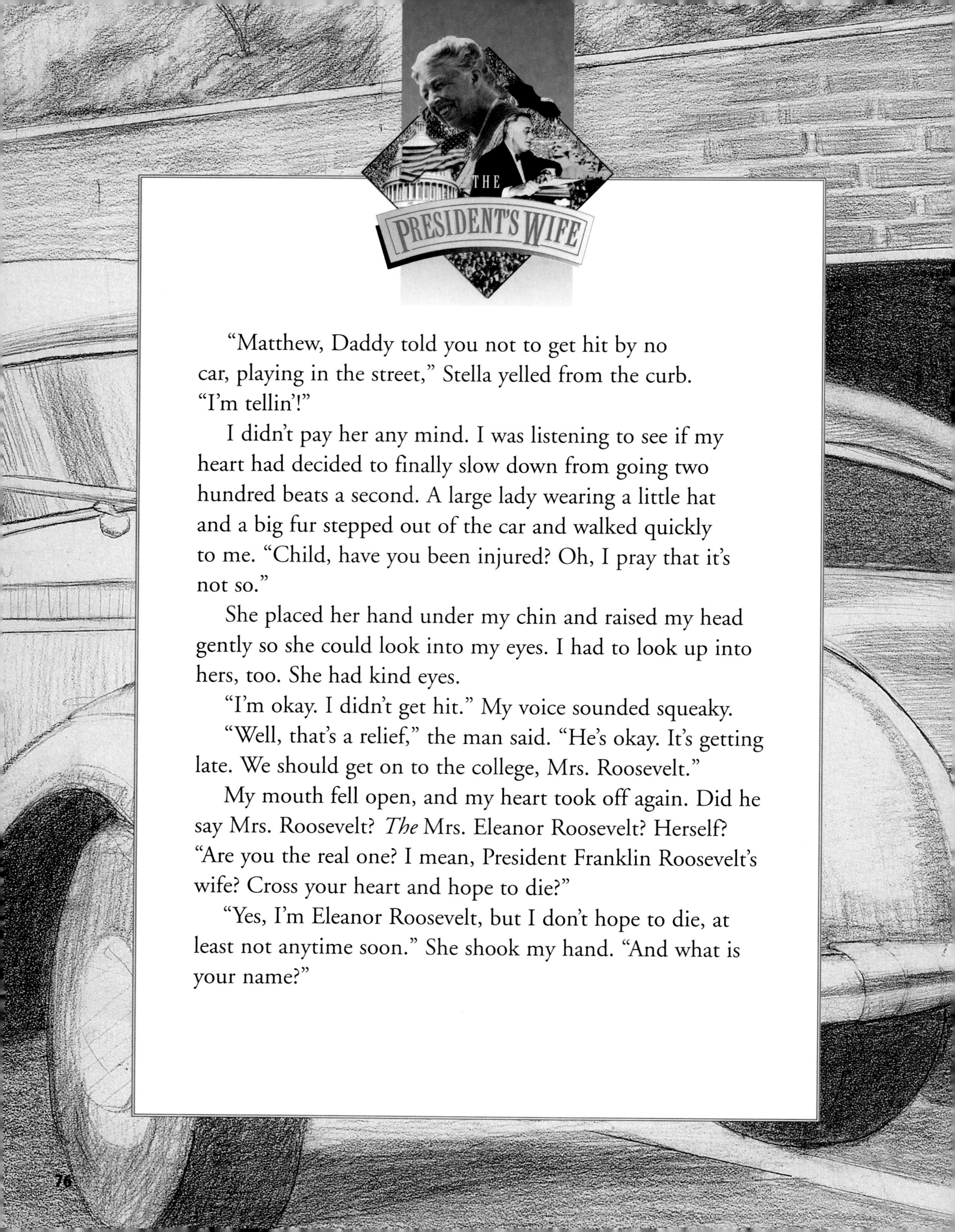

"Matthew, Daddy told you not to get hit by no car, playing in the street," Stella yelled from the curb. "I'm tellin'!"

I didn't pay her any mind. I was listening to see if my heart had decided to finally slow down from going two hundred beats a second. A large lady wearing a little hat and a big fur stepped out of the car and walked quickly to me. "Child, have you been injured? Oh, I pray that it's not so."

She placed her hand under my chin and raised my head gently so she could look into my eyes. I had to look up into hers, too. She had kind eyes.

"I'm okay. I didn't get hit." My voice sounded squeaky.

"Well, that's a relief," the man said. "He's okay. It's getting late. We should get on to the college, Mrs. Roosevelt."

My mouth fell open, and my heart took off again. Did he say Mrs. Roosevelt? *The* Mrs. Eleanor Roosevelt? Herself? "Are you the real one? I mean, President Franklin Roosevelt's wife? Cross your heart and hope to die?"

"Yes, I'm Eleanor Roosevelt, but I don't hope to die, at least not anytime soon." She shook my hand. "And what is your name?"

GENERAL STORE
SWEET

I told her. "And these are my cousins Delmo and Elmo Bennett. They're twins. And this is my little sister Stella. She was the one who kicked the ball. I was trying to catch it so they couldn't score."

"But it went out-of-bounds," said Stella, "so we don't get a score, anyway. Hello."

"How do you do, Stella?" Mrs. Roosevelt went over to Stella and shook her hand. "You certainly are a good sport. That's the mark of a true athlete."

Stella's face lit up like a Christmas light.

Mrs. Roosevelt shook hands with Elmo and Delmo, too. Their mouths hung open so far that her car could have driven in through one and out through the other.

Mrs. Roosevelt asked me what grade I was in. I told her. "And our school, Frederick Douglass, is over there." I pointed to it. "Our teacher is Aunt Daisy Green and she lives over there." I pointed again. "She said you were going to give a speech at the college. That's where she is right now, waiting to see you. She's been talking about you all week. She said you knew Dr. Mary McLeod Bethune, too. I did a report on her one time."

"Matthew's got his mouth wide open and can't stop now," I heard Delmo whisper.

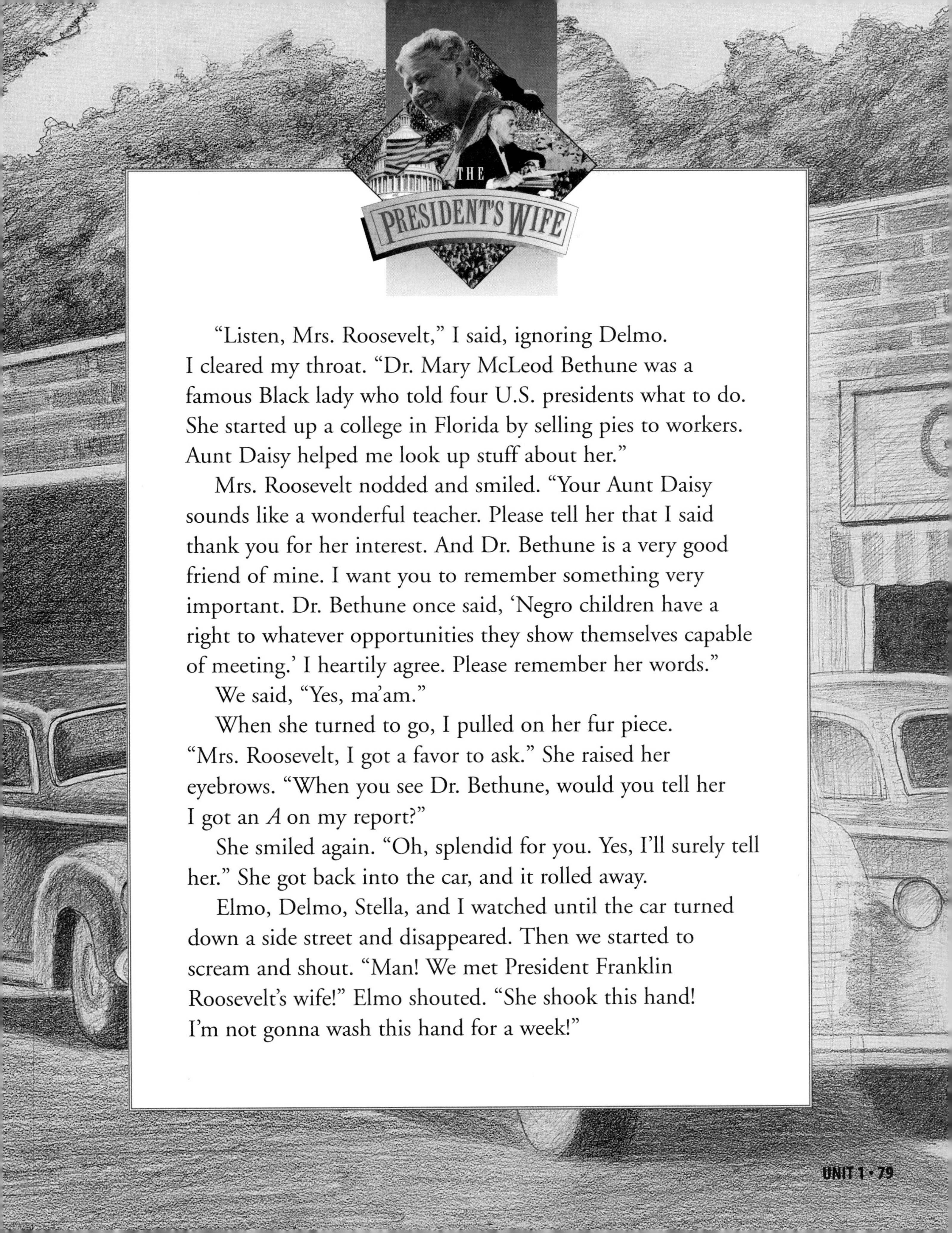

"Listen, Mrs. Roosevelt," I said, ignoring Delmo. I cleared my throat. "Dr. Mary McLeod Bethune was a famous Black lady who told four U.S. presidents what to do. She started up a college in Florida by selling pies to workers. Aunt Daisy helped me look up stuff about her."

Mrs. Roosevelt nodded and smiled. "Your Aunt Daisy sounds like a wonderful teacher. Please tell her that I said thank you for her interest. And Dr. Bethune is a very good friend of mine. I want you to remember something very important. Dr. Bethune once said, 'Negro children have a right to whatever opportunities they show themselves capable of meeting.' I heartily agree. Please remember her words."

We said, "Yes, ma'am."

When she turned to go, I pulled on her fur piece. "Mrs. Roosevelt, I got a favor to ask." She raised her eyebrows. "When you see Dr. Bethune, would you tell her I got an *A* on my report?"

She smiled again. "Oh, splendid for you. Yes, I'll surely tell her." She got back into the car, and it rolled away.

Elmo, Delmo, Stella, and I watched until the car turned down a side street and disappeared. Then we started to scream and shout. "Man! We met President Franklin Roosevelt's wife!" Elmo shouted. "She shook this hand! I'm not gonna wash this hand for a week!"

Delmo did a little dance. "I'm not gonna wash this hand for a month!"

I waved my right hand in the air, then touched my chin. "And I'm not going to wash my hand or my face for a year!"

"That'll be more than what you wash them now," said smart-mouthed Stella.

Momma was standing on the front porch, waiting for us to get home. "The phone's been ringing off the hook," she said. "Everybody up and down the highway by the school saw Mrs. Roosevelt shake your hands." She hugged Stella.

"And saw you almost get hit by her car!" She patted me all over, then hugged me.

She made us tell her everything Mrs. Roosevelt had said. Dad came out and shook our hands, too. We had to repeat everything to him.

When word got around that we had met Eleanor Roosevelt, we had to get up in school and tell the other kids what happened. We had to do it in church the next Sunday. I even had to tell it at the gas station when I went by for a pop.

I hope Mrs. Roosevelt didn't forget to give my message to Dr. Bethune. I didn't forget hers.

SOURCE
Scholastic News®
News Magazine

A b c D e

AWARD WINNING
Magazine

Barbara BUSH

First Lady of Literacy

She calls herself "everybody's grandmother," but on January 20, 1989, Barbara Bush became America's First Lady.

The First Lady has no specific duties and does not get paid. But she is a very important person. Usually, the First Lady becomes involved in worthwhile projects. Because of her influence as the President's wife, she can make people pay attention to the issues she cares about. Rosalynn Carter, the wife of Jimmy Carter, worked to improve medical care for the mentally handicapped. Nancy Reagan is well known for her "Just Say No to Drugs" campaign.

When President Bush took office, Mrs. Bush already had her volunteer cause lined up. As First Lady, her top priority was working to eliminate illiteracy. Her interest in teaching people to read and write goes back 25 years. That is when doctors diagnosed her third son as having dyslexia (dis-LEKS-ee-ah), a reading disorder.

Mrs. Bush has campaigned for years to raise money and recruit volunteers to fight illiteracy. She even wrote a book about the family cocker spaniel, C. Fred Bush. The money from sales of the book went to literacy groups. "Some people give time, some money, some their skills and connections, some literally give their life's blood . . . but everyone has something to give," says Mrs. Bush.

"Everything I worry about would be better if more people could read, write, and comprehend," said Mrs. Bush. "I honestly don't know of a more important gift that anyone can give than the gift of literacy."

▲ Barbara Bush, First Lady from 1989–1993 reads to a kindergarten class.

from HOME

UNDER *the* BACK PORCH

by **Virginia Hamilton**

illustrated by **Pat Cummings**

Our house is two stories high
shaped like a white box.
There is a yard stretched around it
and in back
a wooden porch.

Under the back porch is my place.
I rest there.
I go there when I have to be alone.
It is always shaded and damp.
Sunlight only slants through the slats
in long strips of light,
and the smell of the damp
is moist green,
like the moss that grows here.

My sisters and brothers
can stand on the back porch
and never know
I am here
underneath.
It is my place.
All mine.

SOURCE

Photo Biography

From CHEROKEE

SUMMER

by Diane Hoyt-Goldsmith
photographs by Lawrence Migdale

My name is Bridget. I live in a small town called Okay, Oklahoma in the northeastern part of the state. In summer, the countryside is a patchwork of green pastures and golden fields. Farmers raise cotton, grain, soybeans, and corn while ranchers fatten cattle and hogs. There are dense forests of oak and hickory that shade the valleys, and rolling fields of hay that ripen in the summer heat.

Before Oklahoma became a state in 1907, the place where I live was part of Indian Territory. I am a Cherokee Indian and a member of the Cherokee Nation. My people have a long history and a great heritage. Our strong traditions have given us an identity to be proud of.

Summer Fun

Summer is a special time for my family. The weather is hot and humid so we go outdoors as much as possible. One of our favorite pastimes is hunting for crawdads. My father and his twin brother used to catch them when they were little boys. Now my dad is an expert.

First we drive out to Grandfather's house and fix up some gigs—poles with a fork on the end for catching crawdads. Grandfather helps us make them out of a piece of wire and river cane. He cuts the wire from a clothes hanger and with a pliers, shapes it into a fork with two prongs. Then we tie it to the cane with a piece of string.

We go hunting at Spring Creek. It flows behind the house where my father grew up. My great-grandmother, Mary Belle Russell, raised him and she still lives there.

The best place to look for crawdads is under the rocks near the banks of the creek. If we creep along quietly, we might find one lying out in clear view. Then, a quick jab with the gig and we have caught one. Sometimes we can turn a rock over slowly and find one hiding underneath.

My father is fast and catches three or four crawdads before I can even get to the water. Then he stands back and watches my brother, sister, and me. It doesn't take us long to catch enough to fill a coffee can. I usually catch the most.

Soon it's time to cook the crawdads. We build a twig fire on the shore with some dry leaves, tiny pieces of wood, and bits of wild grapevine.

After we get the fire going, we fill the can that holds the crawdads with water from the creek. We heat the can on stones over the fire. Soon the water starts to boil. When the crawdads turn a bright red, they are cooked and ready to eat. Nothing is more delicious than a fresh crawdad cooked over a twig fire on a hot summer day.

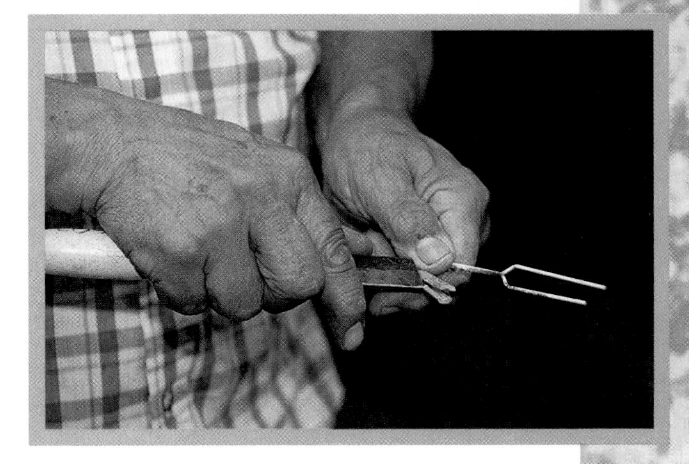

Bridget's grandfather splits a piece of river cane and puts the double-prong fork into the end to make a gig for catching crawdads.

Bridget's mother has gone hunting for crawdads every summer since she was a child. Breaking the sticks into small pieces, she helps her husband start a fire on the shore to cook the crawdads.

The Cherokee Language

My mother's parents can both speak our native language. Although my grandmother reads and writes in Cherokee, many of the younger people have stopped learning and using the language altogether.

Grandmother teaches the Cherokee language in an adult class during the school year. She has taught me a few words in Cherokee, and I like having a Cherokee name. Grandmother says that there are things she can say in Cherokee that are hard to translate into English. Our language is part of our history and our identity as a tribe. That is why we don't want to lose it.

The Cherokee language is spoken by combining eighty-five different sounds. The written language has a separate character for each sound, so Cherokee is written by using this syllabary, rather than by using an alphabet.

The Cherokees have had a written language since 1821. The syllabary was the invention of a man named Sequoyah. The English alphabet took four thousand years to develop, but Sequoyah invented our syllabary in just nine years.

The Cherokee Syllabary

	1 (a)	2 (e)	3 (i)	4 (o)	5 (u)	6 (v)
1	Ꭰ	Ꭱ	Ꭲ	Ꭳ	Ꭴ	Ꭵ
2 (d/t)	Ꮣ Ꮤ	Ꮥ Ꮦ	Ꮧ Ꮨ	Ꮩ	Ꮪ	Ꮫ
3 (dl/tl)	Ꮬ Ꮭ	Ꮮ	Ꮯ	Ꮰ	Ꮱ	Ꮲ
4 (g/k)	Ꭶ Ꭷ	Ꭸ	Ꭹ	Ꭺ	Ꭻ	Ꭼ
5 (gw/kw)	Ꮖ	Ꮗ	Ꮘ	Ꮙ	Ꮚ	Ꮛ
6 (h)	Ꭽ	Ꭾ	Ꭿ	Ꮀ	Ꮁ	Ꮂ
7 (j/ch)	Ꮳ	Ꮴ	Ꮵ	Ꮶ	Ꮷ	Ꮸ
8 (l)	Ꮃ	Ꮄ	Ꮅ	Ꮆ	Ꮇ	Ꮈ
9 (m)	Ꮉ	Ꮊ	Ꮋ	Ꮌ	Ꮍ	
10 (n/hn)	Ꮎ Ꮏ	Ꮑ	Ꮒ	Ꮓ	Ꮔ	Ꮕ
11 (s)	Ꮝ Ꮜ	Ꮞ	Ꮟ	Ꮠ	Ꮡ	Ꮢ
12 (w/hw)	Ꮹ	Ꮺ	Ꮻ	Ꮼ	Ꮽ	Ꮾ
13 (y/hy)	Ꮿ	Ᏸ	Ᏹ	Ᏺ	Ᏻ	Ᏼ

Durbin Feeling

PRONUNCIATION GUIDE

The following is a list of the roman alphabet used in Cherokee speech: a, ch, d, e, g, h, i, j, k, l, m, n, o, s, t, u, v, w, y. The consonant sounds are the same as in English. The vowel sounds used in Cherokee speech have only one sound for each:

a, as in ah
e, as in they
i, as in ski
o, as in note
u, as in true
v, as uh in huh

By combining the consonants and vowels listed by lines and columns in the chart, the correct pronunciation for each Cherokee syllable can be produced.

Example: The pronunciation for Ꮳ is "ja". Ꮃ is "la"; and Ꭹ is pronounced "gi" as in "buggy."

Exceptions to the rule that Cherokee syllables are produced by combining consonants and vowels are the syllables Ꭰ Ꭱ Ꭲ Ꭳ Ꭴ Ꭵ, and Ꮝ. The characters in the first line are produced by the single vowel sounds; and the character Ꮝ is simply an "s" sound.

When Sequoyah created our written language, he could neither read nor write in English. He watched the Europeans write and receive letters, and decided to come up with the same system for his own people.

Sequoyah was very artistic and the characters he drew for the Cherokee syllabary were done with a calligrapher's grace and beauty. Later on, as people began to use the syllabary to print books and newspapers, many original characters were changed to look more like English letter forms. However, in Cherokee the letters stand for different sounds. For example, a "D" in Cherokee stands for the sound "ah" and an "R" stands for "eh."

The Nation's TSA-LA-GI (*TSA-lah-gee*) Library is located in the old prison building. The people who work there try new ways of teaching children to become literate in the Cherokee language. For example, the Nation has a program in which Cherokee is taught in the schools. There is even a new computer program for students learning our language. When you type the sound of a Cherokee word on the computer, a mechanical voice pronounces it. Then the proper letter comes up on the screen. It is fun to use.

Another way to teach the language is by telling stories. The library puts on puppet shows in the schools, and the actors use Cherokee stories, characters, and words.

For our people, legends have been a good way for the elders to teach children about Cherokee life and the proper way to behave. Sometimes the stories explain something about the natural world. The stories almost always have a moral, and they are entertaining too.

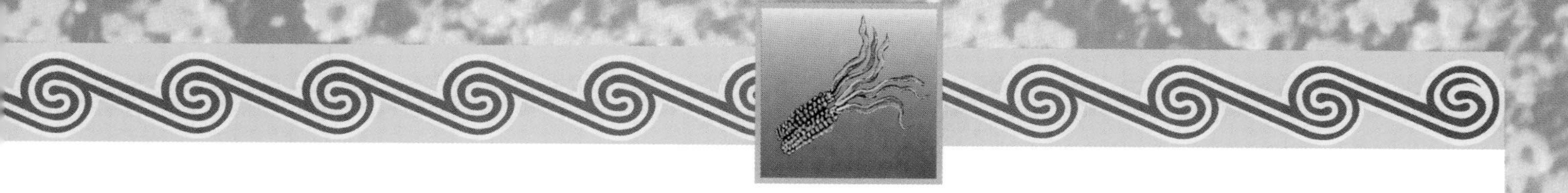

Possum Learns a Lesson

A CHEROKEE LEGEND
retold by Sequoyah Guess

Long, long ago in the days when animals could talk, Possum had a big, bushy tail. It was even more beautiful than Fox's, and Possum was proud of it. He loved to show it off to his friends. Every day he combed it a hundred times to keep it looking shiny.

The rest of the animals grew tired of Possum's showing off. They got together and discussed what they could do to teach him a lesson. Then they came up with a plan.

Rabbit went over and talked to Possum.

"We're going to have a dance tonight," he said, "and it's in honor of your tail."

"Great! Great!" Possum replied. "But you know I'll need a special chair to sit on so I can show it off."

"Of course," Rabbit answered. "We'll get a nice chair for you. But in the meantime, I'll help you get ready. You won't have to do a thing. Just sit back and relax."

Possum was really thrilled to have so much attention paid to his tail. He lay back while Rabbit carefully washed and combed it. Possum was so relaxed and happy that he soon fell asleep.

While Possum snored peacefully, Rabbit whistled for his friend Cricket. It was time to put the rest of the plan into action. Cricket came and shaved off all the hairs on Possum's tail. Then he helped Rabbit wrap some cloth around it.

When Possum woke up, Rabbit told him, "I've got this cloth over your tail to keep it nice for tonight." Possum didn't give it a thought. He was full of excitement and couldn't wait for the dance to begin.

When night came, all the birds and the animals gathered for the dance. Chanting their ancient songs, they moved around the fire in a perfect circle, singing and dancing.

Rabbit said to Possum, "You should go out there and dance. We are all waiting to see your most wonderful tail." As he spoke, he started to unwrap Possum's tail.

Possum was in such a hurry to dance that he didn't look back. He did not notice that anything was wrong. He danced and sang, circling the fire with a huge grin on his face.

"Look at my tail," he sang. "I've got a beautiful tail. There's no tail like mine."

The animals started to giggle. They said "Oooooh!" and "Aaaaah!" Then they started to laugh out loud.

At first, Possum thought they were admiring his tail. He kept on singing. Each time he passed the animals, he sang "Look at my beautiful tail!" But the more the animals laughed, the more Possum wondered, What's wrong? Why are they making fun of me?

Then he turned and looked behind him. His beautiful tail was pink and bare! Instead of being big and bushy, it was skinny and ugly.

Possum was so embarrassed that he fell backward, his big smile frozen on his lips.

Possum never got his bushy tail back. And to this day, all opossums have a hairless tail. If you startle an opossum when you are walking in the woods, he'll play dead and grin just like Possum did. Possum learned it is not smart to brag about anything too much.

A Summer Stomp Dance

For the Cherokees, dancing around a fire is not something that only happens in legends and stories. Special stomp dances are still held every weekend all year round by the traditional people in the tribe. Our people keep the spirit of ancient teachings alive by singing the songs that we have learned from past generations. Because these have never been written down, the elders teach the words and melodies to their children. Attending a stomp dance has become a very special part of my summer.

Before the dances begin, the Cherokees often prepare a special feast called a "Hog Fry." Everything is cooked outdoors over an open fire. It takes all afternoon to make an evening meal for the crowd.

The Cherokees are known for their hospitality. It is a tradition that anyone who comes to a stomp dance will be fed. The meal is a time for sharing. It creates an atmosphere of friendship for the dances that follow.

Stomp dances have been performed for centuries. They are still danced by the tribes of the Southeast—the

Small pieces of pork are added to hot lard in a cast-iron kettle to cook. The stove was made out of a fifty-gallon oil drum. A hole for adding wood has been cut into the sides near the bottom.

Cherokees, Creeks, Seminoles, and Shawnees. The dancers believe that the rhythmic songs and movements of the dance help put them back in balance with the world. Dancing gives them peace of mind.

Men, women, and children are free to participate in the dances. Children begin to dance when they are very young, following the movements of their parents and grandparents.

At a stomp dance, dancers from many tribes gather to visit, feast, and worship. The dances begin after dinner and usually last all night long.

Some of the girls wear a modern version of shackles, made with tin cans rather than turtle shells. The cans make a nice sound when filled with tiny pebbles.

On long summer afternoons, when I have the chance to be alone, I like to draw pictures and let my mind wander. I dream about what I will do when I grow up and how I will live. Perhaps I'll be an artist or a dancer. I might be a doctor or a teacher. I might even be the chief of my tribe.

For now, I feel lucky to have a loving family and to live in a beautiful place. I am proud of my Cherokee heritage, and I will work hard to keep it strong. Soon it will be time to go back to school. The weather will turn cold and the leaves will fall. But I will have the memories of this Cherokee summer—a special time in my life.

The summer hay crop near Tahlequah is harvested and collected into bales for drying. The giant hay rolls are a good place to be alone to think and dream.

SOURCE
Family Pictures • Cuadros de familia
CARMEN LOMAS GARZA
Personal Narrative

AWARD WINNING
Book

from FAMILY PICTURES

Cuadros de familia

by CARMEN LOMAS GARZA

The pictures in this book are all painted from my memories of growing up in Kingsville, Texas, near the border with Mexico. From the time I was a young girl I always dreamed of becoming an artist. I practiced drawing every day; I studied art in school; and I finally did become an artist. My family has inspired and encouraged me for all these years. This is my book of family pictures.

Los cuadros de este libro los pinté de los recuerdos de mi niñez en Kingsville, Texas, cerca de la frontera con México. Desde que era pequeña, siempre soñé con ser artista. Dibujaba cada día; estudié arte en la escuela; y por fin, me hice artista. Mi familia me ha inspirado y alentado todos estos años. Este es mi libro de cuadros de familia.

Oranges

We were always going to my grandparents' house,
so whatever they were involved in we would get involved in.
In this picture my grandmother is hanging up the laundry.
We told her that the oranges needed picking so she said,
"Well, go ahead and pick some." Before she knew it, she had
too many oranges to hold in her hands, so she made a basket
out of her apron. That's my brother up in the tree, picking
oranges. The rest of us are picking up the ones that he
dropped on the ground.

Naranjas

Siempre íbamos a la casa de mis abuelos, así que cualquier
cosa que estuvieran haciendo ellos, nosotros la hacíamos
también. En este cuadro, mi abuela está colgando la ropa a
secar. Nosotros le dijimos que las naranjas estaban listas para
cosechar, y ella nos respondió:–Vayan pues, recójanlas. En un
dos por tres, tenía demasiadas naranjas para sostenerlas en las
manos, así que convirtió su delantal en canasta. Ése es mi
hermano, en el árbol, recogiendo naranjas. El resto de nosotros
estamos recogiendo las que él deja caer al suelo.

CARMEN LOMAS GARZA

Watermelon

It's a hot summer evening. The whole family's on the front porch. My grandfather had brought us some watermelons that afternoon. We put them in the refrigerator and let them chill down. After supper we went out to the front porch. My father cut the watermelon and gave each one of us a slice.

It was fun to sit out there. The light was so bright on the porch that you couldn't see beyond the edge of the lit area. It was like being in our own little world.

Sandía

Es una noche calurosa de verano. Toda la familia está en el corredor. Mi abuelo nos había traído unas sandías esa tarde. Las pusimos en el refrigerador para enfriarlas. Después de la cena, salimos al corredor. Mi padre cortó la sandía y nos dio un pedazo a cada uno.

Era divertido estar sentados allá afuera. La luz del corredor era tan fuerte que no se podía ver más allá del área que estaba iluminada. Era como estar en nuestro propio pequeño mundo.

How to Write a Personal Narrative

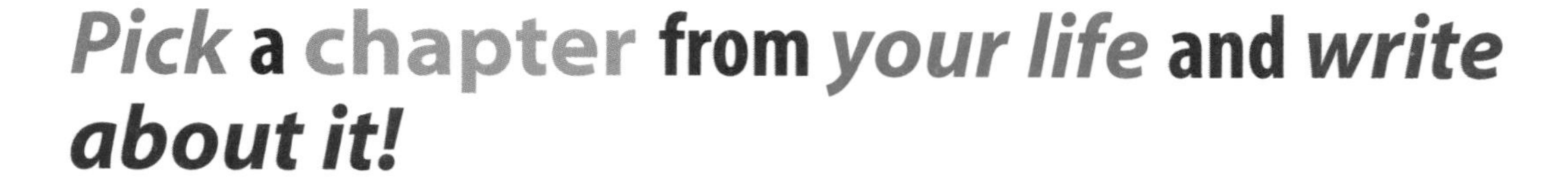

Ever think about writing a book starring you as the main character? Many authors do just that when they write a personal narrative. In a personal narrative, authors share their memories and experiences with others. Each story is told using the first-person point of view, as though the author is speaking directly to the reader.

1 Choose a Story to Tell

Decide on a topic for your personal narrative. Think of important events in your life that you'd like to share with others. If you made a Table of Contents, you may want to use one of your chapter title ideas. After you've decided what to write about, ask yourself these questions. What is my story about? When did it happen? Where did it take place? Who else was there? Think about these questions when you're writing your outline.

TOOLS

- notebook and pencil
- memories about events in your life
- people who can help you remember dates and details

- Ask your family for details about the event you chose for your story.
- What age were you when the story took place?
- What did you look like?
- Write your story as though you are talking to a friend.

2 Make an Outline

Now that you have your story idea, it's time to organize your material. Like any story, your personal narrative should have a beginning, a middle, and an end. Think about the story you want to tell, and divide your paper into three sections. Then write a few sentences in each section that tell what happened in that part of your story. This outline will help you organize your personal narrative.

Before you start writing, take a few minutes to ask yourself these questions.

- Do I have a clear idea of what I want to write about?
- Have I decided on the mood of my story? Is it funny, sad, or something else?
- Is the outline of my story clear and organized?

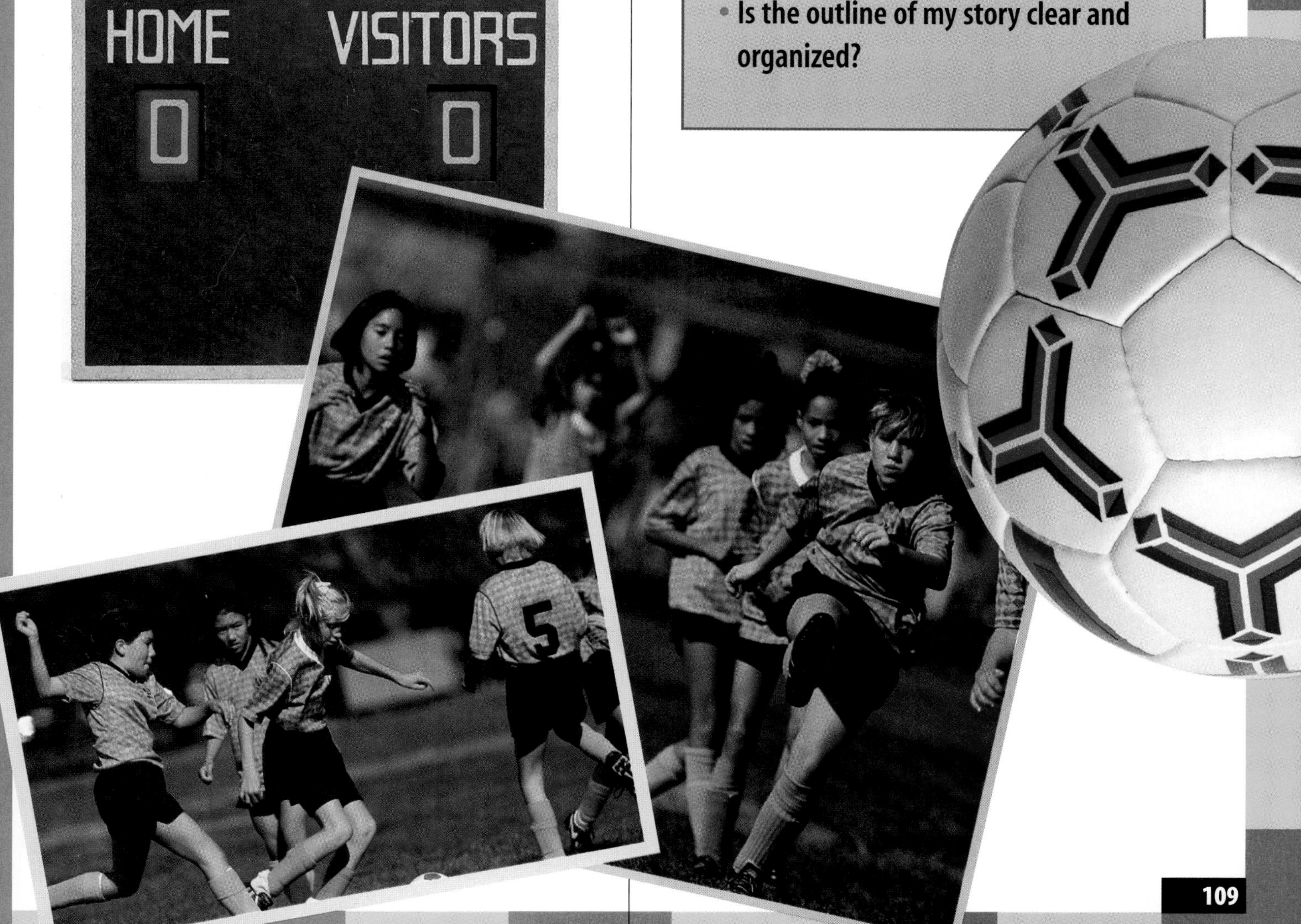

3 Write Your Personal Narrative

Once you've finished your outline, it's time to write your story. Use the ideas in your outline, and then add lots of details. Search your memory to find sensory details that will make your personal narrative come alive. What sounds, tastes, and smells do you remember? What colors remind you of the event you are writing about? Be sure to write your story using the first-person point of view.

4 Present Your Story

Here are some ways to present your story. Whatever form you choose, illustrate your narrative with drawings or photos.

- Make a book by stapling several sheets of paper together. If you made a book jacket, you can use that as the cover!
- Create a poster by arranging your writing with pictures and photos on a piece of posterboard.
- Write to a friend and tell your story in letter form.
- Turn your narrative into a script for a play.
- If you want to, you can share your personal narrative with the rest of the class.

If You Are Using a Computer . . .

Try drafting your personal narrative in the Report format on the computer. Choose clip art to illustrate your work. To make your narrative ready to present, you can print it out and use the book cover from Workshop 2, or you can make a new title page. If you like, you also can use the Record and Playback Tools as you work on your story.

CONGRATULATIONS

You've read about other people's lives and thought about your own. Every experience is a new chapter.

Jerry Spinelli
Author

Glossary

a•pol•o•get•ic (a pol′ə jet′ik) *adjective* Regretful. After he dropped the plate, he gave her an *apologetic* look.

ath•lete (ath′lēt) *noun* A person who has the skills to do well in sports or physical exercise.

athlete

au•di•ence (ô′dē əns) *noun* The people who read an author's work. She is a successful author because she has a large *audience*.

brusque•ly (brusk′lē) *adverb* A rough and abrupt manner of doing something. She *brusquely* slammed the door.

bur•lap (bûr′lap) *noun* A rough cloth woven from jute or hemp.

cal•lig•ra•pher (kə lig′rə fər) *noun* A person who has beautiful handwriting. He asked a *calligrapher* to write the invitations.

Word History

The word **calligrapher** comes from the Greek word *kalligraphia*. The word *kallia* means "beauty," and the word *graphein* means "to write."

ca•pa•ble (kā′pə bəl) *adjective* Competent. She is a *capable* driver in wet weather.

char•ac•ter (kar′ik tər) *noun* Any letter, symbol, or figure that is used in writing. The letter *A* is a *character* in the English alphabet.

con•so•nant (kon′sə nənt) *noun* Any letter of the alphabet that is not a vowel.

con•tent (kən tent′) *adjective* Satisfied and happy.

con•ver•sa•tion (kän′ver sā′shən) *noun* The act of talking with another person. She had a long *conversation* with her teacher.

ed•i•tor (ed′i tər) *noun*
A person who checks and corrects a piece of writing so that it is ready for publication.

ed•u•ca•tor
(ej′ ə kā′tər) *noun*
A person whose job it is to teach or train others.

ep•i•sode
(ep′ə sōd′) *noun*
One event in a series of events.

et•i•quette
(et′i kit) *noun*
Rules for good behavior. It is good *etiquette* to chew with your mouth closed.

fair (fâr) *adverb*
According to the rules. He didn't play *fair*.

Word Study

The word **fair** can be used to mean:
- attractive
- a clear, sunny day
- a just and honest person

fu•ri•ous
(fyo͝or′ē əs) *adjective*
Very angry.

in•flu•ence
(in′flo͞o əns) *noun*
The power to have an effect on or change others. The teacher was a good *influence* on him.

in•volved
(in volvd′) *verb*
Engaged in. She became *involved* in many projects.
▲ **involve**

laughed (laft) *verb*
Made an amused sound because something was funny. ▲ **laugh**

laughed

lit•er•ate
(lit′ər it) *adjective*
Able to read and write.

a add	o͝o took	ə =
ā ace	o͞o pool	a in *above*
â care	u up	e in *sicken*
ä palm	û burn	i in *possible*
e end	yo͞o fuse	o in *melon*
ē equal	oi oil	u in *circus*
i it	ou pout	
ī ice	ng ring	
o odd	th thin	
ō open	*th* this	
ô order	zh vision	

Glossary

man•ners
(man′ərz) *noun*
Good behavior. It's good *manners* to thank your host after a party.

nov•els (nov′əlz) *noun*
Long fictional stories. She read three *novels* by the same author. ▲ **novel**

pat•tern
(pat′ərn) *noun*
The way in which shapes and colors are placed to form a design.

pattern

pub•lished
(pub′lisht) *verb*
Printed and offered for sale. Her book was *published* this summer.
▲ **publish**

puz•zled
(puz′əld) *verb*
Confused. His bad behavior *puzzled* her.
▲ **puzzle**

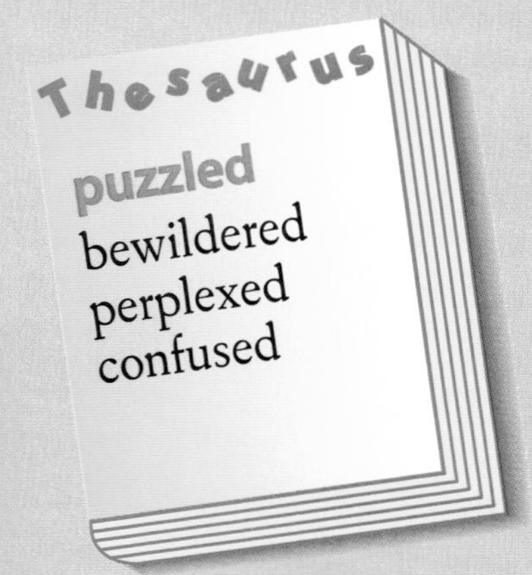

quilt (kwilt) *noun*
A bed covering made from pieces of fabric stitched together.

sat•is•fied
(sat′is fīd′) *adjective*
Contented. She was *satisfied* with her finished story.

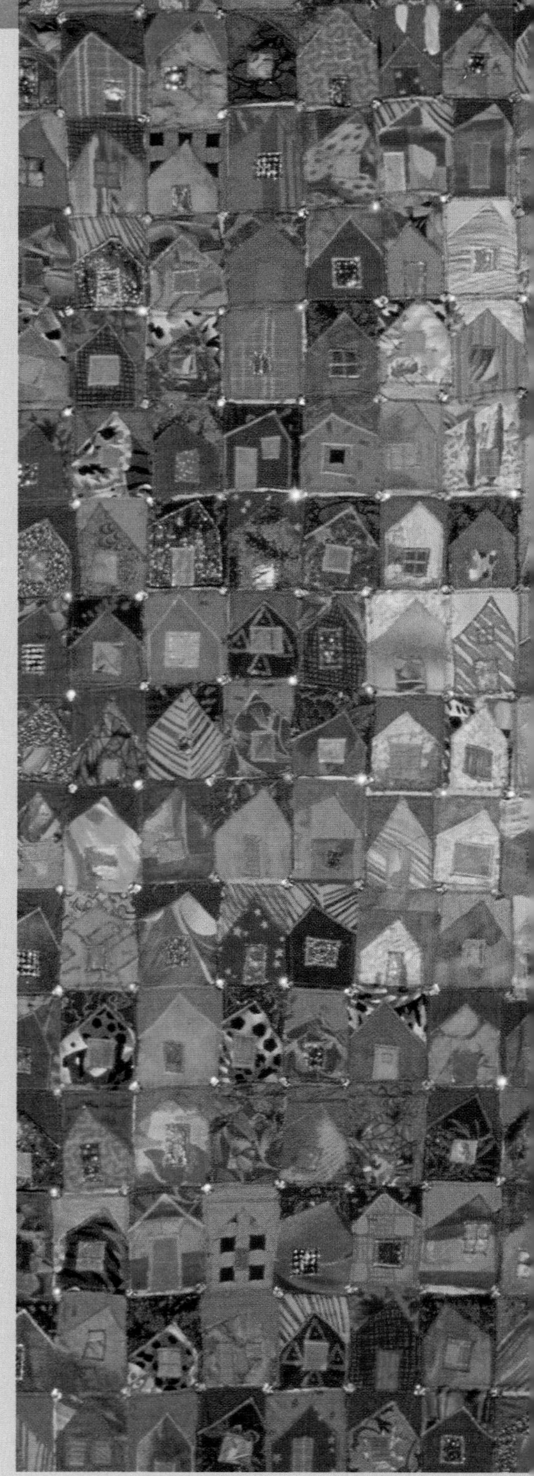
quilt

sched•ule
(skej′o͞o əl) *noun*
A list of times at which to do certain things. He had an exercise *schedule* which he followed faithfully.

scowled (skould) *verb*
Frowned and looked threatening. The bully *scowled* at the boy.
▲ **scowl**

scraps (skraps) *noun*
Small bits and pieces that are leftovers from something larger. ▲ **scrap**

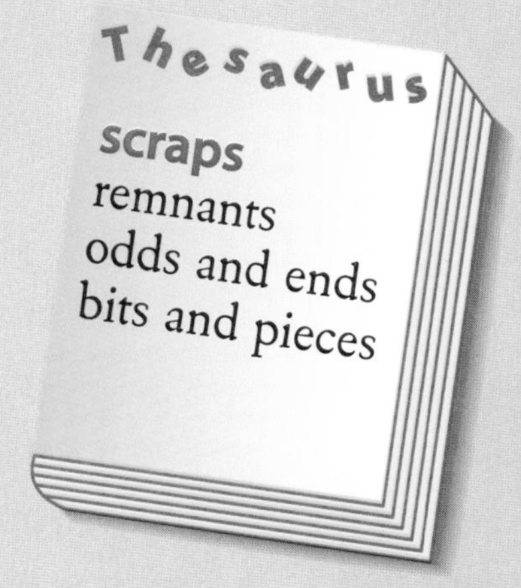

small talk
(smôl′ tôk′) *noun*
A light conversation about everyday things.

stitched (sticht) *verb*
Sewed together. She *stitched* the quilt together from scraps. ▲ **stitch**

syl•la•bar•y
(sil′ə ber′ē) *noun*
A writing system in which each sound of a spoken language is expressed by a different character or letter.

syl•la•bles
(sil′ə bəlz) *noun*
Words or parts of words pronounced with a single uninterrupted sound. The word butterfly has three *syllables*. ▲ **syllable**

trans•late
(trans′ lāt) *verb*
To put into the words of a different language. She was able to *translate* French into English.

vol•un•teer
(vol′ən tēr′) *adjective*
Doing a job without pay. She was a *volunteer* firefighter.

vow•el (vou′əl) *noun*
One of the sounds represented by the letters *a,e,i,o,u,* or sometimes *y.*

wool•en
(wo͝ol′ən) *adjective*
Made of wool.

a	add	o͝o	took	ə =
ā	ace	o͞o	pool	a in *above*
â	care	u	up	e in *sicken*
ä	palm	û	burn	i in *possible*
e	end	yo͞o	fuse	o in *melon*
ē	equal	oi	oil	u in *circus*
i	it	ou	pout	
ī	ice	ng	ring	
o	odd	th	thin	
ō	open	*th*	this	
ô	order	zh	vision	

Authors & Illustrators

Pam Conrad *pages 10–21*

When Pam Conrad was seven, she got chickenpox. Her mother gave her some paper and colored pencils. Instead of drawing, she began to write poetry. She kept on writing, and in the fourth grade she won a writing contest. The prize was a puppy! Now Pam Conrad writes books that are inspired by her childhood memories and things that happened to her children. Her daughter Sarah was the inspiration for *Staying Nine*.

Virginia Hamilton *pages 84–85*

Virginia Hamilton comes from a long line of storytellers. Her parents told stories so often that soon it became natural for her to do the same. The author of many award-winning books, Ms. Hamilton still lives in her hometown of Yellow Springs, Ohio.

Diane Hoyt-Goldsmith
Lawrence Migdale *pages 86–99*

A beautiful piece of Native American art inspired Diane Hoyt-Goldsmith to research her first book, *Totem Pole*. She teamed up with photographer Lawrence Migdale for the project, and they have continued to work together on many other books.

Lauren Mills *pages 40–53*

Lauren Mills learned quilting, weaving, and doll making from her mother, grandmother, and aunt. The songs and stories of the Appalachian people inspired her to write *The Rag Coat*. They reminded her of the patchwork coat she once wore.

Gary Soto *pages 54–61*

Many of Gary Soto's stories and poems have been inspired by his Mexican-American heritage and his childhood in Fresno, California. Mr. Soto didn't begin writing until he was in college, where he discovered his love of poetry. Today, Gary Soto is known for his essays and stories, as well as his poetry. In his stories, humor always plays an important part.

Eleanora E. Tate *pages 70–81*

Eleanora Tate's happy childhood inspired her to write stories for children. She gets her ideas from the people around her; then she makes her stories larger than life so that others will want to read them.

"Childhood can be happy if children learn that they can do anything they set their minds to, if they try."

Books&

Author Study

More by Jerry Spinelli

Dump Days
In this funny book, two friends find adventure in an unusual place.

Picklemania!
Pickles, Salem, Eddie, and Sunny make sure that life at Plumstead School is never dull!

Report to the Principal's Office
Pickles the skateboarder and his three friends are all trying to adjust to a new school, but each of them goes about it in a different hilarious way.

Fiction

Mieko and the Fifth Treasure
by Eleanor Coerr
Mieko dreamed of becoming a great artist, but that was before her hand was injured. Now she can barely hold a paintbrush. Will she ever be able to paint again?

Sara Crewe
by Frances Hodgson Burnett
In this classic book, Sara's world is turned upside down when her father dies. Once she was treated like a princess at Miss Minichin's Select Seminary for Young Ladies. Now that she is poor, she lives in the attic and wears ragged clothes.

Nonfiction

Bicycle Rider
by Mary Scioscia
illustrated by Ed Young
When bicycle racing first gained popularity as a sport, Marshall Taylor was one of the fastest racers in the world. This book tells how he became the first African-American professional racer.

Silent Observer
by Christy MacKinnon
Over a hundred years ago, this author was born on a farm in Canada. Through her own words and original watercolor paintings, MacKinnon describes the fun she had with her seven brothers and sisters, as well as her experiences when she left home to study at the Halifax School for the Deaf.

xMedia

Videos

Anne of Green Gables
Disney Home Video
In this classic story, Anne finds a new family and a new life on Prince Edward Island in Canada. (202 minutes)

The Pool Party
Reading Adventures
Gary Soto's novel is brought to life in this humorous film. (30 minutes)

Marshall Taylor

Software

Bank Street Writer
Broderbund Software
(Macintosh, Apple, MS-DOS)
Here's a program to help you write your life story—or anything else you would like to write. In the network version, you can share the stories and messages you create with others.

Charlotte's Web
(A Write On! Multimedia Story)
Humanities Software
(Macintosh, Apple II, MS DOS)
This version of E. B. White's classic book includes a video and computer activities.

Magazines

Stone Soup: The Magazine by Children
Children's Art Foundation
This magazine wants your writing and artwork. It publishes stories, poems, and pictures done by kids.

Storyworks
Scholastic Inc.
Storyworks has great art, fiction, real-life stories, and interviews. And in every issue kids tell about the books they like and why they like them.

A Place to Write

The Giraffe Project,
197 Second Street
Langley, WA 98260

Here's an organization that celebrates acts of courage and kindness. Write to find out how you or someone you know can qualify for future awards.

WHAT AN IDEA!
HOMEWORK
HOMEWO
IDEA Book
OFF
ON

World's first shoe made from recycled materials

Visit an Inventor's Office

People solve problems by inventing new things.

New and Improved

Many inventions have improved people's lives.

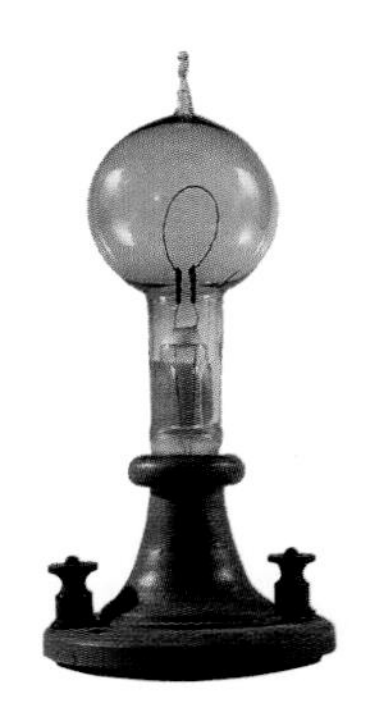

SOURCE Time Line

Amazing Inventions & Discoveries 10

SOURCE Picture Book

A Piece of String Is a Wonderful Thing 14

by Judy Hindley
illustrated by Margaret Chamberlain

SOURCE Inventor's Handbook

The Invention of Sneakers 32

by Steve Caney

from *Steve Caney's Invention Book*

MENTOR Inventor

Julie Lewis 40

WORKSHOP 1

How to Write a Product Improvement Letter 44

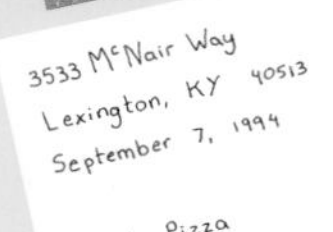

Inventors at Work

Inventors problem-solve as they work.

SOURCE **Classic Fiction**

The Doughnuts 50

by Robert McCloskey

from *Homer Price*

SOURCE **Nonfiction**

from
Mistakes That Worked 68

by Charlotte Foltz Jones
illustrated by John O'Brien

SOURCE **Poetry Collection**

The Inventor Thinks Up Helicopters 76

by Patricia Hubbell
illustrated by Ju-Hong Chen
from *The Tigers Brought Pink Lemonade*

WORKSHOP 2

How to Make an Invention Diagram 78

Fast Forward

Inventors try to make the future better.

SOURCE Novel

The Star Ship 84

by Betsy Byars
illustrated by Lisa Adams

from *The Computer Nut*

SOURCE News Magazine

The First Computers 94

by Richard Chevat
illustrated by Dan Picasso

from *Scholastic News*

SOURCE Short Story Collection

LAFFF 100

by Lensey Namioka
illustrated by Tim Lee

from *Within Reach*
edited by Donald R. Gallo

SOURCE Magazine

Things to Come 120

by Curtis Slepian
illustrated by
Nathan Jarvis

from
3•2•1 Contact

PROJECT

How to Market Your Invention 122

Glossary 128

Authors and Illustrators 132

Books and Media 134

Trade Books

The following books accompany this *What an Idea!* SourceBook.

Fiction

AWARD WINNING Book

Danny Dunn and the Homework Machine

by Jay Williams and Raymond Abrashkin illustrated by Ezra Jack Keats

Nonfiction

AWARD WINNING Author

Eureka! It's an Airplane!

by Jeanne Bendick illustrated by Sal Murdocca

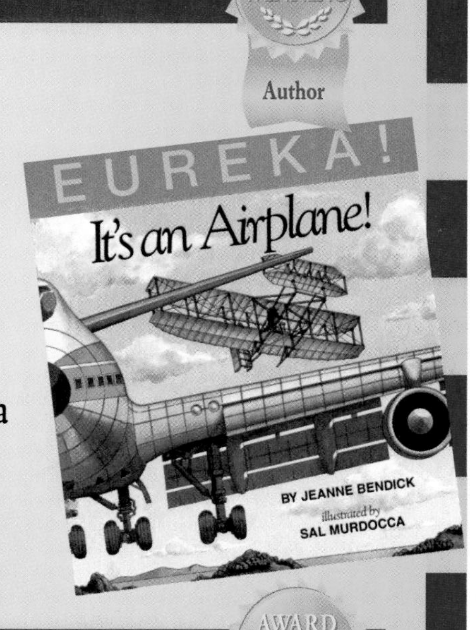

Classic Fiction

AWARD WINNING Book

On the Banks of Plum Creek

by Laura Ingalls Wilder illustrated by Garth Williams

Biography

AWARD WINNING Book

The Real McCoy

by Wendy Towle illustrated by Wil Clay

?
MAN DISCOVERS FIRE
ANCIENT AIR TRAVEL
DANG!
FIRST WHEEL
FIRST FLAT TIRE
BAD AIRMAIL ATTEMPT
UNSUCCESSFUL AIRBAG DESIGN
PLEASE HOLD!

SECTION 1

Many inventions have improved people's lives.

New and Improved

Travel along a time line that highlights famous inventions. Next, follow a piece of string through the centuries.

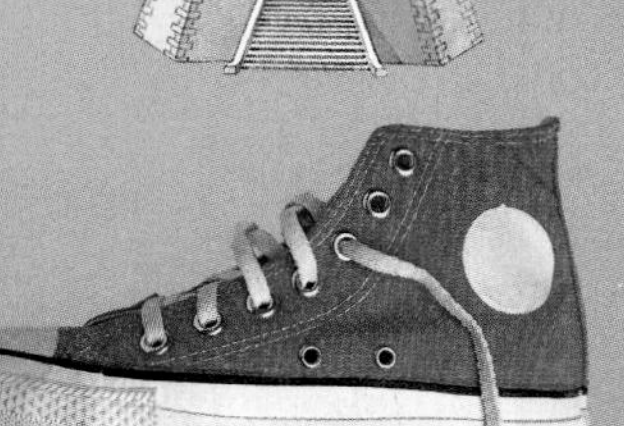

Learn how the first sneaker was invented.

Find out how Julie Lewis turned garbage into shoes.

WORKSHOP 1

Tell a company how it could improve its product.

3533 McNair Way
Lexington, KY 40513
September 7, 1999

Poppo's Pizza
238 Sitwell Place
San Francisco, CA 94179

To Whom It May Concern:

Your frozen pizza really hits the spot, but there aren't enough pieces. Instead of four ... pizza, why not eight? You ... bigger and

SOURCE

Time Line

Amazing

B.C.

3500s B.C.

The wheel is invented by the Sumerians in what is now Iraq.

A.D.

A.D. 100s

Paper is invented in China by Ts'ai Lun. Knowledge of papermaking eventually spread to Europe by way of the Islamic world.

A.D. 200s

The Maya are the first to use the number zero.

Mayan 0

A.D. 1280s

Eyeglasses are developed in Italy.

A.D. 1450s

The printing press is invented in Germany.

INVENTIONS & DISCOVERIES

1593

Galileo Galilei devises the first thermometer.

1656

The first successful pendulum clock is invented by Christiaan Huygens. This clock improved the accuracy of timekeeping.

1783

The Montgolfier brothers are the first to construct and ride in a hot-air balloon in France.

1809

Mary Dixon Kies becomes the first woman to receive a U.S. patent for her invention of a weaving process.

1871

Margaret Knight invents a machine that makes paper bags. She later patents 21 more inventions.

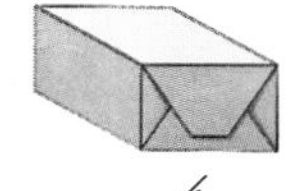

1 2 3 4

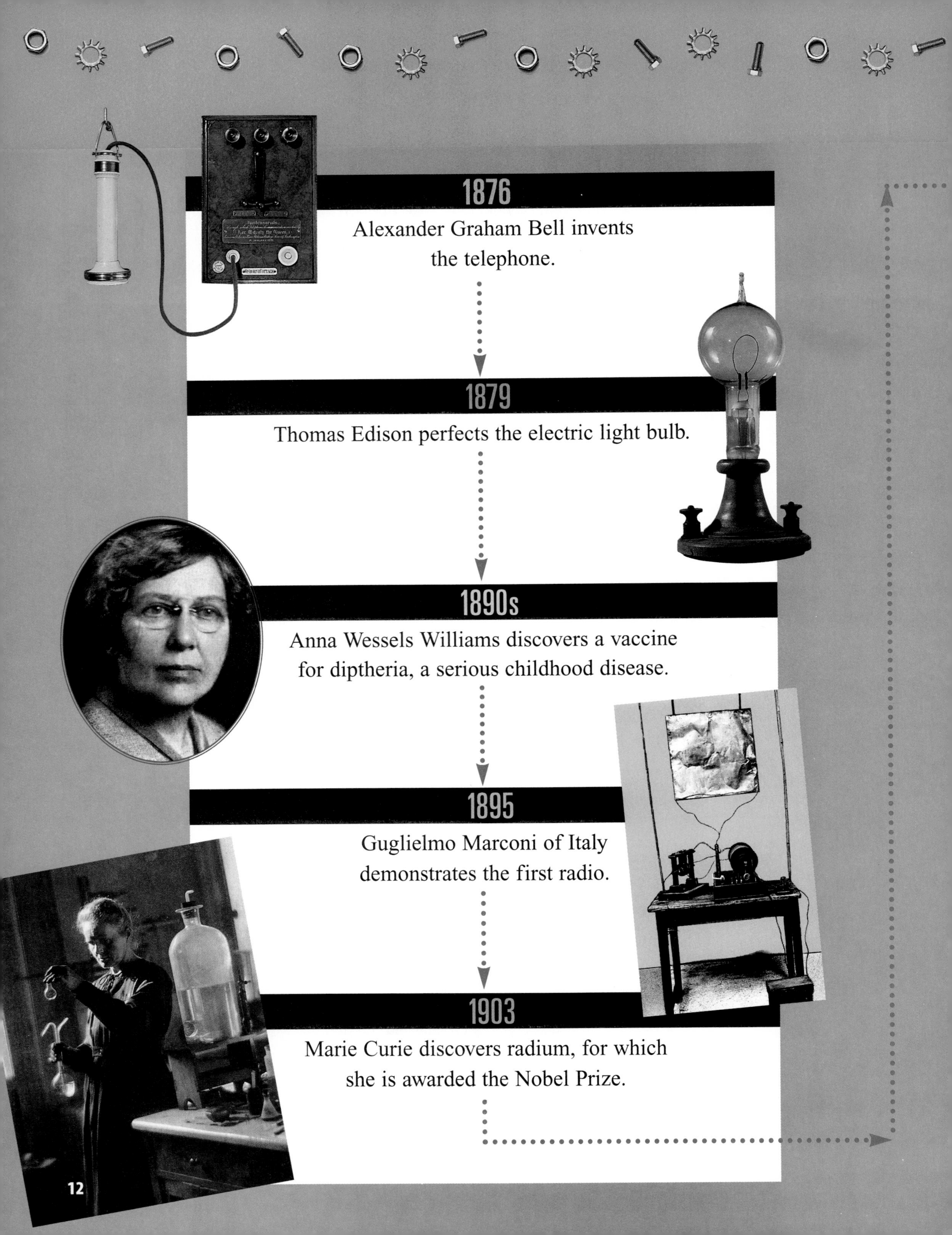

1876

Alexander Graham Bell invents the telephone.

1879

Thomas Edison perfects the electric light bulb.

1890s

Anna Wessels Williams discovers a vaccine for diptheria, a serious childhood disease.

1895

Guglielmo Marconi of Italy demonstrates the first radio.

1903

Marie Curie discovers radium, for which she is awarded the Nobel Prize.

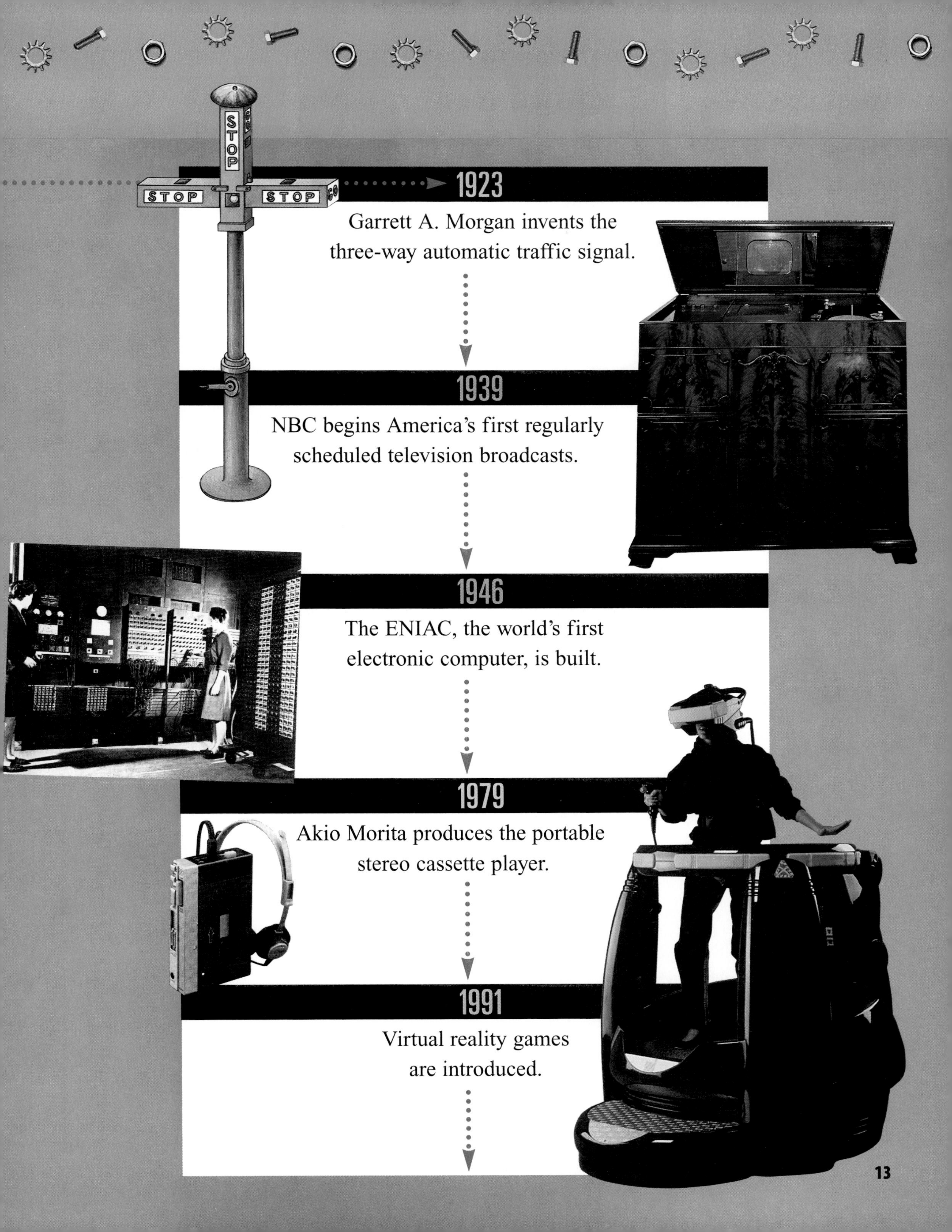

1923

Garrett A. Morgan invents the three-way automatic traffic signal.

1939

NBC begins America's first regularly scheduled television broadcasts.

1946

The ENIAC, the world's first electronic computer, is built.

1979

Akio Morita produces the portable stereo cassette player.

1991

Virtual reality games are introduced.

A PIECE of STRING IS A WONDERFUL THING

by **JUDY HINDLEY** illustrated by **MARGARET CHAMBERLAIN**

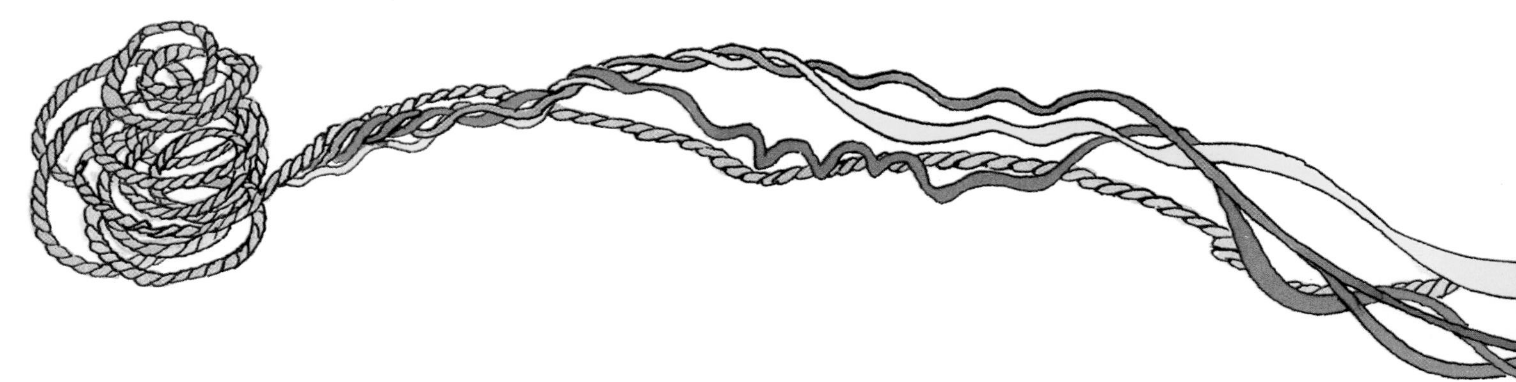

What a wonderful
thing string is!
Just think of the things
you can do with string!

Let us sing a song
about string—
what a wonderful thing it is!
When you think of the things
that you do with string,
you have to admit
it's a marvelous bit
to have in your kit:

My friend's uncle said, "You should never go anywhere without change for a phone call, a pencil stub, and a piece of string."

for a fishing line, a boat, a kite,
somewhere to hang your socks to dry;
for tying up packages, fastening gates,
leading you safe through a treacherous cave;
for a spinning top, a skipping rope,
a bracelet, a necklace, a drawstring purse . . .
there's just about no end of things
a person can do with a piece of string!
And then you wonder,
from time to time,
how did a thing like
string begin?

Back in the days
when mammoths roamed,
and they didn't have chains
and they didn't have ropes
for hauling around or
lifting things up—

(well, they didn't have any connecting things:
buttons or braces or buckles or laces,
or latches or catches or bolts or belts,
or tabs or clasps or hooks and eyes . . .
Velcro patches! ribbons! ties!
zips or grips or snaps or clips)—
well how did anyone
THINK IT UP?

Did they chat as they sat
near the fire at night,
eating their prehistoric fish,
and say, "What we need
to get it right
is a thing like hair,
but long and strong,
a thing to tie on a piece of bone:
what a wonderful fishing line
that would make!"?

After which, I suppose,
they went out to the lake
and tickled the fish
with their cold, bare hands—
for they didn't have nets
if they didn't have string.
How they all must have wished
that they had such a thing!

So how on earth
do you think they discovered it?
Do you think somebody
just tripped over it?
Was it an accident?
Was it a guess?
Did it emerge
from a hideous mess?
Did it begin with
a sinuous twig,
a whippety willow,
a snaky vine?

Did it happen that somebody,
one dark night,
winding his weary way home alone,
got tripped by the foot on a loop of vine
and fell kersplat! and broke a bone;
and then, as he lay in the dark, so sad,
and yelled for help (and it didn't come)
he got thoroughly bored with doing that
and invented—a woolly-rhinoceros trap?

Oh, it might have occurred
in a number of ways
as the populace pondered
the fate they faced—
as they huddled in caves
in the worst of the weather,
wishing for things like
tents
and clothes,
as they hugged furry skins
to their shivering bodies
and scraps of hide
to their cold, bare toes

And they had no suspenders
or snaps or connectors
or buttons or toggles
or zippers or pins—
so HOW did they hold up
their trousers, then?
They must have said,
"Oh! A piece of string
would be SUCH a fine thing
to have around the cave!"

They needed a noose for an antelope foot.
They needed a thing to string a bow.
They needed nets, and traps, and snares
for catching their venison unaware
and leading the first wild horses home.

Well, they must've gone on to try and try
as hundreds of thousands of years went by,
twisting and braiding and trying out knots
with strips of hide and rhinoceros guts,
spiders' webs and liana vines,
reeds and weeds and ribs of palm,
slippery sinews, muscles, and thongs,
elephant grasses three feet long,
and wriggly fish-bone skeletons.

And they spun out the fibers
of vegetable fluff,
and they felted the hairs of a goat,
and they knitted and twisted
and braided and twined

and invented . . .

the three-ply rope!
What a wonderful thing!
A very fine thing!
The KING of string
is rope!

You can lift up pots
from an echoing well with it,
fling it to make a bridge;
you can haul along hulking hunks
of stone for building a pyramid
(and they did).

The Egyptians made rope from bulrushes, camel hair, and flax.

The oldest rope ever discovered came from a tomb in Egypt. It was made from flax 5000 years ago.

Sometimes rope was even made from women's hair.

You can also halter and harness
your animal friends.

And then again, when life gets tough
and it's time to be moving along,
you can use it to lash your luggage fast
to a camel, a goat, a raft, a boat—
oh! a stringable thing
is the only thing
to have when you're afloat!

But they still
went on and on,
sticking and spinning
and looping and gluing
and tying and trying out
more and more types,
quicker and quicker
crazier, slicker

for pulleys and ladders
and hoses and bridges
and fences and winches
and wires and pipes.

Where on earth
have we come to now?
What would a town
ever do without string
and things that go stringing along?
Candlewicks, rackets, and violins,
telephones, plumbing, and railroad lines,
things that fasten and fuse and fix
and click and stick and link.

Can you even begin
to count the ways
that things connect
with other things?
It could just about
scramble your brain!

And to think it began
(though we'll never know when)
with somebody choking
on elephant gristle,
or trying to chew
through the stem
of a thistle,
or just stumbling into
the thing!

Oh, what we've done
with a piece of string
is a marvelous thing,
an amazing thing—
some would say
a crazy thing!
And one of these days
I might just go away
and begin it
all over
again . . .

from Steven Caney's

Invention Book

The Invention of Sneakers

How rubber-soled shoes with canvas uppers became known as "sneaks" or "sneakers" is not exactly known. The reason may be the obvious one—rubber and canvas shoes are very quiet. But the phenomenal popularity of the sneaker has more to do with its comfort and style than with the ability to sneak around quietly.

The story of the rubber-soled sneaker begins with the development of rubber. For many centuries, the natives of Central and South America commonly used the gum that oozed from the bark of certain trees to cover and protect the bottoms of their feet. Their technique was to apply the gum directly in thin layers, curing each layer with gentle heat from a fire. The result was a coating that covered the bottom of the wearer's foot and protected it from rough land.

SNEAKERS

A British traveler, in the late 1700s, became fascinated with these strange-looking foot coverings, but he was even more intrigued with the possibility of using the gum to make other products. He collected several samples of the gum and the products the natives made from it and returned to England, where he showed the new substance to his chemist friend Joseph Priestley. Priestley's first discovery was that the gum had the unique ability to cleanly erase pencil marks by briskly rubbing the paper with it—so he enthusiastically named the substance "rubber."

For the next fifty years, several products made of rubber were manufactured—mostly water-proof containers and coverings to protect all kinds of things from the rain. And by 1820 someone finally designed a rubber cover that the wearer could stretch over his leather shoes to protect them in wet or muddy weather. These rubber "overshoes" quickly found their way to America, and the new novelty product became an instant success—but not for long.

This drawing shows how the Mayans made shoes by covering their feet with melted rubber.

SNEAKERS

In an attempt to make money on the popular imported fad, many New England shoe manufacturers hastily set up factories, making rubber overshoes in various styles that incorporated hand-painted designs and other decorations. But within just a few years the attraction had diminished, as wearers soon discovered that pure rubber became obnoxiously smelly and sticky in hot weather, and brittle enough to crack into small pieces during cold weather. By 1823 no one wanted anything to do with rubber overshoes.

About that time, Charles Goodyear, a young out-of-work hardware salesman, decided to take on the challenge of eliminating rubber's shortcomings. Goodyear's interest became a hobby and then a serious undertaking. Soon he was dedicating all his time and money to making rubber a more stable product. Goodyear believed that the solution involved adding certain chemicals to the pure rubber gum and finding the right way to cure the mixture.

Experiment after experiment failed, and Charles Goodyear went broke. He borrowed money from friends and businessmen, but he still couldn't find the right formula. Eventually Goodyear was arrested and put into debtor's prison for failing to pay back his creditors.

SNEAKERS

While the shoe industry still tried to bring back the fad by introducing various new styles of rubber overshoes, the sticky, smelly, and often brittle substance found little acceptance as footwear. In 1834 an inventor named Wait Webster patented a process for attaching rubber to the soles of shoes and boots with uppers made of leather, but the combination did nothing to eliminate the original problems with rubber.

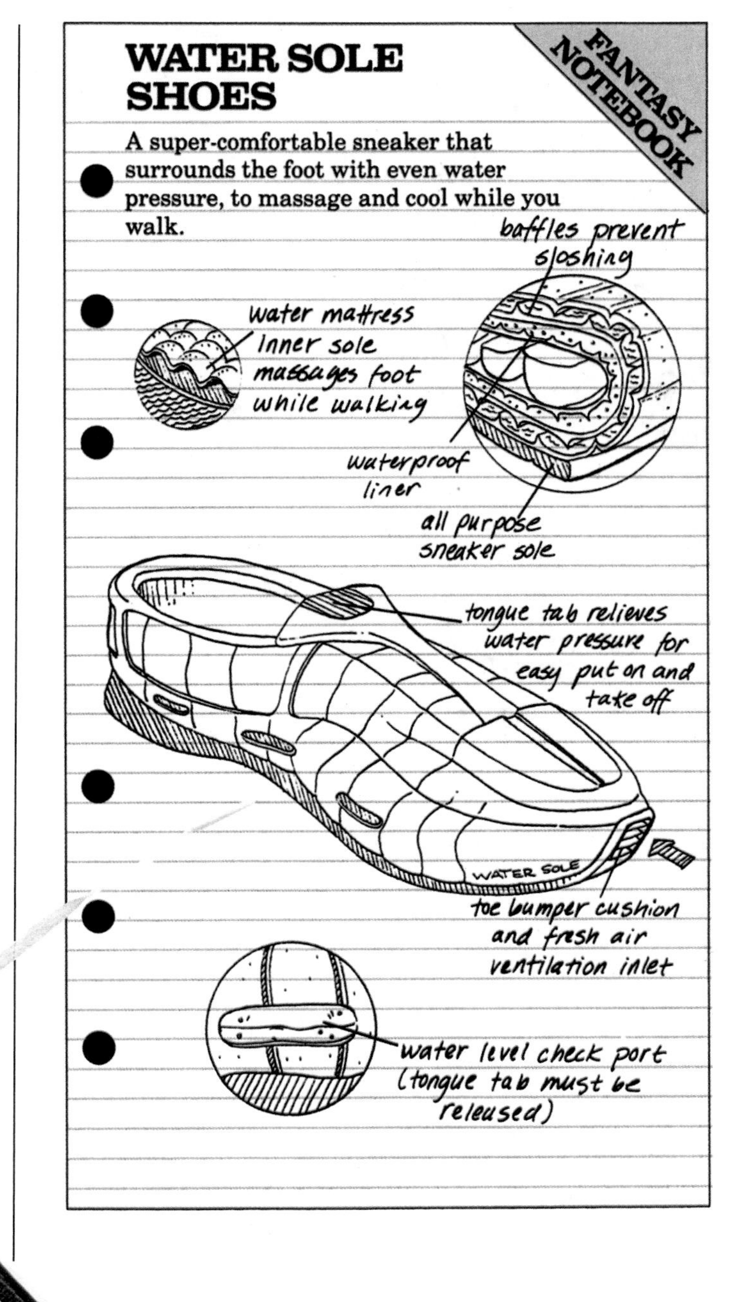

An artist's rendition of Charles Goodyear at work, just as he discovered the process of vulcanization.

By 1838 Charles Goodyear was at his experiments again; this time another rubber enthusiast, Nathaniel Hayward, joined him. They discovered that if they mixed sulfur with the gum rubber and then left it in the sun to bake slowly, the mixture would form a rubbery but not sticky outer skin. Goodyear was sure he was on the track to the solution, but Hayward wasn't so convinced. So Goodyear paid Hayward for his contribution and optimistically went on experimenting alone.

One year later, Charles Goodyear got lucky. He was mixing up a batch of gum rubber, sulfur, and white lead when a glob of the mixture fell off his stirring utensil and onto the hot stovetop. When the mass cooled and Goodyear went to remove it, he discovered that the rubber had cured perfectly—consistently rubbery throughout and not sticky at all! He then discovered that his new "metallic" rubber (he called it "metallic" because of the lead in the mixture) was more elastic and considerably less brittle. Goodyear named the process for making metallic rubber vulcanization, after the Roman god of fire, Vulcan.

SNEAKERS

Now that a better rubber had been invented, a better rubber shoe could be made. Charles Goodyear licensed his vulcanization process to several shoe companies and also to manufacturers of all types of rubber products. Some companies made rubber-soled shoes, rubber shoe covers, or even all-rubber shoes, and one shoe manufacturer, Thomas Crane Wales, made a waterproof boot of rubberized cloth with a rubber sole, called "Wales patent Arctic gaitors." But the first real sneaker with laced canvas uppers and vulcanized rubber soles came in 1868 from the Candee Manufacturing Company of New Haven, Connecticut. These canvas-and-rubber "croquet sandals" were made to appeal strictly to the wealthy, and they were sold through the exclusive Peck and Snyder Sporting Goods Catalog.

Fortunately, the Candee Company's marketing scheme didn't work as planned, and people who never thought of playing croquet began wearing the light and comfortable canvas-and-rubber shoes. By 1873 the shoes were commonly called sneaks or sneakers. And by the beginning of the twentieth century, everyday people often wore 60¢ canvas-and-rubber sneakers, while the rich wore more expensive models with silk, satin, and white duck uppers, trimmed in bows for women and elk skin for men.

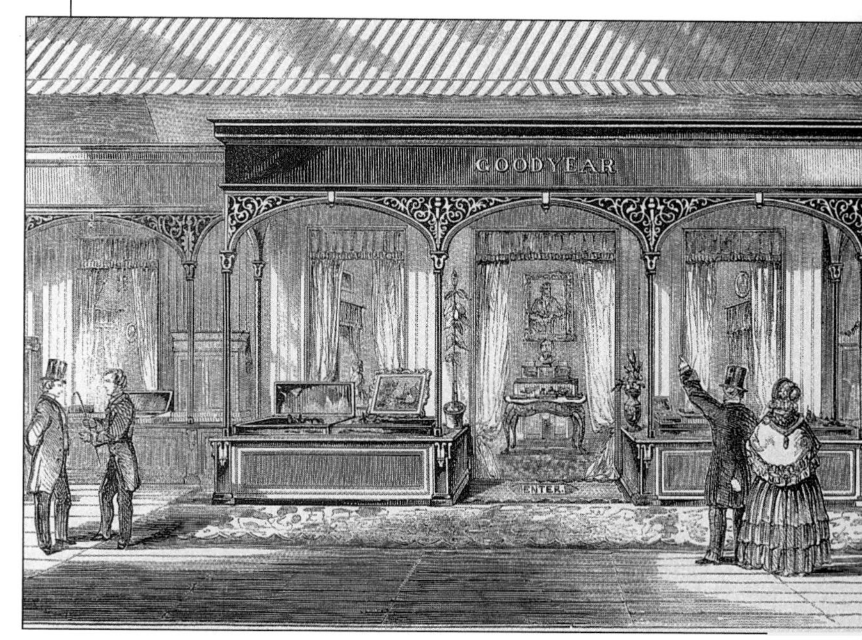

A print of Charles Goodyear's exhibition of rubber products at the famous Crystal Palace in Sydenham, England, from 1893.

SNEAKERS

While the sneaker became increasingly popular as a comfortable, stylish casual shoe, it also was being used as a sporting shoe. Special types of sneakers were being made for all kinds of popular sports and games. In 1909 the basketball sneaker was introduced, and a year later the Spalding Company invented a rubber sneaker sole with molded suction cups for better traction. In 1915 the U.S. Navy ordered non-slip sneakers to be used aboard ships.

A picture of the early Spalding tennis shoes in action.

In 1917 Henry McKinney, the public relations director for the National India Rubber Company (owned by the U.S. Rubber Company), decided it was time to call the canvas-and-rubber shoe

An early advertisement for Spalding tennis shoes.

something different from the ever-popular sneaker. After reviewing more than 300 suggestions, he selected the name "Peds" (from the Latin word meaning "foot"). However, McKinney soon discovered that another company used "Peds," and he quickly switched to the now-famous brand name "Keds." The idea worked, and for a while the Keds name was just as familiar as sneakers.

Many other companies tried to create new sneaker fads, and some succeeded. Over the past seventy-odd years, "new, improved" models have appeared with features such as arch cushions, colored uppers, colored rubber soles, side venting outlets, waffle soles, and most recently, curved-sole "running" shoes. Today the sneaker is by far America's most popular and comfortable shoe style, accounting for over one-quarter of all shoes sold—and very few are worn for croquet.

Fantasy Inventions

The sneaker has come a long way since the early twentieth century and there is no reason you can't invent another variation on this old favorite.

Slug Glue Dispenser. A healthy live slug is placed inside the glue dispenser carrying case. When glue is needed, a portion of the case bottom is removed and the slug is allowed to walk across the area to be glued.

Shoe Shine Vending Machine. Provides a quick shoe shine for people on the move. Shine selection options include rainy day waterproofing, military spit shine, different color shade, and a computerized shoe condition report.

New Sneaker Smell Renewer. A spray that gets rid of old sneaker smell and replaces it with the smell of a new pair of shoes.

Headlight Shoes Shoe toe headlights and red heel taillights provide safety for nighttime joggers and walkers.

MENTOR

Julie Lewis

Inventor

Inventor + Problem = **Solution!**

Julie Lewis is an inventor who cares about the environment. Her most successful invention tackles a problem that is becoming bigger every day—too much garbage. Can garbage be turned into something useful? After some experimenting, Lewis came up with a solution: shoes!

PROFILE

Name: Julie Lewis

Occupation: inventor and founder of Deja Shoe Inc.

Special skills: ability to see a problem and solve it

Favorite invention: the telephone

A problem that needs an inventive solution: air pollution

Previous jobs: bread factory worker, nutrition teacher, waitress

Favorite book in fourth grade:
Harriet the Spy by Louise Fitzhugh

QUESTIONS
for Julie Lewis

Learn how *Julie Lewis* found a **practical solution** to an *environmental problem.*

What gave you the idea to invent shoes out of trash?

My college roommate was in nursing school. One cold day, she hung her polyester nursing-school pants on the radiator. They melted. That's when I realized that some fabrics were made of plastics. Later, when I thought of using recycled materials to make cloth, I remembered her pants melting.

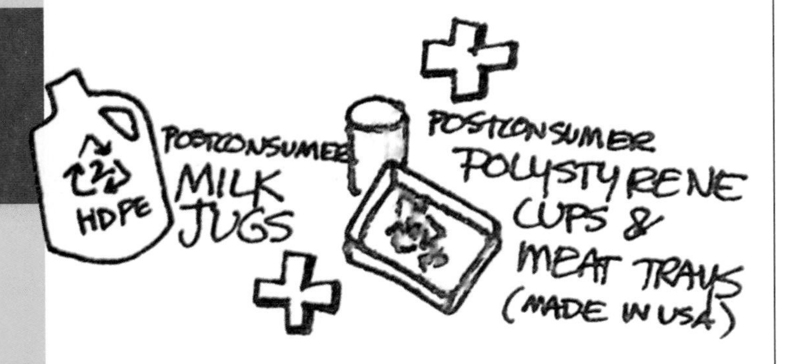

How did that help you come up with your invention?

It made me think of what gets recycled: aluminum, plastics, and even tire rubber. I had some sandals made from old tires, which gave me the idea of combining different types of recycled "garbage" to make shoes.

How did you turn garbage into shoes?

It took me a few years to develop a cloth made from recycled plastics. Then I made some model shoes with it. My two kids thought it was funny. They'd say, "Oh, there's Mom trying to invent again."

What was the next step?

I didn't know anything about making shoes, but I wasn't afraid to ask. First I talked to Bill Bowerman, a shoe designer and co-founder of Nike Shoes. I explained my idea, and showed him what I'd done. He made me a model of the first Deja shoe.

Did you start a company with just one shoe?

That model shoe was all I needed. I applied for a grant from an Oregon agency in charge of recycling. I presented a business plan and an explanation of how to turn recycled materials into shoes. They awarded me $110,000 to start my company.

Do you feel that you've solved the problem of waste in the environment?

Not at all. I'm proud of our success in recycling, but there's so much more to do!

Julie Lewis's Tips for Young Inventors

1. Don't be discouraged if someone says your idea is dumb.
2. Look for alternative solutions. If a solution doesn't work, try another, and another, until one works.
3. Get information from experts.

WORKSHOP 1

How to Write a Product Improvement Letter

The company's address

Did you ever buy something and think—this could be better? Did you think of different ways to improve it? Well, you can put those ideas to work in a product improvement letter.

What is a product improvement letter? A product improvement letter gives a company suggestions about how to make a more successful product. Some letters include a sketch to help illustrate the changes being suggested. Product improvement letters are usually sent to the Consumer Relations department of the company.

The letter ends with a closing and the writer's name.

The return address lets the company know where to send a response.

3533 McNair Way
Lexington, KY 40513
September 7, 1994

Poppo's Pizza
238 Sitwell Place
San Francisco, CA 94179

To Whom It May Concern:

Your frozen pizza really hits the spot, but there aren't enough pieces. Instead of four pieces in each pizza, why not eight? You could make your pizza a little bigger and make each slice smaller. All the kids would think you are a super nice company.

I hope you will consider my suggestion.

Truly yours,

Daniel Otfinoski

The body of the letter describes the product and gives suggestions.

1 Pick a Problem Product

Think of a product that needs improvement. It could be something you aren't happy with, such as a toy that doesn't work the way an advertisement promised. It could be an item you're happy with that could be made even better by adding or changing something.

TOOLS

- pen and paper
- ruler
- two envelopes
- two stamps

2 Identify Problems and Solutions

Now write two headings on a piece of paper: *Problems* and *Solutions.* Under the first heading, list all the problems with your product. It's all right if there's only one problem. Under the second heading, list ideas for solutions to make the product work better. Use a lot of details to describe the problems and solutions.

3 Write Your Letter

Write your address and the date on the top left side of your paper.

- Skip four lines and write the address of the company on the same side.
- Skip two lines and write *Dear* ______ , (person's name). If you don't know a name, you can write *To Whom It May Concern.*
- Write a few paragraphs about how you think the product can be improved.
- Close with *Sincerely,* or *Yours truly,* followed by your signature. Print your name below your signature.

- For product improvement ideas, think of items that you use every day, such as toothpaste and shoes.
- Enclose a diagram to show how your idea would change the product.
- Be polite! A company might not respond to a rude letter.

4 Mail Your Letter

When you're satisfied with your letter, make a neat copy and place it in an envelope. Enclose a stamped, self-addressed envelope, so the company can send you a reply. Address, stamp, and mail your letter. You and your classmates can make a chart to track the replies you receive.

If You Are Using a Computer . . .

Write your letter on the computer using the letter format. To create your own stationery, choose from the selection of letterheads.

Julie Lewis
Inventor

GRADE A
RoBoT PARTS
JENNY'S HOMEMADE FRIENDLY RoBoT-MAKING

Inventors problem-solve as they work.

Inventors at Work

Laugh out loud as Homer solves the problem of an out-of-control doughnut machine.

See how inventors turn mistakes into successes. Then read a poem about an inventor's "new" kind of flying machine.

WORKSHOP 2

Draw a diagram of an invention of your own.

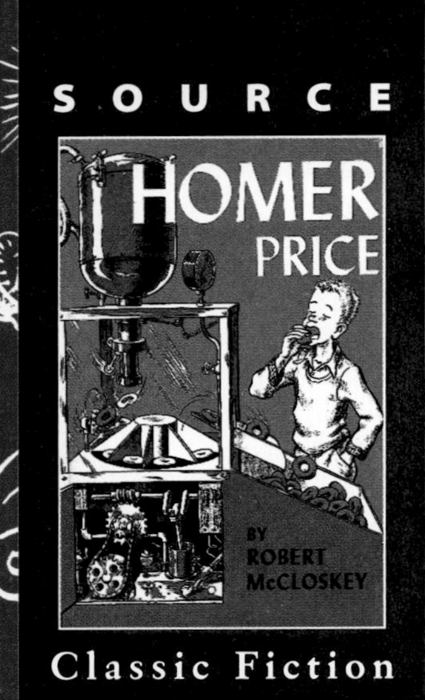

from

Homer Price By Robert McCloskey

THE DOUGHNUTS

One Friday night in November Homer overheard his mother talking on the telephone to Aunt Agnes over in Centerburg. "I'll stop by with the car in about half an hour and we can go to the meeting together," she said, because tonight was the night the Ladies' Club was meeting to discuss plans for a box social and to knit and sew for the Red Cross.

"I think I'll come along and keep Uncle Ulysses company while you and Aunt Agnes are at the meeting," said Homer.

So after Homer had combed his hair and his mother had looked to see if she had her knitting instructions and the right size needles, they started for town.

Homer's Uncle Ulysses and Aunt Agnes have a very up-and-coming lunchroom over in Centerburg, just across from the court house on the town square. Uncle Ulysses is a man with advanced ideas and a weakness for labor-saving devices. He equipped the lunchroom with automatic toasters, automatic coffee maker, automatic dishwasher, and an automatic doughnut maker. All just the latest thing in labor-saving devices.

Aunt Agnes would throw up her hands and sigh every time Uncle Ulysses bought a new labor-saving device. Sometimes she became unkindly disposed toward him for days and days. She was of the opinion that Uncle Ulysses just frittered away his spare time over at the barbershop with the sheriff and the boys, so, what was the good of a labor-saving device that gave you more time to fritter?

When Homer and his mother got to Centerburg, they stopped at the lunchroom, and after Aunt Agnes had come out and said, "My, how that boy does grow!" which was what she always said, she went off with Homer's mother in the car. Homer went into the lunchroom and said, "Howdy, Uncle Ulysses!"

"Oh, hello, Homer. You're just in time," said Uncle Ulysses. "I've been going over this automatic doughnut machine, oiling the machinery and cleaning the works . . . wonderful things, these labor-saving devices."

"Yep," agreed Homer, and he picked up a cloth and started polishing the metal trimmings while Uncle Ulysses tinkered with the inside workings.

"Opfwo-oof!!" sighed Uncle Ulysses and, "Look here, Homer, you've got a mechanical mind. See if you can find where these two pieces fit in. I'm going across to the barbershop for a spell, 'cause there's somethin' I've got to talk to the sheriff about. There won't be much business here until the double feature is over and I'll be back before then."

Then as Uncle Ulysses went out the door he said, "Uh, Homer, after you get the pieces in place, would you mind mixing up a batch of doughnut batter and putting it in the machine? You could turn the switch and make a few doughnuts to have on hand for the crowd after the movie . . . if you don't mind."

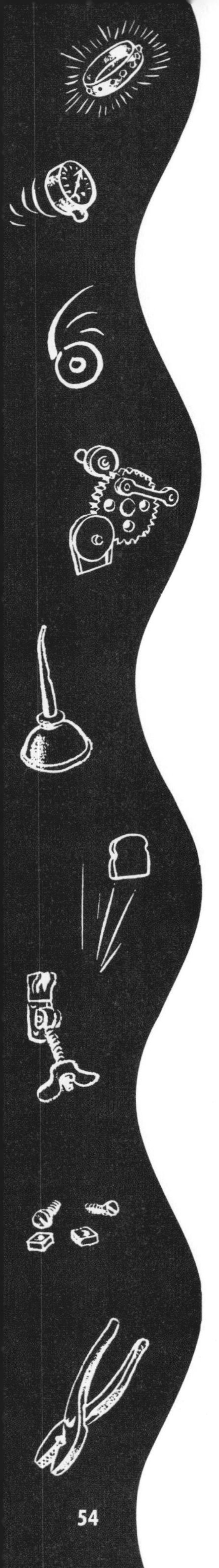

"O.K." said Homer, "I'll take care of everything."

A few minutes later a customer came in and said, "Good evening, Bud."

Homer looked up from putting the last piece in the doughnut machine and said, "Good evening, Sir, what can I do for you?"

"Well, young feller, I'd like a cup o' coffee and some doughnuts," said the customer.

"I'm sorry, Mister, but we won't have any doughnuts for about half an hour, until I can mix some dough and start this machine. I could give you some very fine sugar rolls instead."

"Well, Bud, I'm in no real hurry so I'll just have a cup o' coffee and wait around a bit for the doughnuts. Fresh doughnuts are always worth waiting for is what I always say."

"O.K.," said Homer, and he drew a cup of coffee from Uncle Ulysses' superautomatic coffee maker.

"Nice place you've got here," said the customer.

"Oh, yes," replied Homer, "this is a very up-and-coming lunchroom with all the latest improvements."

"Yes," said the stranger, "must be a good business. I'm in business too. A traveling man in outdoor advertising. I'm a sandwich man. Mr. Gabby's my name."

"My name is Homer. I'm glad to meet you, Mr. Gabby. It must be a fine profession, traveling and advertising sandwiches."

"Oh no," said Mr. Gabby, "I don't advertise sandwiches. I just wear any kind of an ad, one sign on front and one sign on behind, this way . . . Like a sandwich. Ya know what I mean?"

"Oh, I see. That must be fun, and you travel too?" asked Homer as he got out the flour and the baking powder.

"Yeah, I ride the rods between jobs, on freight trains, ya know what I mean?"

"Yes, but isn't that dangerous?" asked Homer.

"Of course there's a certain amount a risk, but you take any method a travel these days it's all dangerous. Ya know what I mean? Now take airplanes for instance . . ."

Just then a large shiny black car stopped in front of the lunchroom and a chauffeur helped a lady out of the rear door. They both came inside and the lady smiled at Homer and said, "We've stopped for a light snack. Some doughnuts and coffee would be simply marvelous."

Then Homer said, "I'm sorry, Ma'm, but the doughnuts won't be ready until I make this batter and start Uncle Ulysses' doughnut machine."

"Well now aren't *you* a clever young man to know how to make *doughnuts*!"

"Well," blushed Homer, "I've really never done it before, but I've got a recipe to follow."

"Now, young man, you simply must allow me to help. You know, I haven't made doughnuts for years, but I know the best recipe for doughnuts. It's marvelous, and we really must use it."

"But, Ma'm . . ." said Homer.

"Now just *wait* till you taste these doughnuts," said the lady. "Do you have an apron?" she asked, as she took off her fur coat and her rings and her jewelry and rolled up her sleeves. "Charles," she said to the chauffeur, "hand me that baking powder, that's right, and, young man, we'll need some nutmeg."

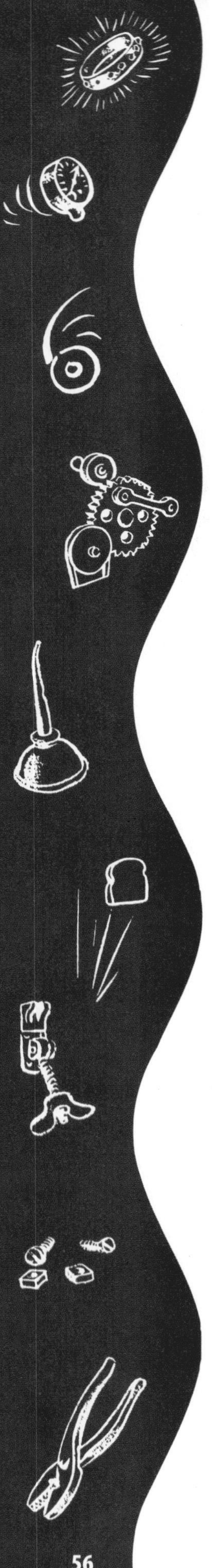

So Homer and the chauffeur stood by and handed things and cracked the eggs while the lady mixed and stirred. Mr. Gabby sat on his stool, sipped his coffee, and looked on with great interest.

"There!" said the lady when all of the ingredients were mixed. "Just *wait* till you taste these doughnuts!"

"It looks like an awful lot of batter," said Homer as he stood on a chair and poured it into the doughnut machine with the help of the chauffeur. "It's about *ten* times as much as Uncle Ulysses ever makes."

"But wait till you taste them!" said the lady with an eager look and a smile.

Homer got down from the chair and pushed a button on the machine marked, *Start.* Rings of batter started dropping into the hot fat. After a ring of batter was cooked on one side, an automatic gadget turned it over and the other side would cook. Then another automatic gadget gave the doughnut a little push and it rolled neatly down a little chute, all ready to eat.

"That's a simply *fascinating* machine," said the lady as she waited for the first doughnut to roll out.

"Here, young man, *you* must have the first one. Now isn't that just *too* delicious!? Isn't it simply marvelous?"

"Yes, Ma'm, it's very good," replied Homer as the lady handed doughnuts to Charles and to Mr. Gabby, and asked if they didn't think they were simply divine doughnuts.

"It's an old family recipe!" said the lady with pride.

Homer poured some coffee for the lady and her chauffeur and for Mr. Gabby, and a glass of milk for himself. Then they all sat down at the lunch counter to enjoy another few doughnuts apiece.

OUR

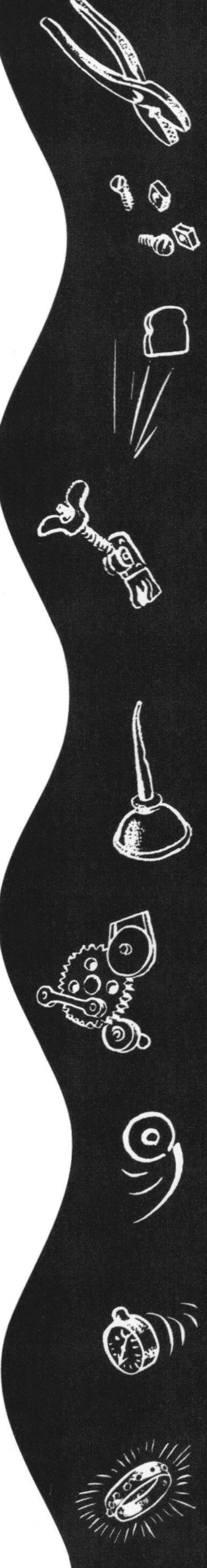

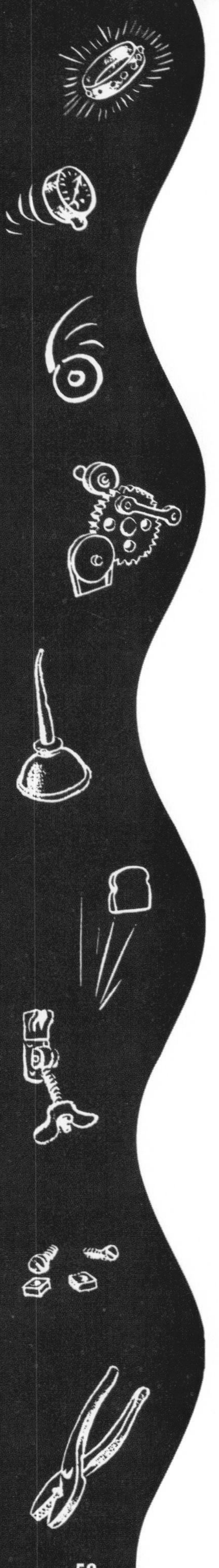

"I'm so glad you enjoy my doughnuts," said the lady. "But now, Charles, we really must be going. If you will just take this apron, Homer, and put two dozen doughnuts in a bag to take along, we'll be on our way. And, Charles, don't forget to pay the young man." She rolled down her sleeves and put on her jewelry; then Charles managed to get her into her big fur coat.

"Good night, young man, I haven't had so much fun in years. I *really* haven't," said the lady, as she went out the door and into the big shiny car.

"Those are sure good doughnuts," said Mr. Gabby as the car moved off.

"You bet!" said Homer. Then he and Mr. Gabby stood and watched the automatic doughnut machine make doughnuts.

After a few dozen more doughnuts had rolled down the little chute, Homer said, "I guess that's about enough doughnuts to sell to the aftertheater customers. I'd better turn the machine off for a while."

Homer pushed the button marked *Stop* and there was a little click, but nothing happened. The rings of batter kept right on dropping into the hot fat, and an automatic gadget kept right on turning them over, and another automatic gadget kept right on giving them a little push, and the doughnuts kept right on rolling down the little chute, all ready to eat.

"That's funny," said Homer, "I'm sure that's the right button!" He pushed it again but the automatic doughnut maker kept right on making doughnuts.

"Well I guess I must have put one of those pieces in backwards," said Homer.

"Then it might stop if you pushed the button marked *Start*," said Mr. Gabby.

Homer did, and the doughnuts still kept rolling down the little chute, just as regular as a clock can tick.

"I guess we could sell a few more doughnuts," said Homer, "but I'd better telephone Uncle Ulysses over at the barbershop." Homer gave the number, and while he waited for someone to answer he counted thirty-seven doughnuts roll down the little chute.

Finally someone answered "Hello! This is the sarberbhop, I mean the barbershop."

"Oh, hello, Sheriff. This is Homer. Could I speak to Uncle Ulysses?"

"Well, he's playing pinochle right now," said the sheriff. "Anythin' I can tell 'im?"

"Yes," said Homer. "I pushed the button marked *Stop* on the doughnut machine, but the rings of batter keep right on dropping into the hot fat, and an automatic gadget keeps right on turning them over, and another automatic gadget keeps giving them a little push, and the doughnuts keep right on rolling down the little chute! It won't stop!"

"O.K. Wold the hire, I mean, hold the wire and I'll tell 'im." Then Homer looked over his shoulder and counted another twenty-one doughnuts roll down the little chute, all ready to eat. Then the sheriff said, "He'll be right over . . . Just gotta finish this hand."

"That's good," said Homer. "G'by, Sheriff."

The window was full of doughnuts by now, so Homer and Mr. Gabby had to hustle around and start stacking them on plates and trays and lining them up on the counter.

"Sure are a lot of doughnuts!" said Homer.

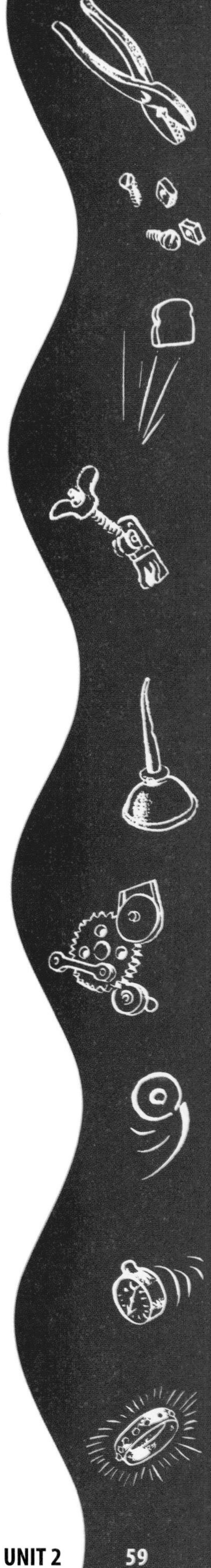

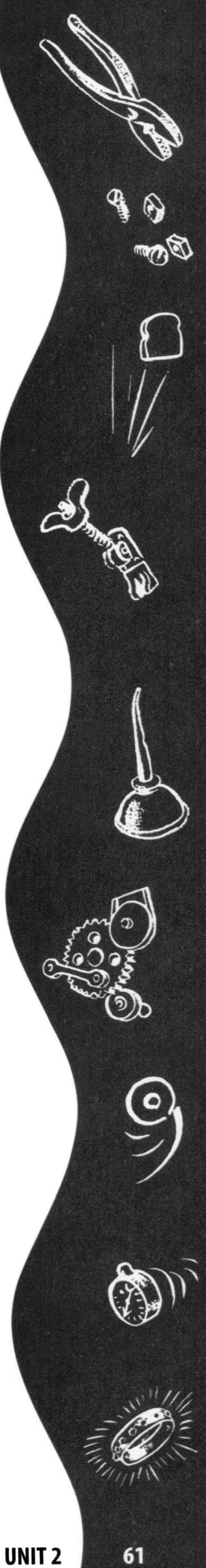

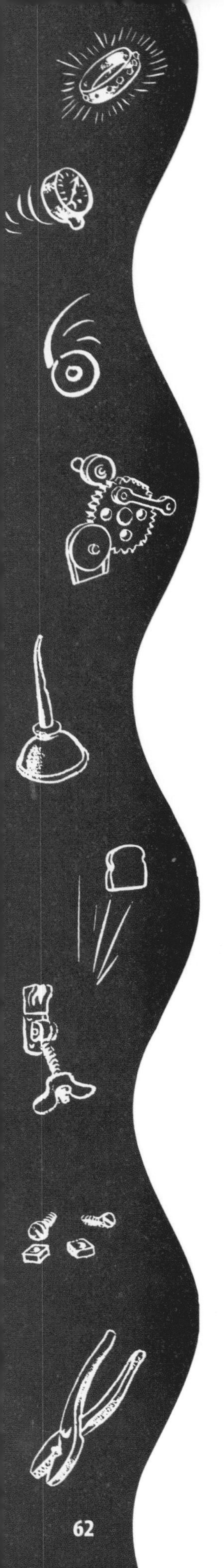

"You bet!" said Mr. Gabby. "I lost count at twelve hundred and two, and that was quite a while back."

People had begun to gather outside the lunchroom window, and someone was saying, "There are almost as many doughnuts as there are people in Centerburg, and I wonder how in tarnation Ulysses thinks he can sell all of 'em!"

Every once in a while somebody would come inside and buy some, but while somebody bought two to eat and a dozen to take home, the machine made three dozen more.

By the time Uncle Ulysses and the sheriff arrived and pushed through the crowd the lunchroom was a calamity of doughnuts! Doughnuts in the window, doughnuts piled high on the shelves, doughnuts stacked on plates, doughnuts lined up twelve deep all along the counter, and doughnuts still rolling down the little chute, just as regular as a clock can tick.

"Hello, Sheriff, hello, Uncle Ulysses, we're having a little trouble here," said Homer.

"Well, I'll be dunked!!" said Uncle Ulysses.

"Dernd ef you won't be when Aggy gits home," said the sheriff.

"Mighty fine doughnuts though. What'll you do with 'em all, Ulysses?"

Uncle Ulysses groaned and said, "What will Aggy say? We'll never sell 'em all."

Then Mr. Gabby, who hadn't said anything for a long time, stopped piling doughnuts and said, "What you need is an advertising man. Ya know what I mean? You got the doughnuts, ya gotta create a market . . . Understand? . . . It's balancing the demand with the supply . . . That sort of thing."

"Yep!" said Homer. "Mr. Gabby's right. We have to enlarge our market. He's an advertising sandwich man, so if we hire him, he can walk up and down in front of the theater and get the customers."

"You're hired, Mr. Gabby!" said Uncle Ulysses.

Then everybody pitched in to paint the signs and to get Mr. Gabby sandwiched between. They painted "SALE ON DOUGHNUTS" in big letters on the window too.

Meanwhile the rings of batter kept right on dropping into the hot fat, and an automatic gadget kept right on turning them over, and another automatic gadget kept right on giving them a little push, and the doughnuts kept right on rolling down the little chute, just as regular as a clock can tick.

"I certainly hope this advertising works," said Uncle Ulysses, wagging his head. "Aggy'll certainly throw a fit if it don't."

The sheriff went outside to keep order, because there was quite a crowd by now—all looking at the doughnuts and guessing how many thousand there were, and watching new ones roll down the little chute, just as regular as a clock can tick. Homer and Uncle Ulysses kept stacking doughnuts. Once in a while somebody bought a few, but not very often.

Then Mr. Gabby came back and said, "Say, you know there's not much use o' me advertisin' at the theater. The show's all over, and besides almost everybody in town is out front watching that machine make doughnuts!"

"Zeus!" said Uncle Ulysses. "We must get rid of these doughnuts before Aggy gets here!"

"Looks like you will have ta hire a truck ta waul 'em ahay, I mean haul 'em away!!" said the sheriff, who had just come in. Just then there was a noise and a shoving out front, and the lady from the shiny black car and her chauffeur came pushing through the crowd and into the lunchroom.

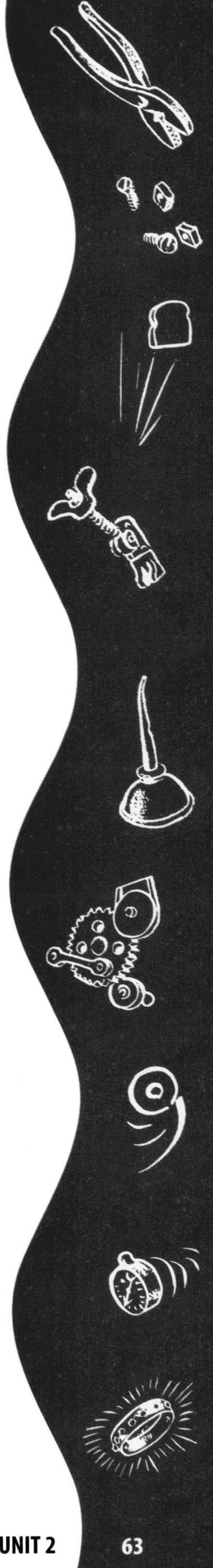

"Oh, gracious!" she gasped, ignoring the doughnuts, "I've lost my diamond bracelet, and I know I left it here on the counter," she said, pointing to a place where the doughnuts were piled in stacks of two dozen.

"Yes, Ma'm, I guess you forgot it when you helped make the batter," said Homer.

Then they moved all the doughnuts around and looked for the diamond bracelet, but they couldn't find it anywhere. Meanwhile the doughnuts kept rolling down the little chute, just as regular as a clock can tick.

After they had looked all around, the sheriff cast a suspicious eye on Mr. Gabby, but Homer said, "He's all right, Sheriff, he didn't take it. He's a friend of mine."

Then the lady said, "I'll offer a reward of one hundred dollars for that bracelet! It really *must* be found! . . . it *really* must!"

"Now don't you worry, lady," said the sheriff. "I'll get your bracelet back!"

"Zeus! This is terrible!" said Uncle Ulysses. "First all of these doughnuts and then on top of all that, a lost diamond bracelet . . ."

Mr. Gabby tried to comfort him, and he said, "There's always a bright side. That machine'll probably run outta batter in an hour or two."

If Mr. Gabby hadn't been quick on his feet Uncle Ulysses would have knocked him down, sure as fate.

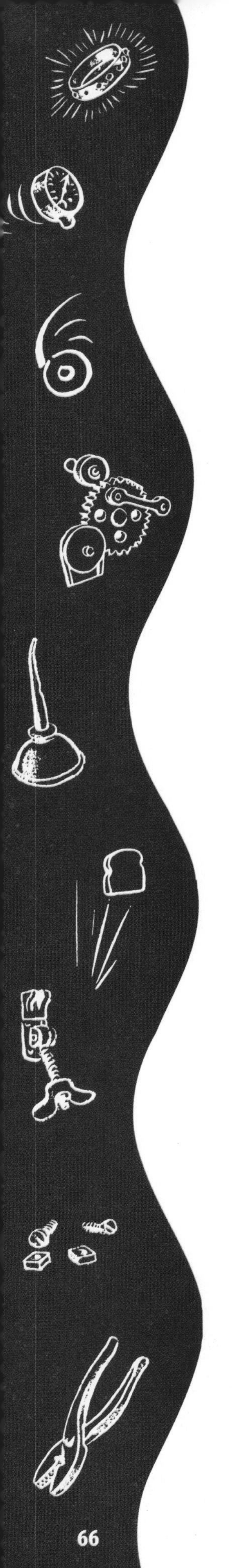

Then while the lady wrung her hands and said, "We must find it we *must*!" and Uncle Ulysses was moaning about what Aunt Agnes would say, and the sheriff was eyeing Mr. Gabby, Homer sat down and thought hard.

Before twenty more doughnuts could roll down the little chute he shouted, "SAY! I know where the bracelet is! It was lying here on the counter and got mixed up in the batter by mistake! The bracelet is cooked inside one of these doughnuts!"

"Why . . . I really believe you're right," said the lady through her tears. "Isn't that *amazing*? Simply *amazing*!"

"I'll be durn'd!" said the sheriff.

"OhH-h!" moaned Uncle Ulysses. "Now we have to break up all of these doughnuts to find it. Think of the *pieces*! Think of the *crumbs*! Think of what *Aggy* will say!"

"Nope," said Homer. "We won't have to break them up. I've got a plan."

So Homer and the advertising man took some cardboard and some paint and printed another sign. They put this sign in the window, and the sandwich man wore two more signs that said the same thing and walked around in the crowd out front.

THEN . . . The doughnuts began to sell! *Everybody* wanted to buy doughnuts, *dozens* of doughnuts!

And that's not all. Everybody bought coffee to dunk the doughnuts in too. Those that didn't buy coffee bought milk or soda. It kept Homer and the lady and the chauffeur and Uncle Ulysses and the sheriff busy waiting on the people who wanted to buy doughnuts.

When all but the last couple of hundred doughnuts had been sold, Rupert Black shouted, "I GAWT IT!!" and sure enough . . . there was the diamond bracelet inside of his doughnut!

Then Rupert went home with a hundred dollars, the citizens of Centerburg went home full of doughnuts, the lady and her chauffeur drove off with the diamond bracelet, and Homer went home with his mother when she stopped by with Aunt Aggy.

As Homer went out of the door he heard Mr. Gabby say, "Neatest trick of merchandising I ever seen," and Aunt Aggy was looking skeptical while Uncle Ulysses was saying, "The rings of batter kept right on dropping into the hot fat, and the automatic gadget kept right on turning them over, and the other automatic gadget kept right on giving them a little push, and the doughnuts kept right on rolling down the little chute just as regular as a clock can tick—they just kept right on a-comin', an' a-comin', an' a-comin', an' a comin'."

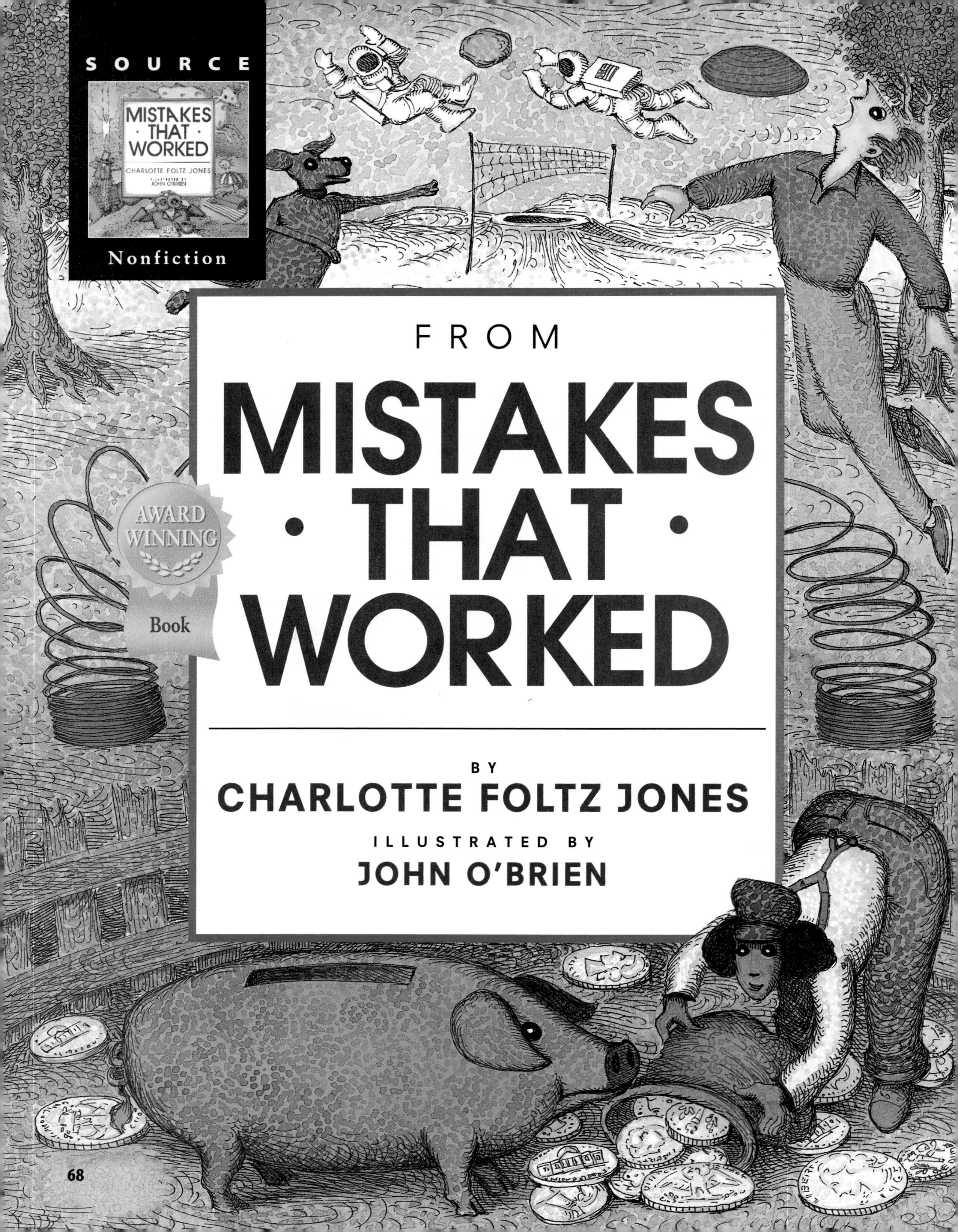

FROM

MISTAKES · THAT · WORKED

BY
CHARLOTTE FOLTZ JONES

ILLUSTRATED BY
JOHN O'BRIEN

Slinky

In 1943, during World War II, an engineer in the United States Navy was on a new ship's trial run. As he worked, a torsion spring suddenly fell to the floor. The spring flip-flopped as the ingenious man watched.

The naval engineer's name was Richard James, and when he returned home, he remembered the spring and the interesting way it flip-flopped. James and his wife Betty perfected a long steel ribbon tightly coiled into a spiral. They began production in 1945.

From that spring's accidental fall came a toy Americans have enjoyed for over forty years: the Slinky.

The nonelectrical, no-battery-required, nonvideo toy has fascinated three generations of children and adults alike. According to one estimate more than two million Slinkys have been sold and the only change in the original design has been to crimp the ends as a safety measure.

Betty James is now the company president and the Slinky is still hopping, skipping, jumping, and bouncing across floors and down stairs all over America.

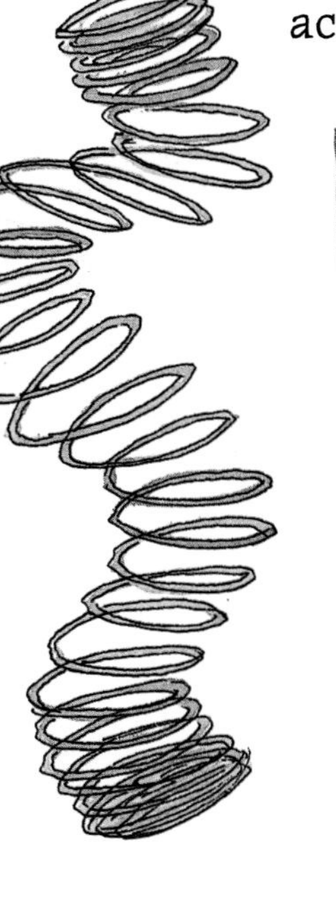

Piggy Bank

Dogs bury bones.

Squirrels gather nuts to last through the winter.

Camels store food and water so they can travel many days across deserts.

But do pigs save anything? No! Pigs save nothing. They bury nothing. They store nothing.

So why do we save our coins in a piggy bank? The answer: Because someone made a mistake.

During the Middle Ages, in about the fifteenth century, metal was expensive and seldom used for household wares. Instead, dishes and pots were made of an economical clay called pygg.

Whenever housewives could save an extra coin, they dropped it into one of their clay jars. They called this their pygg bank or their pyggy bank.

Over the next two hundred to three hundred years, people forgot that "pygg" referred to the earthenware material. In the nineteenth century when English potters received requests for pyggy banks, they produced banks shaped

like a pig. Of course, the pigs appealed to the customers and delighted children.

Pigs are still one of the most popular forms of coin banks sold in gift shops today.

Silly Putty

Sand.

There's lots of sand on Planet Earth. In fact, there's tons of it.

From sand, chemists can refine silicon. Plenty of silicon.

During World War II, the United States government needed a synthetic rubber for airplane tires, soldiers' boots, and other uses. Since silicon was so widely available, the government asked several large companies to have their engineers try to make a rubber substitute out of silicon.

In 1944 at General Electric, one of the engineers working on the silicon experiments was James Wright. One day while he was doing tests with silicon oil, he added boric acid. The result was a gooey substance that bounced.

Unfortunately, it had no apparent use. Samples were sent to engineers all over the world, but no one could find a use for it.

Then in 1949, four years after the war ended, a man named Peter Hodgson thought of an idea. After borrowing $147, he encased the goo in plastic "eggs" and renamed it "Silly Putty." Then he began selling it as a toy, first to adults and several years later to children.

It stretches. It bounces. When whacked with a hammer, it shatters. If it is pressed against newspaper comics, it will pick up the imprint. Silly Putty is truly amazing. It is now over forty years old, and was one of the first "fad" toys in America.

It has been used by athletes to strengthen their hand and forearm muscles. It can level the leg of a wiggly table or clean typewriter keys. It removes lint from clothes and animal hair from furniture.

The astronauts on the *Apollo 8* spacecraft played with Silly Putty when they got bored, and they used it to keep tools from floating around after they left the Earth's gravity.

It was used by the Columbus Zoo in Ohio in 1981 to take hand and foot prints of gorillas.

It's the toy with only one moving part, and best of all, Silly Putty is still priced so almost everyone can afford it.

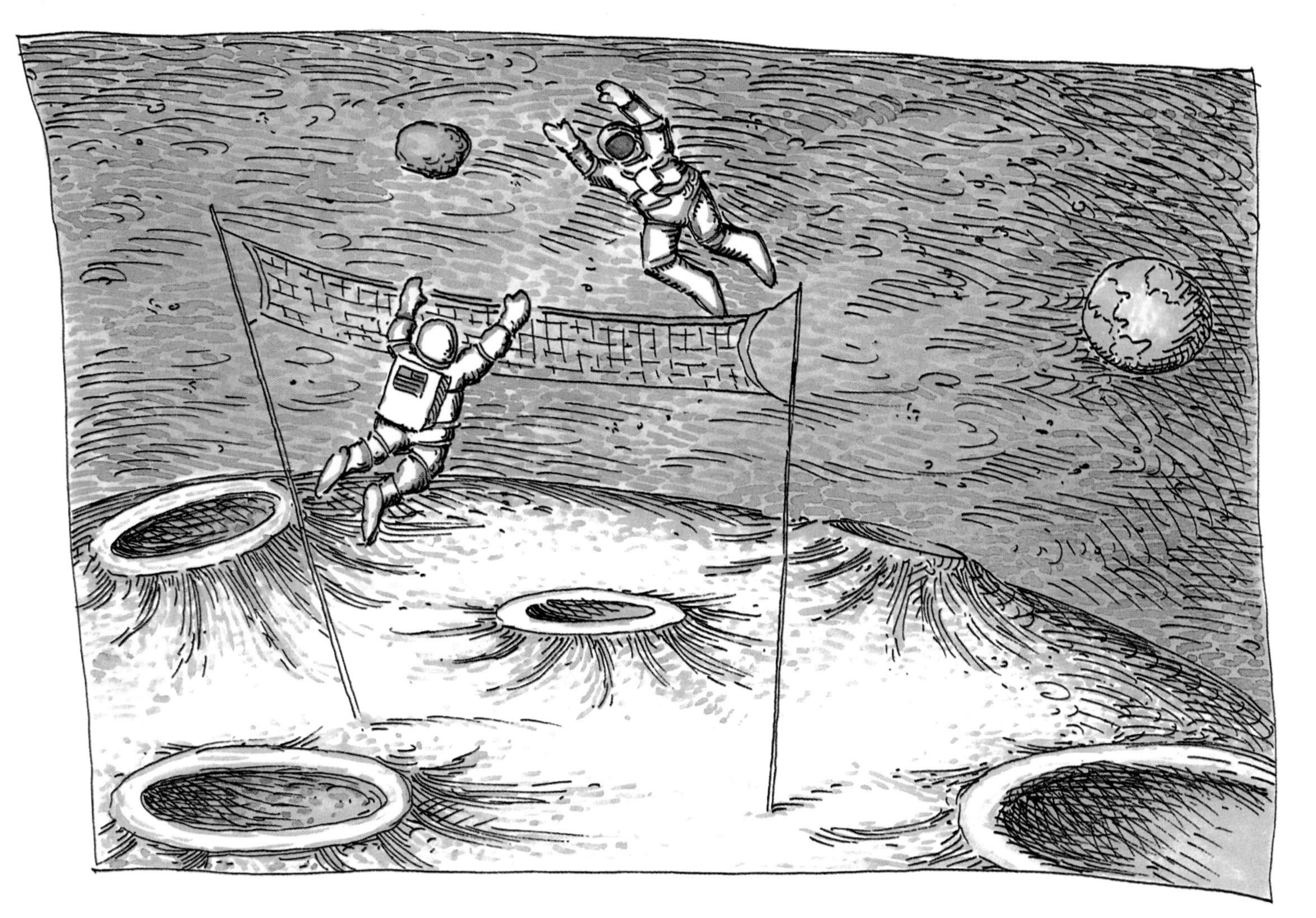

The Frisbee Disc

The Frisbee was invented 2,700 years ago.

Well . . . not really!

Discus throwing was a part of the early Olympic games in Greece 2,700 years ago. And the design of the Frisbee disc is similar to the discus thrown in the Olympic games. But the Frisbee is a Frisbee, not a discus. And its invention was *not* the result of some inventor staying up nights.

The original Frisbee was spelled Frisbie and it was metal. It was not invented to be thrown — except into an oven. It was a pie tin stamped with the words "Frisbie Pies" since the pies came from the Frisbie Bakery in Bridgeport, Connecticut.

The Frisbie pie tins would probably have done nothing more than hold pies if it hadn't been for some Yale University students. The Yale students bought Frisbie pies and once the pie was eaten, they began tossing the tins to each other. They would call out, "Frisbie!" to the person to whom they were tossing the pan, or to warn people walking nearby to watch for the flying objects.

And so, intending simply to toss a pie tin back and forth, the Yale University students invented what has grown into the Frisbee we know today.

Walter F. Morrison produced the first plastic models. The Wham-O Manufacturing Company of San Gabriel, California, began manufacturing Frisbee discs in the mid-1950s and since 1957 has made sixteen models. Now about thirty companies make flying discs.

There are flying disc clubs, tournaments, champions, a world association, and a publication just for flying disc enthusiasts. The National Frisbee Disc Festival is held each September.

The *Guinness Book of World Records* reports that the record time for keeping a flying disc aloft was set by Don Cain on May 26, 1984, when he kept one in the air for 16.72 seconds.

Disc play is good exercise. It's fun. It's easy, yet challenging. It doesn't cost much. And, best of all, it's a sport you can enjoy with your favorite dog!

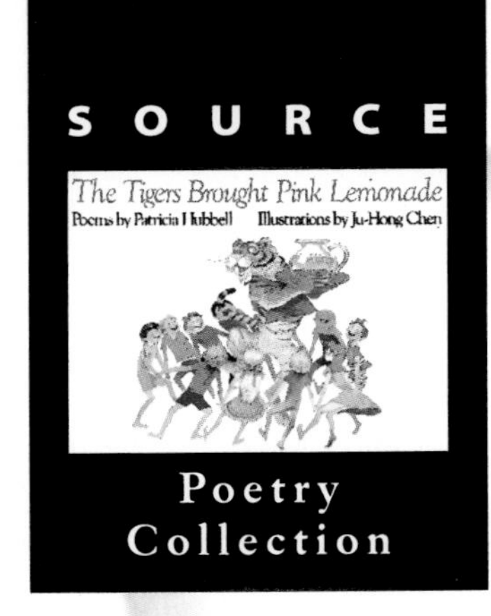

from

The Tigers Brought Pink Lemonade

by *Patricia Hubbell*

illustration by *Ju-Hong Chen*

The Inventor Thinks Up Helicopters

"*W*hy not
a
vertical
whirling
winding
bug,
that hops like a cricket
crossing a rug,
that swerves like a dragonfly
testing his steering,
twisting and veering?
Fleet as a beetle.
Up
down
left
right,
jounce, bounce, day and night.
It could land in a pasture the size of a dot . . .
Why not?"

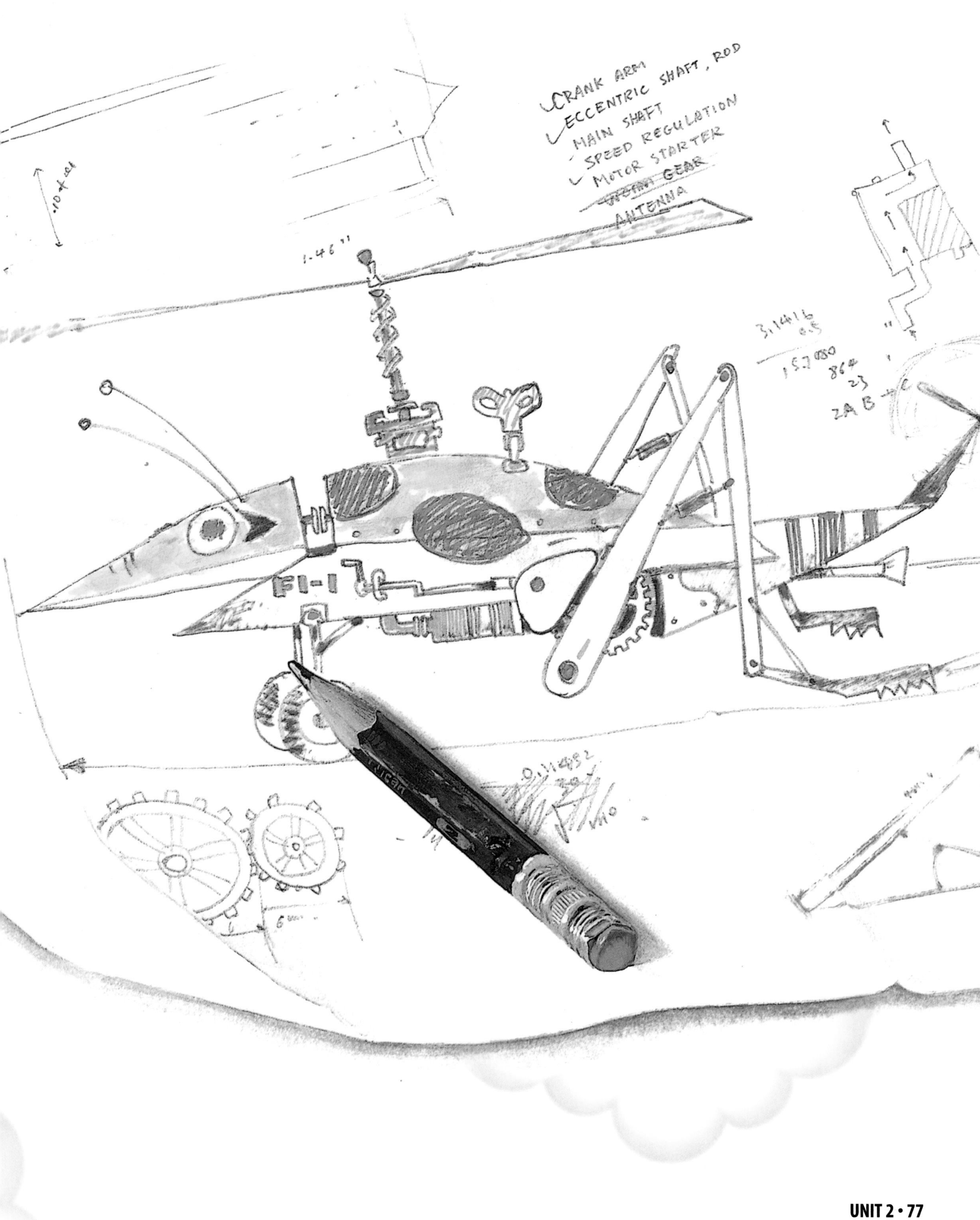
CRANK ARM
ECCENTRIC SHAFT, ROD
MAIN SHAFT
SPEED REGULATION
MOTOR STARTER
GEAR
ANTENNA
FI-I

WORKSHOP 2

How to Make an Invention Diagram

Have you ever had an idea for an invention? Did you ever look at an everyday object and think, "I could improve that?" Inventors often write down their ideas when they think of them. Later, they may decide to develop an idea by making a diagram of it.

What is an invention diagram? An invention diagram is a drawing of an invention with each of its parts labeled, and a list of materials needed to make it. The diagram includes a description of what the invention can do.

Nathan Matter:

The Handy Helper

magnetic bracelet holds nails and tacks

The name of the inventor

The name of the invention

Matthew McCurdy's

Crayons for Keeps

long bolt

handle pushes crayon out

hard nylon dowel

crayon

protects crayons from breaking

Clearly labeled parts

Description of the invention's function

1 Make a List

Jot down ideas for inventions or product improvements that you would like to see. Don't worry if your ideas seem silly—how about motorized sneakers, or sunglasses with a built-in video camera? Write down as many ideas as you can.

2 Design Your Invention

Look over your ideas and choose the one you like best. Think of different ways to design your invention. For example, if your invention is a talking watch, one design idea might include a talking cartoon head on the watch. A different design idea would be a digital watch that would announce the time and date every hour. Write down at least three different design ideas for your invention.

3 Draw a Diagram

Pick your favorite design idea and make a diagram of it. You may want to draw a picture of the whole thing and then a closeup of one of its important parts. Or you could show what your invention looks like on both the outside and the inside. Be sure to label each part of your invention. Underneath the diagram, list the materials you would need to build it.

Tip Make some quick sketches of your invention before you draw your finished diagram.

4 Add Finishing Touches

Write a brief description of what your invention does. Don't forget to name it. Share your invention diagram with your classmates.

If You Are Using a Computer . . .

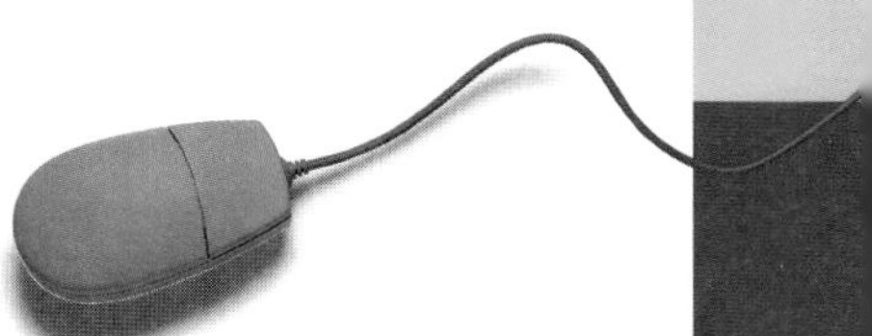

Keep track of your invention ideas by typing them in the journal format. You also can experiment with font sizes and styles to make labels for your diagram.

THINK

Why is a diagram an important step in the process of developing an invention?

Julie Lewis
Inventor

PASSENGER TRAIN TRAVELLING ON SOUND WAVES
ROBO VAC
ROBOTIC VACUUM CLEANER
SOLAR-POWERED SPACECRAFT
HEART
REMOTE CONTROLLED ROBOT SURGEON

FLOATING AIR-AUTO

MORE H2O, SIR?

SUPPE?

MENU

MORE WATER?

COMPUTERIZED WAITER

ULTRAVIOLET RAY PROTECTOR

SECTION 3

Inventors try to make the future better.

Fast Forward

Share Kate's excitement as she talks to a space alien on her dad's computer. Then marvel at the size of the first computer ever built.

Step into a time machine with Angela and zip into the future. Next, learn about inventions that may really exist in the future.

PROJECT

Choose the best way to market your invention.

from The Computer Nut

The Star Ship

by Betsy Byars

illustrated by Lisa Adams

Kate, who's a computer nut, receives a mysterious message while drawing a self-portrait on her father's computer. She waits impatiently for another chance to make contact with the stranger who sent the message.

It was Saturday morning, and rain had been coming down for three hours, a cold, solid October rain that brought winter closer.

Kate came into her father's office, shaking rain from her slicker. She threw back her hood and crossed to the door to the computer room. "It is pouring," she said to Miss Markham.

"I'm surprised your mother let you out on a day like this."

"She almost didn't. She said, 'Just because your father is a doctor is no reason to take chances with your health . . . blah . . . blah . . . blah.' And I said, 'I never take chances with my health because when I get sick I have to take free samples.'"

"Kate!"

"That's what my mother said. 'Kate!' Anyway, it's true. I have never had drugstore medicine in my life. How much longer are you going to be?"

"Until I finish the bills."

"But that'll be hours!"

"Well, I'm going to take a break in five minutes. How about that?"

"That's better."

Kate walked to the window. She looked out at the rainswept street. She closed the blinds, opened them to the same scene, closed them.

"What is wrong with you?" Miss Markham asked without looking around. "Why are you so restless?"

"I'm not restless. I just want to know who sent me that message. And I would like to find out before Linda completely ruins me. Yesterday she—" Kate broke off.

"She what?"

"Nothing."

Kate opened the blinds again. The memory of being pushed into Frank Wilkins, of leaving a slice of pizza on his back, had been returning like an echo to embarrass her again and again. Even now her cheeks reddened. She turned from the window with a sigh.

"Okay, okay, the computer is yours. I need to make some phone calls anyway. Mrs. Brown thinks Arthur swallowed some of the dog's worm pills." She slipped out the accounting program. "I'll be back in twenty minutes, Kate."

Kate slid into the chair as Miss Markham got up. She took a deep breath and exhaled. Before Miss Markham was out of the room, she had begun to type.

THIS IS THE COMPUTER NUT. DOES SOMEBODY OUT THERE HAVE A MESSAGE FOR ME?

She waited, watching the screen. She moistened her dry lips. She typed again.

REPEAT. THIS IS THE COMPUTER NUT. IS THERE A MESSAGE FOR ME?

She waited. When nothing happened, she gave a mock scream of impatience.

"Give it a chance," Miss Markham called from her desk.

"I *hate* to wait for anything. You know that." Kate turned back to the video screen. She drummed her fingers on the desk. "I just *hate* to—"

Suddenly Kate straightened. Words were appearing on the screen.

COMPUTER NUT, THAT IS AFFIRMATIVE. THIS IS BB-9 AND I WAS TRYING TO CONTACT YOU.

"BB-9?" Kate asked herself. "I wonder what that stands for—some sort of program?"

She typed:

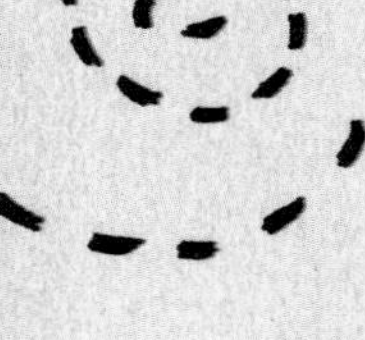

I AM UNFAMILIAR WITH BB-9. WHAT DOES THAT STAND FOR?

The answer came at once:

BB-9 IS A SHORTENED VERSION OF MY DESIGNATION. MY FULL DESIGNATION IS BB-947-82-A-1070-BLX-09. THAT IS A CODE THAT WOULD HAVE NO MEANING TO YOU AT THIS TIME. LET ME SAY THAT YOU ARE IN CONTACT WITH A PEACEABLE BEING WITHOUT MALICE OF INTENT WHOSE INTEREST IS IN MUTUAL EXCHANGE OF INFORMATION.

Kate paused. Suddenly she wished Linda were there with her to laugh, to wonder at the real identity of BB-9, to yell, "I know who it is, Kate!" She swallowed and typed:

HOW DID YOU HAPPEN TO SEE MY SELF-PORTRAIT?

She waited.

I SAW IT ON MY MASTER CONSOLE WHICH MONITORS ALL TERRESTRIAL TERMINALS. YOUR SELF-PORTRAIT WAS THE ONLY INTERESTING THING ON THE MASTER CONSOLE AT 16:39 THURSDAY. ALSO YOU LOOKED AS IF YOU HAD A SENSE OF HUMOR, AS IF YOU WOULD ENJOY A GOOD LAUGH. THAT IS WHY I DECIDED TO CONTACT YOU.

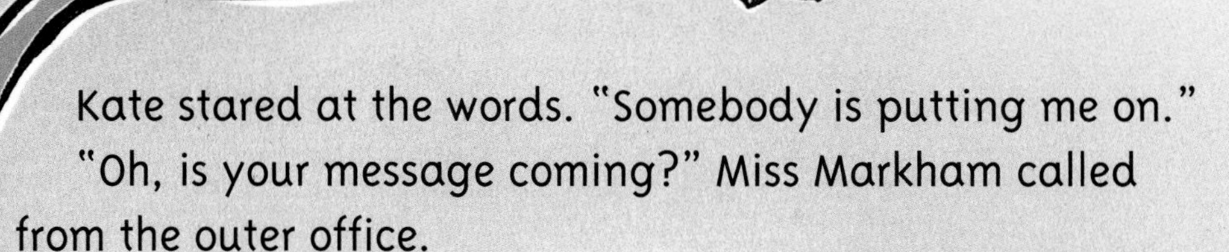

Kate stared at the words. "Somebody is putting me on."

"Oh, is your message coming?" Miss Markham called from the outer office.

"*Something's* coming."

"Well, tell me about it when you get through."

Kate let out her breath between her teeth, then typed:

WHERE, EXACTLY, IS THIS MASTER CONSOLE? HOW FAR AWAY?

She put one hand under her chin and watched the screen. "Well?"

THE MASTER CONSOLE IS 2591.82 MILES DIRECTLY ABOVE YOU AT THIS MOMENT, MOVING IN A GEOSYNCHRONOUS ORBIT.

"Oh, come on. You expect me to believe that?" Kate put her hands on the keyboard.

WHAT ARE YOU? A SATELLITE? A—

"I'm ready to use the computer now, Kate," Miss Markham called.

"I'm almost through."

The answer was coming. Kate leaned forward.

NO SATELLITE, COMPUTER NUT. I AM IN A SELF-CONTAINED UNIT, A STAR SHIP, AS YOU EARTHLINGS WOULD SAY, AND I HAVE BEEN MONITORING EARTH'S COMPUTERS IN PREPARATION FOR AN OCTOBER LANDING.

Kate snorted with disgust. "An October landing. Who does he think he is? E.T.?"

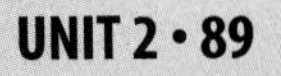

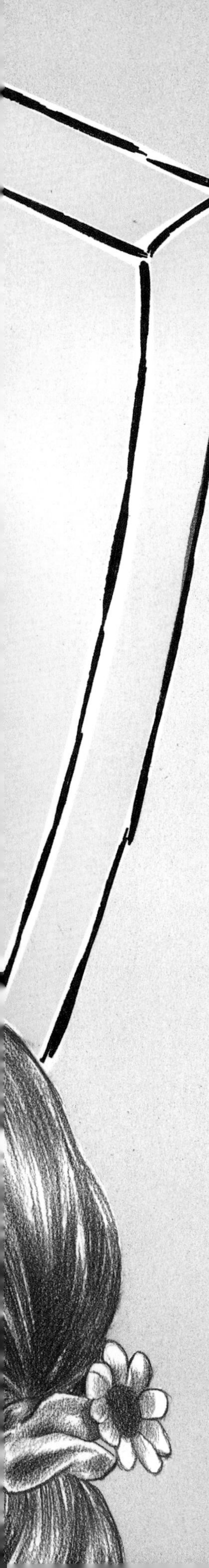

AND JUST HOW, WHEN, AND WHERE ARE YOU GOING TO MAKE THIS LANDING?

She waited, leaning forward on her elbows.

THE ACTUAL DETAILS OF MY LANDING CANNOT BE REVEALED AT THIS TIME. HOWEVER, I WOULD BE GLAD TO DEPICT MY SPACE TRANSPORT. IT IS NOT AN UNUSUAL VEHICLE—MUCH LIKE OTHERS THAT HAVE COME TO YOUR PLANET—BUT IF IT WOULD BE OF INTEREST TO YOU . . .

Kate typed:

IT WOULD DEFINITELY BE OF INTEREST.

"Kate, are you finished?" Miss Markham called.

"Just let me see this spaceship," Kate called back.

"Spaceship?"

"Yes, some nut is pretending to be from outer space, and he is going to draw his spaceship. It's nothing out of the ordinary, just some little vehicle he's been tooling around the galaxy in."

"This I gotta see."

Miss Markham came into the room and stood behind Kate. They watched the screen as lines began to appear. For a moment there was not a sound in the office.

Then, when the picture was finished, Miss Markham let out her breath in a low whistle. "Well," she said, "as space vehicles go, that is not bad."

Kate slapped her hands down on the desk. "I hate it when people try to put me on. I *hate* it."

"Don't be so intense, hon. You take life too seriously. It's just somebody playing a joke on you. Go along with it. Ask him to send a picture of himself, of his planet."

Kate kept staring at the spaceship until the picture disappeared and words replaced it on the screen.

WHAT DID YOU THINK OF MY SPACESHIP, COMPUTER NUT? WAS IT A DISAPPOINTMENT? WAS IT AS YOU EXPECTED?

"Tell him, 'Yes.' Tell him you'd like to go for a ride. Tell him you'll meet him out in front of the office. Ask him if he's got an alien friend for me." Miss Markham broke off and let her hands drop onto Kate's shoulders. "I am getting carried away. Whatever you tell him will have to be some other time. I need the computer now."

Kate typed:

COMPUTER NUT LOGGING.

"There." Kate got up and walked to the window. She stared out at the wet street.

"You'll find out who it is," Miss Markham said.

Kate flicked her hair behind her ears. "I'm beginning to wonder," she said.

Kate does finally discover the identity of BB-9, the mysterious message sender. And is he ever out of this world!

Computer
Nut
logging

SOURCE
SCHOLASTIC NEWS®
News Magazine

The First Computers

A History Play by
Richard Chevat

Illustrated by
Dan Picasso

Fast forward to a TV newsroom of the future where a reporter can travel back to 1943 to cover the unveiling of a new invention.

Characters

Sue Smith

Gary Granite

Grace Hopper

Howard Aiken

Mary Roberts

Granite: Hello, this is Gary Granite in the newsroom. Our time-traveling reporter, Sue Smith, has traveled back to the year 1943 to get a first-hand look at one of the first computers. Sue, can you hear me?

Smith: Yes, Gary. I am at Harvard University, in Cambridge, Massachusetts. Right here in this room, one of the first modern computers is being put together.

Granite: Hey, that sounds neat! Can you get an interview with the first person to play Pac Man?

Smith: No, Gary, I'm here to talk to Grace Hopper, who was one of the first computer programmers. Wait a minute, I think I see her now! Oh, Ms. Hopper! Excuse me, I'm Sue Smith from Time-Travel News. Could you answer some questions for our viewers?

Hopper: Sure, but we'll have to hurry. I'm very busy.

Smith: All right. First, could you show us the machine that you are working on?

Hopper: Show you . . . ? That's it right there!

Smith: That's a computer? It must be fifty feet long!

Hopper: Fifty-one, to be exact. It's also eight feet tall and two feet thick and weighs about five tons. Come on, let's go inside.

Smith: Inside? OK, if you say so. Gary, I don't know if you can see this, but Grace Hopper is taking me *inside* the computer.

Granite: Great, I always wanted to know where those little space aliens went when they weren't attacking my planet.

Hopper: This is the inside of the Mark 1 computer. It is powered by a small electric motor which turns this shaft here.

Smith: It looks like some kind of engine.

Hopper: Yes, sort of. As you can see, it is mainly mechanical, that is, it works with moving parts.

Granite: Sue, ask her where the microchips are.

Smith: Gary, microchips won't be invented until 1958.

Hopper: What won't be invented until 1958? Say, who did you say you are?

Smith: Uh, never mind. Could you explain what all these rolls of paper are for?

Hopper: The instructions for running this machine are written on this paper tape. Actually, they're not really written. Instead, it's a code of small holes punched in the paper.

Smith: That's the program?

Hopper: Yes, that would be another name for the instructions—a program.

Smith: Tell us, what can the Mark 1 do?

Hopper: Why don't you ask my boss, Howard Aiken? The Mark 1 is his invention.

Aiken: Did someone mention my name?

Smith: Mr. Aiken, could you explain what the Mark 1 will do when it is finished?

Aiken: Well, the Mark 1 is really a big calculating machine. It will be able to perform large numbers of calculations in a short time. The Navy is paying part of our costs. They plan to use the Mark 1 to help win World War II.

Smith: Can you give us an example?

Roberts: I can.

Smith: Who are you?

Roberts: My name is Mary Roberts, and I work for the Navy. There are 30 women who work in my office. Sometimes it takes all of us working four or five days to solve just one problem.

Aiken: Yes, you see, they have to use old-fashioned adding machines and pencils and paper. But the Mark 1 will be able to do the same amount of work in just a few hours.

Smith: So in some ways, the Mark 1 is like a giant adding machine?

Aiken: You could say that. But it can handle problems that are much more complex than any adding machine.

Hopper: Of course, the Mark 1 is just the beginning. Our goal is to build a machine that can handle many different problems and work even faster than Mark 1.

Smith: A computer.

Hopper: That's one name for it. We think these new machines will be a great aid to science.

Granite: Not to mention video games.

Hopper: What did you say?

Smith: Uh, nothing.

Hopper: Well, we have a lot of work to do.

Smith: I guess you're still getting all of the bugs out of the system.

The actual Mark 1 computer unveiled in 1943

Hopper: Oh, you heard about that, did you?

Smith: Heard about what?

Hopper: Our bug. I have it right here, taped to this piece of paper.

Smith: That's a moth!

Aiken: We were having problems with the computer, and no one could figure out what was wrong. Then Grace found this in the machine. It was stuck in one of the relay switches.

Smith: You don't mean . . . ?

Hopper: Yes, this is the very first computer bug.

Smith: Well, this certainly is historic.

Hopper: Yes, well, we really have to get back to work.

Aiken: Yes, we were in the middle of a major problem.

Granite: Sue, maybe you should loan them your computer.

Hopper: You have a computer?

Smith: Yes, I, uh, that is . . .

Hopper: Is it close by?

Smith: Well actually, it's, that is . . . you're looking at it. It's right here on my wrist.

Hopper: Hey, who did you say you are?

Smith: Uh, this is Sue Smith, of Time-Travel News, signing off.

Aiken: Did she say on her wrist?

Roberts: She must have a very strong arm.

Hopper: I thought there was something strange about her.

SOURCE

WITHIN REACH

Ten Stories by
Constance C. Greene
Ardath Mayhar • Lensey Namioka
Judie Angell • Carol Snyder
Steven Otfinoski • Pam Conrad
Robert Lipsyte • Larry Bograd
Jan Greenberg
Edited by Donald R. Gallo

Short Story Collection

from

WITHIN REACH

edited by Donald R. Gallo

LAFFF

AWARD WINNING Author

by Lensey Namioka

illustrated by Tim Lee

In movies, geniuses have frizzy white hair, right? They wear thick glasses and have names like Dr. Zweistein.

Peter Lu didn't have frizzy white hair. He had straight hair, as black as licorice. He didn't wear thick glasses, either, since his vision was normal.

Peter's family, like ours, had immigrated from China, but they had settled here first. When we moved into a house just two doors down from the Lus, they gave us some good advice on how to get along in America.

I went to the same school as Peter, and we walked to the school bus together every morning. Like many Chinese parents, mine made sure that I worked very hard in school.

In spite of all I could do, my grades were nothing compared to Peter's. He was at the top in all his classes. We walked to the school bus without talking because I was a little scared of him. Besides, he was always deep in thought.

Peter didn't have any friends. Most of the kids thought he was a nerd because they saw his head always buried in books. I didn't think he even tried to join the rest of us or cared what the others thought of him.

Then on Halloween he surprised us all. As I went down the block trick-or-treating, dressed as a zucchini in my green sweats, I heard a strange, deep voice behind me say, "How do you do."

I yelped and turned around. Peter was wearing a long, black Chinese gown with slits in the sides. On his head he had a little round cap, and down each side of his mouth drooped a thin, long mustache.

"I am Dr. Lu Manchu, the mad scientist," he announced, putting his hands in his sleeves and bowing.

He smiled when he saw me staring at his costume. I smiled back. I knew he was making fun of the way some kids believed in stereotypes about Chinese people. Still, his was a scary smile, somehow.

Some of the other kids came up, and when they saw Peter, they were impressed. "Hey, neat!" said one boy.

I hadn't expected Peter to put on a costume and go trick-or-treating like a normal kid. So maybe he did want to join the others after all—at least some of the time. After that night he wasn't a nerd anymore. He was Dr. Lu. Even some of the teachers began to call him that.

When we became too old for trick-or-treating, Peter was still Dr. Lu Manchu. The rumor was that he was working on a fantastic machine in his parents' garage. But nobody had any idea what it was.

One evening, as I was coming home from a baby-sitting job, I cut across the Lus' backyard. Passing their garage, I saw through a little window that the light was on. My curiosity got the better of me, and I peeked in.

I saw a booth that looked like a shower stall. A stool stood in the middle of the stall, and hanging over the stool was something that looked like a great big shower head.

Suddenly a deep voice behind me said, "Good evening, Angela." Peter bowed and smiled his scary smile.

"What are you doing?" I squeaked.

Still in his strange, deep voice, Peter said, "What are *you* doing? After all, this is my garage."

"I was just cutting across your yard to get home. Your parents never complained before."

"I thought you were spying on me." said Peter. "I thought you wanted to know about my machine." He hissed when he said the word *machine*.

Honestly, he was beginning to frighten me. "What machine?" I demanded. "You mean this shower-stall thing?"

He drew himself up and narrowed his eyes, making them into thin slits. "This is my time machine!"

I goggled at him. "You mean . . .you mean . . . this machine can send you forward and backward in time?"

"Well, actually, I can only send things forward in time," admitted Peter, speaking in his normal voice again. "That's why I'm calling the machine LAFFF. It stands for Lu's Artifact For Fast Forward."

JUNE
1996
BEEP
GURGLE

Of course Peter always won first prize at the annual statewide science fair. But that's a long way from making a time machine. Minus his mustache and long Chinese gown, he was just Peter Lu.

"I don't believe it!" I said. "I bet LAFFF is only good for a laugh."

"Okay, Angela. I'll show you!" hissed Peter.

He sat down on the stool and twisted a dial. I heard some *bleeps*, *cheeps*, and *gurgles*. Peter disappeared.

He must have done it with mirrors. I looked around the garage. I peeked under the tool bench. There was no sign of him.

"Okay, I give up," I told him. "It's a good trick, Peter. You can come out now."

Bleep, *cheep*, and *gurgle* went the machine, and there was Peter, sitting on the stool. He held a red rose in his hand. "What do you think of that?"

I blinked. "So you produced a flower. Maybe you had it under the stool."

"Roses bloom in June, right?" he demanded.

That was true. And this was December.

"I sent myself forward in time to June when the flowers were blooming," said Peter. "And I picked the rose from our yard. Convinced, Angela?"

It was too hard to swallow. "You said you couldn't send things back in time," I objected. "So how did you bring the rose back?"

But even as I spoke I saw that his hands were empty. The rose was gone.

"That's one of the problems with the machine," said Peter. "When I send myself forward, I can't seem to stay there for long. I snap back to my own time after only a minute. Anything I bring with me snaps back to its own time, too. So my rose has gone back to this June."

I was finally convinced, and I began to see possibilities. "Wow, just think: If I don't want to do the dishes, I can send myself forward to the time when the dishes are already done."

"That won't do you much good," said Peter. "You'd soon pop back to the time when the dishes were still dirty."

Too bad. "There must be something your machine is good for," I said. Then I had another idea. "Hey, you can bring me back a piece of fudge from the future, and I can eat it twice: once now, and again in the future."

"Yes, but the fudge wouldn't stay in your stomach," said Peter. "It would go back to the future."

"That's even better!" I said. "I can enjoy eating the fudge over and over again without getting fat!"

It was late, and I had to go home before my parents started to worry. Before I left, Peter said, "Look, Angela, there's still a lot of work to do on LAFFF. Please don't tell anybody about the machine until I've got it right."

A few days later I asked him how he was doing.

"I can stay in the future time a bit longer now," he said. "Once I got it up to four minutes."

"Is that enough time to bring me back some fudge from the future?" I asked.

"We don't keep many sweets around the house," he said. "But I'll see what I can do."

A few minutes later, he came back with a spring roll for me. "My mother was frying these in the kitchen, and I snatched one while she wasn't looking."

I bit into the hot, crunchy spring roll, but before I finished chewing, it disappeared. The taste of soy sauce, green onions, and bean sprouts stayed a little longer in my mouth, though.

It was fun to play around with LAFFF, but it wasn't really useful. I didn't know what a great help it would turn out to be.

Every year our school held a writing contest, and the winning story for each grade got printed in our school magazine. I wanted desperately to win. I worked awfully hard in school, but my parents still thought I could do better.

Winning the writing contest would show my parents that I was really good in something. I love writing stories, and I have lots of ideas. But when I actually write them down, my stories never turn out as good as I thought. I just can't seem to find the right words, because English isn't my first language.

I got an honorable mention last year, but it wasn't the same as winning and showing my parents my name, Angela Tang, printed in the school magazine.

The deadline for the contest was getting close, and I had a pile of stories written, but none of them looked like a winner.

Then, the day before the deadline, *boing*, a brilliant idea hit me.

I thought of Peter and his LAFFF machine.

I rushed over to the Lus' garage and, just as I had hoped, Peter was there, tinkering with his machine.

"I've got this great idea for winning the story contest," I told him breathlessly. "You see, to be certain of winning, I have to write the story that would be the winner."

"That's obvious," Peter said dryly. "In fact, you're going around in a circle."

"Wait, listen!" I said. "I want to use LAFFF and go forward to the time when the next issue of the school magazine is out. Then I can read the winning story."

After a moment Peter nodded. "I see. You plan to write down the winning story after you've read it and then send it in to the contest."

I nodded eagerly. "The story would *have* to win, because it's the winner!"

Peter began to look interested. "I've got LAFFF to the point where I can stay in the future for seven minutes now. Will that be long enough for you?"

"I'll just have to work quickly," I said.

Peter smiled. It wasn't his scary Lu Manchu smile, but a nice smile. He was getting as excited as I was. "Okay, Angela. Let's go for it."

He led me to the stool. "What's your destination?" he asked. "I mean, *when's* your destination?"

Suddenly I was nervous. I told myself that Peter had made many time trips, and he looked perfectly healthy.

Why not? What have I got to lose—except time?

I took a deep breath. "I want to go forward three weeks in time." By then I'd have a copy of the new school magazine in my room.

"Ready, Angela?" asked Peter.

"As ready as I'll ever be," I whispered.

Bleep, *cheep*, and *gurgle*. Suddenly Peter disappeared.

What went wrong? Did Peter get sent by mistake, instead of me?

Then I realized what had happened. Three weeks later in time Peter might be somewhere else. No wonder I couldn't see him.

There was no time to be lost. Rushing out of Peter's garage, I ran over to our house and entered through the back door.

L.A.F.

Mother was in the kitchen. When she saw me, she stared. "Angela! I thought you were upstairs taking a shower!"

"Sorry!" I panted. "No time to talk!"

I dashed up to my room. Then I suddenly had a strange idea. What if I met *myself* in my room? Argh! It was a spooky thought.

There was nobody in my room. Where was I? I mean, where was the I of three weeks later?

Wait. Mother had just said she thought I was taking a shower. Down the hall, I could hear the water running in the bathroom. Okay. That meant I wouldn't run into me for a while.

I went to the shelf above my desk and frantically pawed through the junk piled there. I found it! I found the latest issue of the school magazine, the one with the winning stories printed in it.

How much time had passed? Better hurry.

The shower had stopped running. This meant the other me was out of the bathroom. Have to get out of here!

Too late. Just as I started down the stairs, I heard Mother talking again. "Angela! A minute ago you were all dressed! Now you're in your robe again and your hair's all wet! I don't understand."

I shivered. It was scary, listening to Mother talking to myself downstairs. I heard my other self answering something, then the sound of her—my—steps coming up the stairs. In a panic, I dodged into the spare room and closed the door.

I heard the steps—my steps—go past and into my room.

The minute I heard the door of my room close, I rushed out and down the stairs.

Mother was standing at the foot of the stairs. When she saw me, her mouth dropped. "But . . . but . . . just a minute ago you were in your robe and your hair was all wet!"

"See you later, Mother," I panted. And I ran.

Behind me I heard Mother muttering, "I'm going mad!"

I didn't stop and try to explain. I might go mad, too.

It would be great if I could just keep the magazine with me. But, like the spring roll, it would get carried back to its own time after a few minutes. So the next best thing was to read the magazine as fast as I could.

It was hard to run and flip through the magazine at the same time. But I made it back to Peter's garage and plopped down on the stool.

At last I found the story: the story that had won the contest in our grade. I started to read.

Suddenly I heard *bleep*, *cheep*, and *gurgle*, and Peter loomed up in front of me. I was back in my original time again.

But I still had the magazine! Now I had to read the story before the magazine popped back to the future. It was hard to concentrate with Peter jumping up and down impatiently, so different from his usual calm, collected self.

I read a few paragraphs, and I was beginning to see how the story would shape up. But before I got any further, the magazine disappeared from my hand.

So I didn't finish reading the story. I didn't reach the end, where the name of the winning writer was printed.

That night I stayed up very late to write down what I remembered of the story. It had a neat plot, and I could see why it was the winner.

I hadn't read the entire story, so I had to make up the ending myself. But that was okay, since I knew how it should come out.

The winners of the writing contest would be announced at the school assembly on Friday. After we had filed into the assembly hall and sat down, the principal gave a speech. I tried not to fidget while he explained about the contest.

Suddenly I was struck by a dreadful thought. Somebody in my class had written the winning story, the one I had copied. Wouldn't that person be declared the winner, instead of me?

The principal started announcing the winners. I chewed my knuckles in an agony of suspense, as I waited to see who would be announced as the winner in my class. Slowly, the principal began with the lowest grade. Each winner walked in slow motion to the stage, while the principal slowly explained why the story was good.

At last, at last, he came to our grade. "The winner is . . ." He stopped, slowly got out his handkerchief, and slowly blew his nose. Then he cleared his throat. "The winning story is 'Around and Around,' by Angela Tang."

I sat like a stone, unable to move. Peter nudged me. "Go on, Angela! They're waiting for you."

I got up and walked up to the stage in a daze. The principal's voice seemed to be coming from far, far away as he told the audience that I had written a science fiction story about time travel.

The winners each got a notebook bound in imitation leather for writing more stories. Inside the cover of the notebook was a ballpoint pen. But the best prize was having my story in the school magazine with my name printed at the end.

Then why didn't I feel good about winning?

After assembly, the kids in our class crowded around to congratulate me. Peter formally shook my hand. "Good work, Angela," he said, and winked at me.

That didn't make me feel any better. I hadn't won the contest fairly. Instead of writing the story myself, I had copied it from the school magazine.

That meant someone in our class—one of the kids here—had actually written the story. Who was it?

My heart was knocking against my ribs as I stood there and waited for someone to complain that I had stolen his story.

Nobody did.

As we were riding the school bus home, Peter looked at me. "You don't seem very happy about winning the contest, Angela."

"No, I'm not," I mumbled. "I feel just awful."

"Tell you what," suggested Peter. "Come over to my house and we'll discuss it."

"What is there to discuss?" I asked glumly. "I won the contest because I cheated."

"Come on over, anyway. My mother bought a fresh package of humbow in Chinatown."

I couldn't turn down that invitation. Humbow, a roll stuffed with barbecued pork, is my favorite snack.

Peter's mother came into the kitchen while we were munching, and he told her about the contest.

Mrs. Lu looked pleased. "I'm very glad, Angela. You have a terrific imagination, and you deserve to win."

"I like Angela's stories," said Peter. "They're original."

It was the first compliment he had ever paid me, and I felt my face turning red.

After Mrs. Lu left us, Peter and I each had another humbow. But I was still miserable. "I wish I had never started this. I feel like such a jerk."

Peter looked at me, and I swear he was enjoying himself. "If you stole another student's story, why didn't that person complain?"

"I don't know!" I wailed.

"Think!" said Peter. "You're smart, Angela. Come on, figure it out."

Me, smart? I was so overcome to hear myself called smart by a genius like Peter that I just stared at him.

He had to repeat himself. "Figure it out, Angela!"

I tried to concentrate. Why was Peter looking so amused?

L.A.F.F.F.
STORY CONTEST

The light finally dawned. "Got it," I said slowly. "*I'm* the one who wrote the story."

"The winning story is your own, Angela, because that's the one that won."

My head began to go around and around. "But where did the original idea for the story come from?"

"What made the plot so good?" asked Peter. His voice sounded unsteady.

"Well, in my story, my character used a time machine to go forward in time . . ."

"Okay, whose idea was it to use a time machine?"

"It was mine," I said slowly. I remembered the moment when the idea had hit me with a *boing*.

"So you s-stole f-from yourself!" sputtered Peter. He started to roar with laughter. I had never seen him break down like that. At this rate, he might wind up being human.

When he could talk again, he asked me to read my story to him.

I began. " 'In movies, geniuses have frizzy white hair, right? They wear thick glasses and have names like Dr. Zweistein. . . .' "

THINGS TO COME

Experts Gaze into the Future

by Curtis Slepian
illustrated by Nathan Jarvis

Marvin Cetron has an unusual job. He is paid to predict the future.

Cetron is a futurist—an expert who uses current information to figure out where the country and world are going, and what the future holds.

Technology is changing the world so quickly, we can't keep up. People in fields like transportation and medicine want to know about current advances *and* what advances the future may hold. That way, they can plan for tomorrow—today.

So companies are hiring futurists like Cetron to predict trends that will one day affect their products and businesses. Cetron says, "I look at technology, economics, politics and social situations and ask, 'What will the future probably look like?' "

Cetron doesn't take wild guesses. First, he gathers thousands of statistics (figures) and feeds them into big computers. Then, with the help of experts, he studies the computer read-outs and makes his forecasts.

Thinking about the future is good sense. As one futurist puts it, "In order to have the future you want, you must figure out what you want and then help create it."

Here are some peeks at the future. Some things may take place in a few decades or less. And some may never happen. After all, no one really knows what the future holds!

Tomorrow's hot fashions will be designed with the environment in mind. For example, awesome future clothes may be head and shoulder coverings that shield wearers from the sun's dangerous ultraviolet rays. And people might walk down the street proudly wearing a transparent helmet that keeps out smog and bad odors.

Tiny robots may perform surgery inside a patient's body. After a patient swallows the "microrobot," a human surgeon will guide it to the trouble spot. The doctor will guide it with the help of a 3-D computer simulation of the patient's insides.

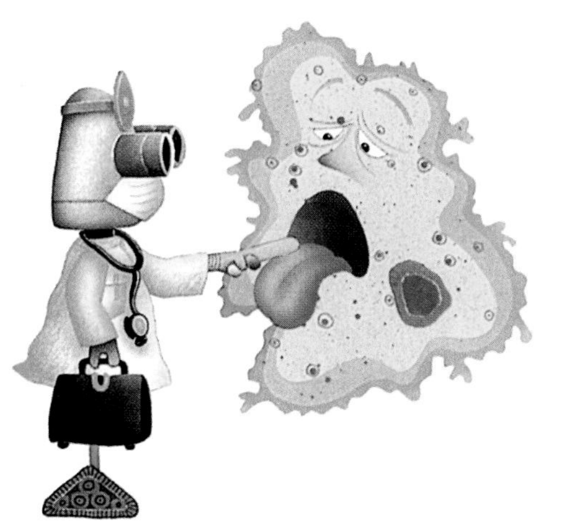

Hypersonic trains will take people from New York to Los Angeles in half an hour. They might even travel across the Atlantic in an hour! How? The "trains" would travel along a tube. When air is pumped out of the tube, the trains would "fly" through the vacuum that was created.

In 30 years, it's possible that a space hotel will be open for business. Tourists will be able to take space walks and play zero-gravity sports, as well as go on side trips to the moon. Guest rooms will have artificial gravity, so taking a shower won't be a washout.

PROJECT

How to Market Your Invention

Do *market research* and decide on a name for *your* invention.

Once an inventor patents an invention, the next step is to market it. Selling a product is just one part of marketing. Naming a product, packaging it, and advertising it are also part of the marketing process. Market research plays an important part, too. Companies test products by asking potential customers for their opinions of the new product. Then they use this research to choose a name for their product.

JET PAK
JET PAK
JET PAK
JET PAK
JET PAK
JET PAK
JET PAK
Put on a Jet Pak and Take Off!

1 Brainstorm an Inventive Idea

Think of an invention. If you need to get your imagination working, make a wish list. For example, you might write "I wish I could fly." Now think of inventions that would make it possible for you to fly. Would sneakers with wings and a motor be a good idea? a backpack with rocket jets? a hat with a propeller? Write down several wishes and the inventive ideas that would make them come true. After you're done, look back over your list and choose the one you like the most.

TOOLS

- notebook and pencil
- colored markers
- posterboard
- glue
- clipboard (optional)

Tips

- Try using alliteration or rhyme when creating a name.
- Say the names aloud to hear how they sound.

2 Name Your Invention

Once you think of your inventive idea, it's time to give it a name. What do you want the name to say about your product? Is your invention scientific? You may want a name with a technical or scientific sounding prefix. For example, the prefixes *therma-* and *micro-* sound scientific. An invention that is meant to be fun, rather than serious, should have a name that sounds fun. Use adjectives to liven up the name of your invention. Make a list of several possible names, and then pick three of them.

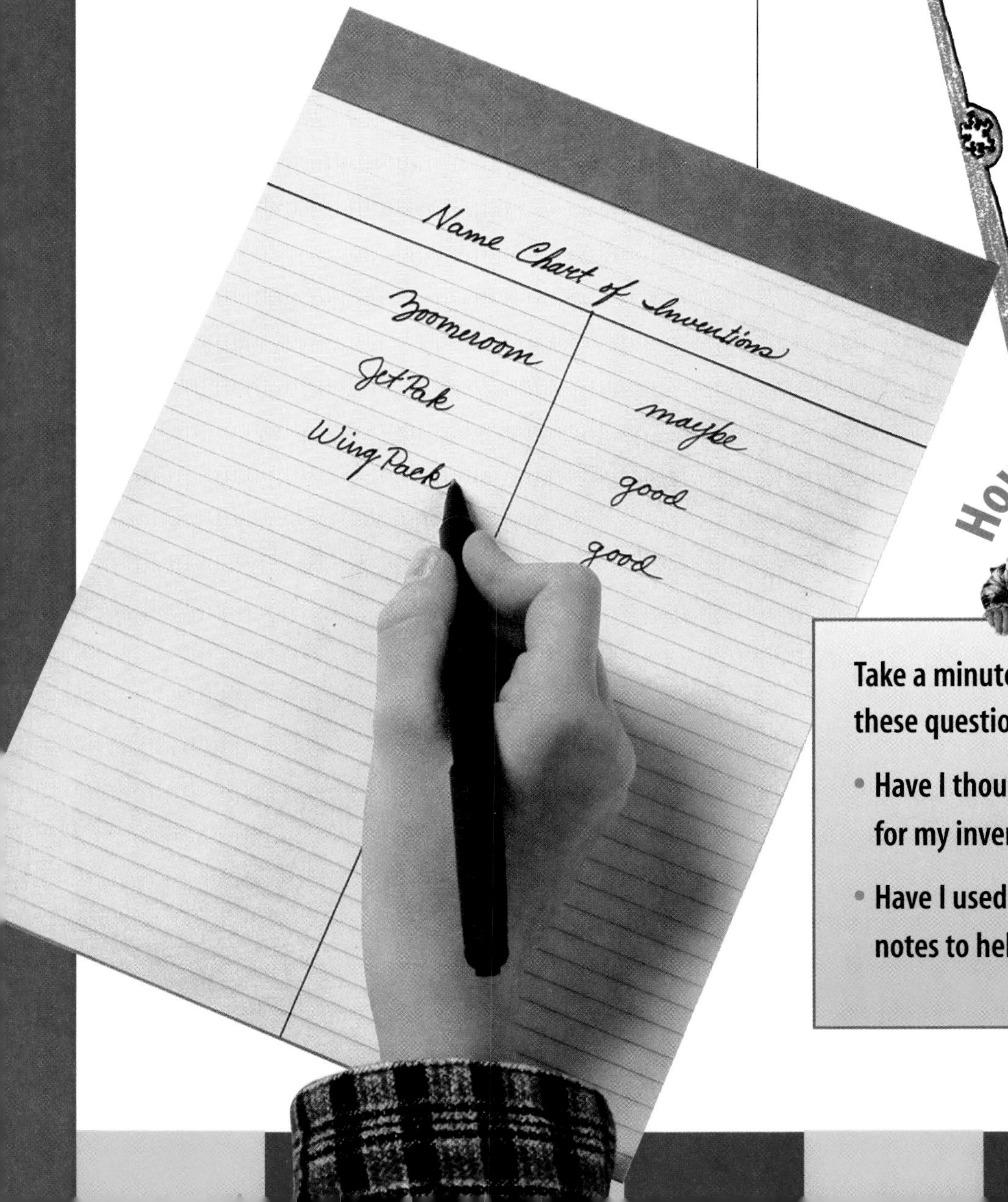

How Am I Doing?

Take a minute to ask yourself these questions:

- **Have I thought of several names for my invention?**
- **Have I used the information from my notes to help me choose a name?**

3 Do Market Research

Take the three names you've chosen, and show them to at least six people. After they have read the names, ask them to describe what they think your invention does. Find out which name they like the best. Be sure to take notes. You may also want to look at products already being sold that are like your invention. Which product has the best name? Do you like the design of the package it comes in? What do you like about the name and the way the product is presented? Using your market research, decide on the best name for your invention. If you want, you can also design a logo for your product.

4 Launch Your Invention

Now that you've named your invention, you're ready to launch it. Think about what kind of company would want to manufacture your invention. Ask some of your classmates to play the part of executives in a company. Then present your invention to them. Here are some things to include in your presentation.

- Make a poster with a colorful picture, the name of your invention, and some sentences describing what your product does. If you designed a logo, put that on the poster, too.
- Use the market research that you did. Tell the audience the good things that people said about your invention.
- Show a model of your invention, if you want to build one.

At the end of the presentation ask the audience for questions and suggestions.

If You Are Using a Computer ...

Create your poster with the sign or poster format. Type the name of your invention using a large fun font. You may wish to add a border and clip art to your poster. Then print it out and hang it up for everyone to see.

JET PAK

CONGRATULATIONS

You've learned that most problems have a solution. As you face new challenges, be sure to remember the problem-solving skills you've learned.

Julie Lewis
Inventor

Glossary

au•to•mat•ic
(ô′tə mat′ik) *adjective*
Made to move and work without the control of a human being. He had an *automatic* bread maker.

cal•cu•la•tions
(kal′kyə lā′shənz) *noun*
The answers found by using mathematics. She checked her *calculations*.
▲ **calculation**

Word History

The word calculation comes from the Latin word *calculus,* which means "pebble." Small stones were used to figure out arithmetic problems.

chem•ist
(kəm′ist) *noun*
A scientist who is an expert in studying the chemical properties of substances.

en•gi•neer
(en′jə nēr′) *noun*
Someone who is trained in building structures using scientific principles.

ex•per•i•ments
(ik sper′ə mənts) *noun*
Tests to find out or prove something.
▲ **experiment**

for•mu•la
(fôr′myə lə) *noun*
An exact method for producing a particular medicine, food, or mixture.

fu•tur•ist
(fyōō′chər ist) *noun*
A person whose job is to predict future trends on the basis of current scientific knowledge.

gadg•et (gaj′it) *noun*
A small device or tool.

hy•per•son•ic
(hī′ pər son′ik) *adjective*
Traveling at least five times the speed of sound. The jet flew at *hypersonic* speeds.

im•prove•ments
(im prōōv′mənts) *noun*
Changes or additions that make something better. New windows and doors were *improvements* to the house. ▲ **improvement**

in•gen•ious
(in jēn′yəs) *adjective*
Marked by a special ability to be inventive and clever. The science project she made was *ingenious*.

in•tend•ing
(in ten′ding) *verb*
Having a purpose in mind. He was *intending* to fix his bicycle. ▲ **intend**

in•ven•tion
(in ven′shən) *noun*
Something that has been created for the first time. The telephone was Alexander Graham Bell's *invention*.

la•bor-sav•ing
(lā′bər sā′ving) *adjective*
Designed to decrease work. The washing machine is a *labor-saving* device.

li•censed
(lī′sənsd) *verb*
Granted legal permission to do something. She was *licensed* to drive a bus.
▲ **license**

log•ging (lô′ging) *verb*
Entering the necessary information to begin or end a session on a computer. ▲ **log**

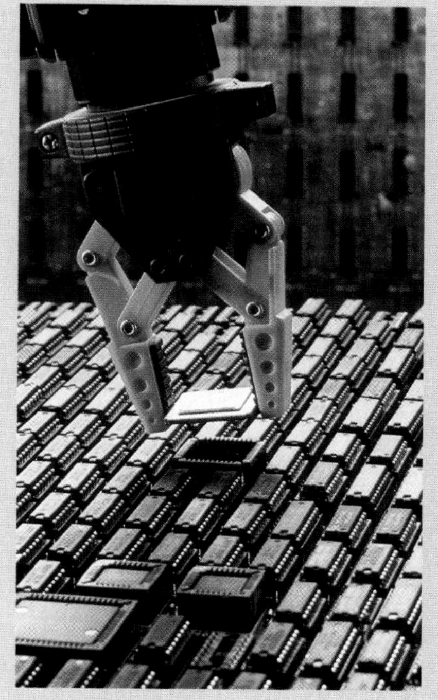

microrobot

me•chan•i•cal
(mə kan′i kəl) *adjective*
Of, or relating to, machines. They saw a *mechanical* horse at the museum.

mi•cro•chips
(mī′krō′ chips′) *noun*
Tiny electronic devices that contain circuits and components etched onto pieces of silicon.
▲ **microchip**

mi•cro•ro•bot
(mī′krō rō′ bət) *noun*
A tiny robot with specialized skills.

Word Study

The prefix micro– means "small." It also means "enlarging" or "amplifying." Many inventions have the prefix micro–. ***Microphotography*** reduces a picture to the size of a pinhead. The result is called a ***microdot***. A ***microscope*** enlarges, while a ***microphone*** amplifies.

a	add	o͝o	took	ə =
ā	ace	o͞o	pool	a in *above*
â	care	u	up	e in *sicken*
ä	palm	û	burn	i in *possible*
e	end	yo͞o	fuse	o in *melon*
ē	equal	oi	oil	u in *circus*
i	it	ou	pout	
ī	ice	ng	ring	
o	odd	th	thin	
ō	open	*th*	this	
ô	order	zh	vision	

Glossary

mold•ed
(mōl′did) *verb*
Made or formed into a shape. ▲ **mold**

pat•ent•ed
(pat′n tid) *verb*
Obtained a document from the government that gives a person the right to be the only one who can make and sell an invention. The inventor *patented* her invention.
▲ **patent**

Fact File

- The first United States patent was granted in 1790.
- There are about 27 million patents on file at the United States Patent Office.
- Fewer than 5 percent of all patents are ever used or sold.

pro•gram
(prō′gram) *noun*
A sequence of coded instructions that tell a computer what to do. This *program* tells the computer how to make graphs.

sub•stance
(sub′stəns) *noun*
The physical matter which a thing consists of. The *substance* in the glass was water.

sus•pen•sion bridge
(sə spen′shun brij′) *noun*
A bridge that is hung by cables anchored to towers.

syn•thet•ic
(sin thet′ik) *adjective*
Produced by human beings; not of natural origin. The *synthetic* flower looked real.

tech•nique
(tek nēk′) *noun*
A certain way of doing things; a special method. She had her own *technique* for painting chairs.

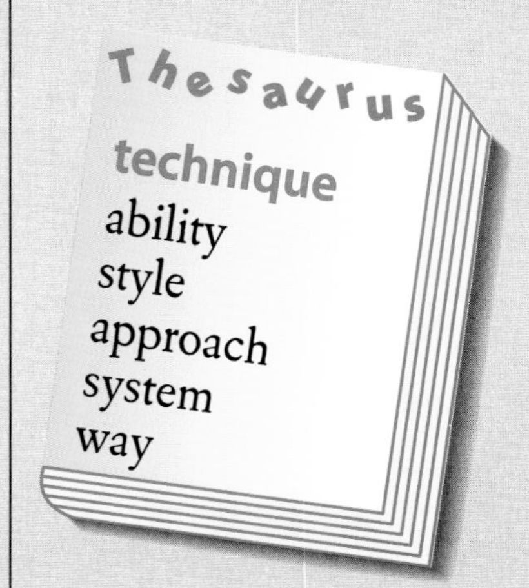

tel•e•phone
(tel′ə fōn′) *noun*
An instrument for talking to people that converts sounds into electrical impulses that travel through wires.

suspension bridge

ter•mi•nals
(tûr′mə nlz) *noun*
Combinations of keyboards and monitors by which information can be entered into or output by a computer. ▲ **terminal**

ther•mom•e•ter
(thər mom′i tər) *noun*
An instrument used to measure temperature.

time ma•chine
(tīm′ mə shēn′) *noun*
A fictional device that allows a person to travel back and forth in time.

tin•kered
(ting′kərd) *verb*
Made minor repairs and adjustments to something. The inventor *tinkered* with her new computer. ▲ **tinker**

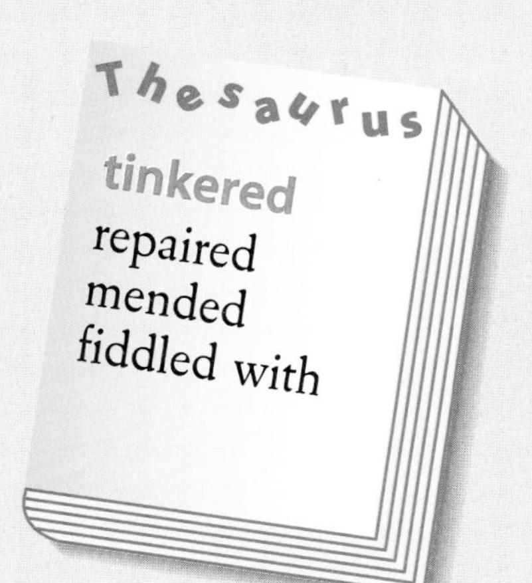

vac•cine
(vak sēn′) *noun*
A preparation of weakened germs that is used to inoculate a person against disease. There is a *vaccine* for measles.

Word History

The word vaccine comes from the Latin word *vacca* which means "cow." The first vaccine ever invented was prepared from a virus that causes disease in cows. The vaccine was used to prevent smallpox.

vir•tu•al re•al•i•ty
(vûr′cho͞o əl rē al′i tē) *noun*
Imaginary three-dimensional environments that are created by computer technology.

virtual reality

vul•can•ized
(vul′ka nīzd) *verb*
Treated rubber with a process of heat and sulfur to make it stronger and more elastic.
▲ **vulcanize**

ze•ro grav•i•ty
(zē′rō grav′i tē) *noun*
A weightless condition in which an object is not pulled by gravity.

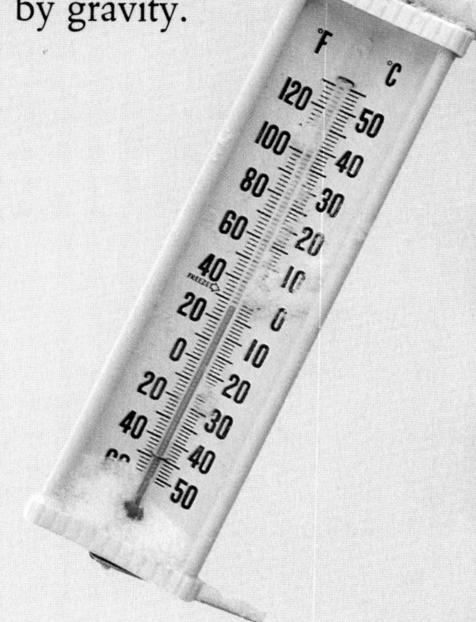

thermometer

a add	o͝o took	ə =
ā ace	o͞o pool	a in *above*
â care	u up	e in *sicken*
ä palm	û burn	i in *possible*
e end	yo͞o fuse	o in *melon*
ē equal	oi oil	u in *circus*
i it	ou pout	
ī ice	ng ring	
o odd	th thin	
ō open	th this	
ô order	zh vision	

Authors & Illustrators

Betsy Byars *pages 84–93*

Even though Betsy Byars often writes about serious issues, she manages to show the funny side of things too. Byars has said that she could never have become a writer for young people without having children of her own. "I have used thousands of things from my children's lives in my stories," she admits. However, she also says that your writing can't just be about the things you know—you've got to make up stuff!

Steven Caney *pages 32–39*

Wouldn't it be great if someone invented a contraption that makes your bed for you every morning? That someone could be you—after reading *Steve Caney's Invention Book*. Mr. Caney is a toy and game inventor who has won awards for product design. He has also written books for kids that help them design and build their own toys and games.

Judy Hindley *pages 14–31*

Judy Hindley has written over 30 books for children, many of which are nonfiction. This author grew up in California but now makes her home in England. When she is not writing, she devotes much of her free time working to end hunger in all parts of the world.

Charlotte Foltz Jones *pages 68–75*

Charlotte Foltz Jones brings her curiosity to every project she works on. She writes about things that amaze her and poses questions she'd like to have answered. In addition to *Mistakes That Worked,* this author has written a book for adults, and over one hundred magazine articles!

Robert McCloskey *pages 50–67*

Luckily for his readers, author-illustrator Robert McCloskey did not become a musician or inventor as he first thought he would. Instead, he has written and illustrated many award-winning books, often taking as many as three years to finish just one. "There are sometimes as many as 20 or 30 drawings before I turn out the one you see in the book—not completed drawings, of course, but ones finding out and exploring the best possible way of presenting a particular picture."

"No effort is too great to find out as much as possible about the things you are drawing."

Lensey Namioka *pages 100–119*

This author often uses her Chinese heritage and her husband's Japanese heritage in her writing. Her stories are almost always funny, since she feels humor is a very powerful tool. Humor helps her get her message across and entertains readers at the same time.

Books &

Author Study

More by Betsy Byars

The Cybil Wars
Two friends compete for the attention of the nicest girl in the fourth grade.

The 18th Emergency
Benjie "Mouse" Frawley has a plan for every possible emergency—or so he thinks. Then he does something to offend the biggest kid in school.

The Moon and I
In this book, Betsy Byars tells the story of her own life.

Benjamin Banneker

Fiction

Ahyoka and the Talking Leaves
by Peter and Connie Roop
illustrated by Yoshi Miyake
This historical novel is based on the true story of how Sequoyah and his daughter worked together to invent a syllabary for the Cherokee language.

Burton and the Giggle Machine
by Dorothy Haas
Burton decides to invent a giggle machine to cheer up his friends. He begins working on it. But who is the mysterious stranger watching him from the shadows?

Wings
by Jane Yolen
illustrated by Dennis Nolan
This retelling of an ancient Greek legend describes what happens when an inventor and his son, Icarus, attempt to fly.

Nonfiction

Be an Inventor
by Barbara Taylor
This how-to book can help get you started if you have an idea for an invention.

Great Lives: Invention and Technology
by Milton Lomask
This collection of short biographies profiles the accomplishments of many creative thinkers.

What Are You Figuring Now? A Story About Benjamin Banneker
by Jeri Ferris
This African-American inventor is famous for his discoveries in astronomy and mathematics.

&Media

Videos

Honey, I Shrunk the Kids
Disney
An inventor discovers that his new invention works when, by mistake, he shrinks his children. (83 minutes)

Invisible World
National Geographic Video Series. Vestron/Family Home Entertainment
Through the specialized "eyes" of high-tech cameras, this video explores unseen worlds. This presentation features microscopic cameras. (60 minutes)

Willy Wonka and the Chocolate Factory
Warner
This film, based on Roald Dahl's novel, stars Gene Wilder as the wacky inventor whose amazing machines produce wonderful candies. (98 minutes)

Software

The Castle of Dr. Brain
Sierra OnLine
(IBM/PC, Tandy)
You're the lab assistant of Dr. Brain, who lives in a castle full of fascinating odds and ends. Work out the puzzles presented and continue on, facing increasingly difficult brain teasers along the way.

Lunar Greenhouse
MECC
(Apple II series)
Your goal is to grow food for a moon colony. To grow the largest amount, as fast as possible, you need to calculate many things—light, water, and temperature.

Magazines

3•2•1 Contact
Children's Television Workshop
3•2•1 Contact examines the science in everyday life with articles about nature, sociology, and technology. It also features puzzles, fiction, and math-related activities.

Super Science Blue
Scholastic Inc.
The great activities in this magazine make it easy to apply scientific concepts to inventive ideas.

A Place to Write

Future Problem Solving Program
115 Main St., Box 98
Aberdeen, NC 28315

This program will challenge you with environmental, political, and economic problems just waiting for your solutions.

DISCOVERY
TEAMS

Zoom in

on a Space Center

When we work as a team, we learn new things about our world.

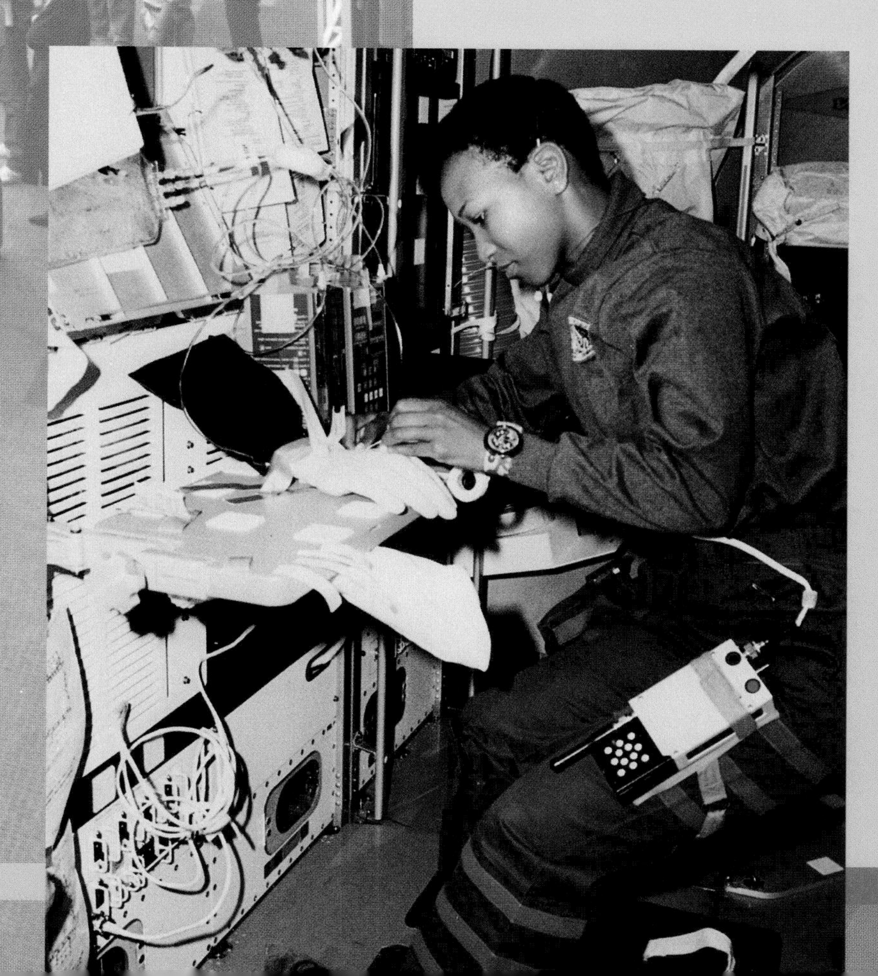

Off to Discovery

Team members share new discoveries.

SOURCE Picture Book

The Lost Lake 10

by Allen Say

SOURCE Magazine

Pushing the Limits 24

by Ross Bankson

from *National Geographic World*

SOURCE Novel

from **Sarah, Plain and Tall** 30

by Patricia MacLachlan

illustrated by Marni Backer

WORKSHOP 1

How to Make an Exploration Map 48

Daring Destinations

Teams explore to gain knowledge.

SOURCE Biography

All the Way There 54

by Sean Dolan

from *Matthew Henson: Arctic Explorer*

SOURCE Magazine

Standing Up for Antarctica 64

from *National Geographic World*

MENTOR Astronaut

Dr. Mae Jemison 66

SOURCE Science Fiction

The Best New Thing 70

by Isaac Asimov

illustrated by Tom Leonard

WORKSHOP 2

How to Create a Team Profile 84

MEET YOUR CREW

Each crew member aboard the ship is called a specialist. Here's what each specialist does:

ENVIRONMENTAL CONTROL: Keeps air breathable and comfortable; takes care of the fresh water supply.

METEOROLOGIST: Keeps track of weather.

Science Search

Scientific teams search for new knowledge about the environment.

SOURCE Environmental Fiction

The Great Kapok Tree 90

by Lynne Cherry

SOURCE Science Nonfiction

from **The Desert Beneath the Sea** 104

by Ann McGovern and Eugenie Clark
illustrated by Craig Phillips

SOURCE Article

The Jason Project: Passport to Adventure 116

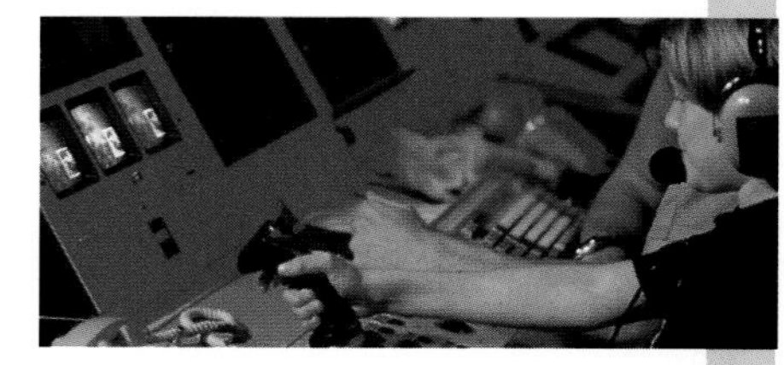

PROJECT

How to Create a Multimedia Presentation 122

Glossary **128**

Authors & Illustrators **132**

Books & Media **134**

Trade Books

The following books accompany this *Discovery Teams* SourceBook.

Science Nonfiction

AWARD WINNING Author

Digging Up Tyrannosaurus Rex

by John R. Horner and Don Lessem

Fiction

AWARD WINNING Author

Jem's Island

by Kathryn Lasky
illustrated by Ronald Himler

Fiction

AWARD WINNING Book

Justin and the Best Biscuits in the World

by Mildred Pitts Walter
illustrated by Catherine Stock

Mystery

AWARD WINNING Book

Who Stole The Wizard of Oz?

by Avi
illustrated by Derek James

SECTION 1

Team members share new discoveries.

Off to Discovery

Hike along with a father and son as they search for the Lost Lake. Then go off to a school that specializes in adventure.

Join Sarah and her new family as they discover how a mound of hay can be as much fun as a sand dune.

WORKSHOP 1

Form a team, and make an exploration map.

SOURCE
THE LOST LAKE
ALLEN SAY
Picture Book

AWARD WINNING Book

THE LOST LAKE

by Allen Say

I went to live with Dad last summer.

Every day he worked in his room from morning to night, sometimes on weekends, too. Dad wasn't much of a talker, but when he was busy he didn't talk at all.

I didn't know anybody in the city, so I stayed home most of the time. It was too hot to play outside anyway. In one month I finished all the books I'd brought and grew tired of watching TV.

One morning I started cutting pictures out of old magazines, just to be doing something. They were pictures of mountains and rivers and lakes, and some showed people fishing and canoeing. Looking at them made me feel cool, so I pinned them up in my room.

Dad didn't notice them for two days. When he did, he looked at them one by one.

"Nice pictures," he said.

"Are you angry with me, Dad?" I asked, because he saved old magazines for his work.

"It's all right, Luke," he said. "I'm having this place painted soon anyway."

He thought I was talking about the marks I'd made on the wall.

That Saturday Dad woke me up early in the morning and told me we were going camping! I was wide awake in a second. He gave me a pair of brand-new hiking boots to try out. They were perfect.

In the hallway I saw a big backpack and a knapsack all packed and ready to go.

"What's in them, Dad?" I asked.

"Later," he said. "We have a long drive ahead of us."

In the car I didn't ask any more questions because Dad was so grumpy in the morning.

"Want a sip?" he said, handing me his mug. He'd never let me drink coffee before. It had lots of sugar in it.

"Where are we going?" I finally asked.

"We're off to the Lost Lake, my lad."

"How can you lose a lake?"

"No one's found it, that's how." Dad was smiling! "Grandpa and I used to go there a long time ago. It was our special place, so don't tell any of your friends."

"I'll never tell," I promised. "How long are we going to stay there?"

"Five days, maybe a week."

"We're going to sleep outside for a whole week?"

"That's the idea."

"Oh, boy!"

We got to the mountains in the afternoon.

"It's a bit of a hike to the lake, son," Dad said.

"I don't mind," I told him. "Are there any fish in the lake?"

"Hope so. We'll have to catch our dinner, you know."

"You didn't bring any food?"

"Of course not. We're going to live like true outdoorsmen."

"Oh . . ."

Dad saw my face and started to laugh. He must have been joking. I didn't think we were going very far anyway, because Dad's pack was so heavy I couldn't even lift it.

Well, Dad was like a mountain goat. He went straight up the trail, whistling all the while. But I was gasping in no time. My knapsack got very heavy and I started to fall behind.

Dad stopped for me often, but he wouldn't let me take off my pack. If I did I'd be too tired to go on, he said.

It was almost suppertime when we got to the lake.

The place reminded me of the park near Dad's apartment. He wasn't whistling or humming anymore.

"Welcome to the *Found* Lake," he muttered from the side of his mouth.

"What's wrong, Dad?"

"Do you want to camp with all these people around us?"

"I don't mind."

"Well, I do!"

"Are we going home?"

"Of course not!"

He didn't even take off his pack. He just turned and started to walk away.

Soon the lake was far out of sight.

Then it started to rain. Dad gave me a poncho and it kept me dry, but I wondered where we were going to sleep that night. I wondered what we were going to do for dinner. I wasn't sure about camping anymore.

I was glad when Dad finally stopped and set up the tent. The rain and wind beat against it, but we were warm and cozy inside. And Dad had brought food. For dinner we had salami and dried apricots.

"I'm sorry about the lake, Dad," I said.

He shook his head. "You know something, Luke? There aren't any secret places left in the world anymore."

"What if we go very far up in the mountains? Maybe we can find our own lake."

"There are lots of lakes up here, but that one was special."

"But we've got a whole week, Dad."

"Well, why not? Maybe we'll find a lake that's not on the map."

"Sure, we will!"

We started early in the morning. When the fog cleared we saw other hikers ahead of us. Sure enough, Dad became very glum.

"We're going cross-country, partner," he said.

"Won't we get lost?"

"A wise man never leaves home without his compass."

So we went off the trail. The hills went on and on. The mountains went on and on. It was kind of lonesome. It seemed as if Dad and I were the only people left in the world.

And then we hiked into a big forest.

At noontime we stopped by a creek and ate lunch and drank ice-cold water straight from the stream. I threw rocks in the water, and fish, like shadows, darted in the pools.

"Isn't this a good place to camp, Dad?"

"I thought we were looking for our lake."

"Yes, right . . ." I mumbled.

The forest went on and on.

"I don't mean to scare you, son," Dad said. "But we're in bear country. We don't want to surprise them, so we have to make a lot of noise. If they hear us, they'll just go away."

What a time to tell me! I started to shout as loudly as I could. Even Dad wouldn't be able to beat off bears. I thought about those people having fun back at the lake. I thought about the creek, too, with all those fish in it. That would have been a fine place to camp. The Lost Lake hadn't been so bad either.

It was dark when we got out of the forest. We built a fire and that made me feel better. Wild animals wouldn't come near a fire. Dad cooked beef stroganoff and it was delicious.

Later it was bedtime. The sleeping bag felt wonderful. Dad and I started to count the shooting stars, then I worried that maybe we weren't going to find our lake.

"What are you thinking about, Luke?" Dad asked.

"I didn't know you could cook like that," I said.

Dad laughed. "That was only freeze-dried stuff. When we get home, I'll cook you something really special."

“You know something, Dad? You seem like a different person up here.”

“Better or worse?”

“A lot better.”

“How so?”

“You talk more.”

“I’ll have to talk more often, then.”

That made me smile. Then I slept.

Dad shook me awake. The sun was just coming up, turning everything all gold and orange and yellow. And there was the lake, right in front of us.

For a long time we watched the light change on the water, getting brighter and brighter. Dad didn’t say a word the whole time. But then, I didn’t have anything to say either.

After breakfast we climbed a mountain and saw our lake below us. There wasn’t a sign of people anywhere. It really seemed as if Dad and I were all alone in the world.

I liked it just fine.

SOURCE
NATIONAL GEOGRAPHIC
world
Magazine

AWARD WINNING
Magazine

PUSHING

by Ross Bankson

Finally, it's summertime! The season to kick back, relax, and get set for—school? Why not? It just depends on your idea of school. Adventure Quest is a school for the *outdoors*. "We teach recreation skills you can use for the rest of your life," says the director, Peter Kennedy. You'll find week-long courses in white-water and wilderness canoeing, kayaking, rock climbing, caving, backpacking, and mountain biking.

THE LIMITS

▲ *The dark, mysterious world of a cave in Vermont awaits discovery by Pierre Harrison-Beauregard, 13, of New Bedford, Massachusetts. Squeezing through the cave's tight spaces was exciting—"but a little scary too," he says.*

◀ **SCALING A ROCK FACE**
Chris Hackett, 10, of Manhasset, New York, looks below. "With the harness and ropes, you couldn't fall," he says.

Climbing Lingo

***BELAYER** (bih-LAY-er) person who controls the rope attached to the climber*

***CARABINER** (kair-uh-BEE-ner) oblong metal ring used to hold a freely running rope*

▲ **ON THE ROPES**
A climber meets a steep challenge. He is secured by a rope that runs up, through a carabiner anchored to a tree, then down to the belayer on the ground.

▲ **WE DID IT!** ***Students celebrate victory atop a conquered cliff. A ropes course and a practice wall helped prepare them for the real thing.***

Younger students can choose a sampler that has two sports. "I love climbing jungle gyms, trees, anything—so I knew I'd like rock climbing best," says 9-year-old Paul Cancro, of Wall Township, New Jersey. "But I learned other things too, like how to escape from a kayak underwater and how to steer a canoe."

The base camp for Adventure Quest is in Woodstock, Vermont, but students may go biking along steep country roads in New Hampshire or caving in New York State. Advanced students may climb the Rocky Mountains or kayak angry rapids in Canada.

▲ **A SUCCESSFUL ROLL** ***brings a smile to Jacey Cobb, right, and praise from her instructor. "Rolling over in a kayak was great—once you learned how," says Jacey.***

"We had a totally wild adventure canoeing in white water," says Luke Moore, 13, of North Pomfret, Vermont. "Where the water backwashes, you have to lean the right way or else you'll tip over."

Luke and his brother, Brendan, didn't tackle white water before they were ready, though. With one instructor for every three students, training is safe but demanding. "We stress the three S's: supervision, skills, and safety," says Kennedy. And the training pays off, according to the students. Says Jacey Cobb, 11, of Norwich, Vermont, who took kayaking at Adventure Quest: "I never dreamed I could do the things I did."

White-water rating scale

- **I** *Very easy.*
- **II** *Easy. Moderate rapids.*
- **III** *Medium difficulty. Lots of waves.*
- **IV** *Expert. Long, violent, irregular waves up to 5 feet.*
- **V** *Almost continuous violent rapids, waves over 5 feet. Dangerous rocks, holes, lots of turns.*
- **VI** *Extremely dangerous.*

▲ **CLASS III RAPIDS**—*That's what this team braved on the Connecticut River. "Running the rapids was wet, but awesome," says Brendan Moore, 11, in front. He and his brother Luke, in back, rank among the top junior canoeing teams in the United States.*

from

Sarah, Plain and Tall

by Patricia MacLachlan

illustrated by Marni Backer

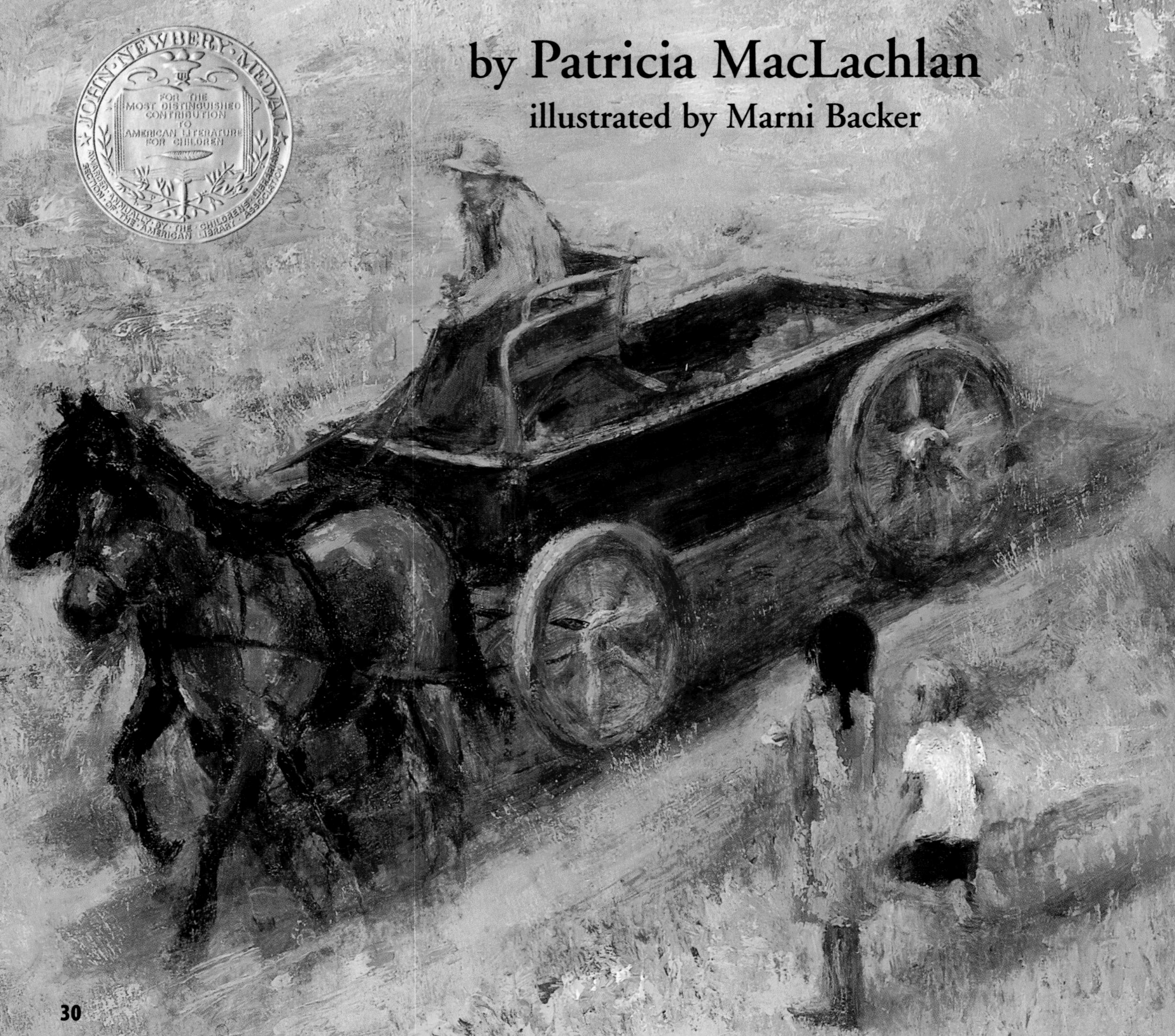

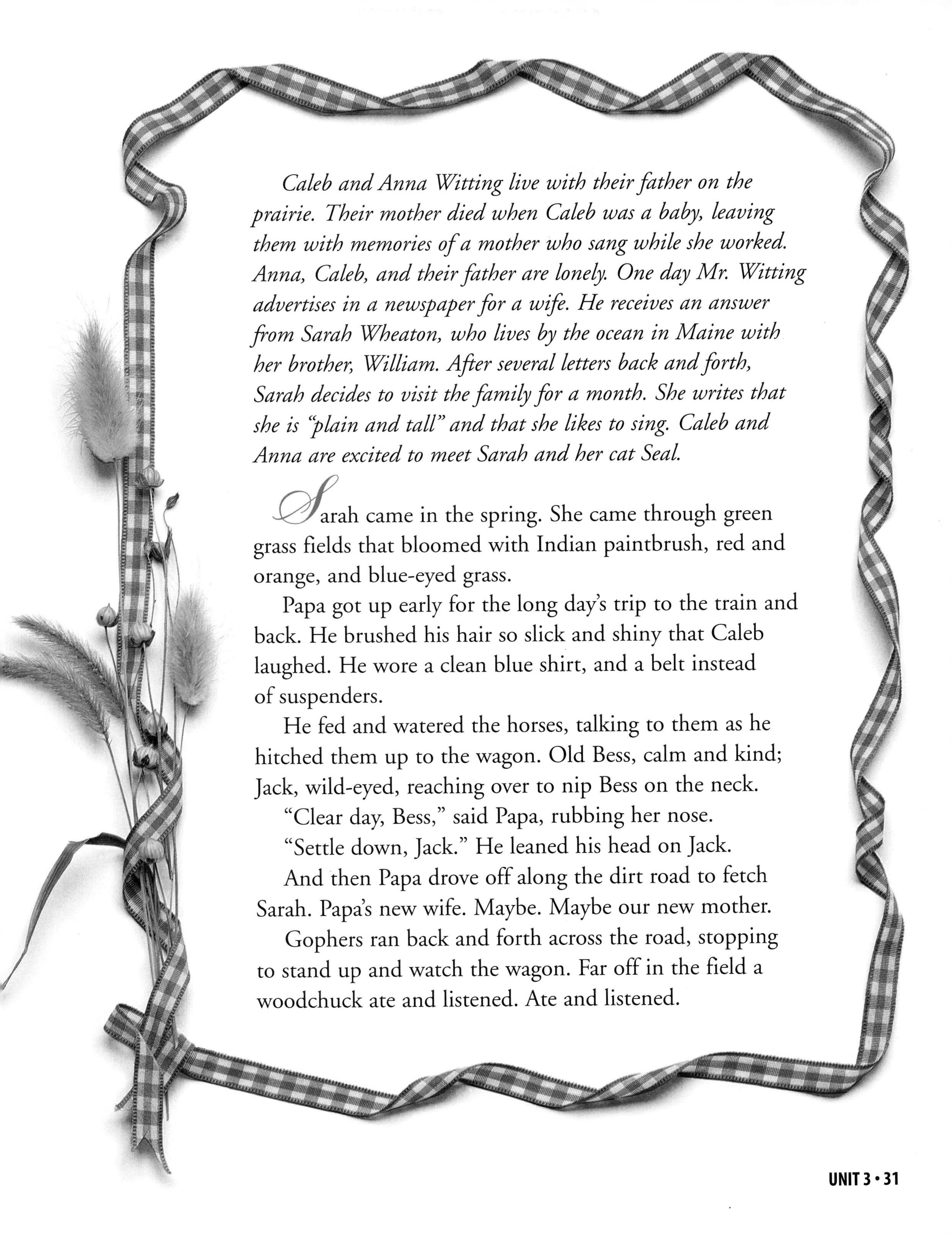

Caleb and Anna Witting live with their father on the prairie. Their mother died when Caleb was a baby, leaving them with memories of a mother who sang while she worked. Anna, Caleb, and their father are lonely. One day Mr. Witting advertises in a newspaper for a wife. He receives an answer from Sarah Wheaton, who lives by the ocean in Maine with her brother, William. After several letters back and forth, Sarah decides to visit the family for a month. She writes that she is "plain and tall" and that she likes to sing. Caleb and Anna are excited to meet Sarah and her cat Seal.

Sarah came in the spring. She came through green grass fields that bloomed with Indian paintbrush, red and orange, and blue-eyed grass.

Papa got up early for the long day's trip to the train and back. He brushed his hair so slick and shiny that Caleb laughed. He wore a clean blue shirt, and a belt instead of suspenders.

He fed and watered the horses, talking to them as he hitched them up to the wagon. Old Bess, calm and kind; Jack, wild-eyed, reaching over to nip Bess on the neck.

"Clear day, Bess," said Papa, rubbing her nose.

"Settle down, Jack." He leaned his head on Jack.

And then Papa drove off along the dirt road to fetch Sarah. Papa's new wife. Maybe. Maybe our new mother.

Gophers ran back and forth across the road, stopping to stand up and watch the wagon. Far off in the field a woodchuck ate and listened. Ate and listened.

Caleb and I did our chores without talking. We shoveled out the stalls and laid down new hay. We fed the sheep. We swept and straightened and carried wood and water. And then our chores were done.

Caleb pulled on my shirt.

"Is my face clean?" he asked. "Can my face be *too* clean?" He looked alarmed.

"No, your face is clean but not too clean," I said.

Caleb slipped his hand into mine as we stood on the porch, watching the road. He was afraid.

"Will she be nice?" he asked. "Like Maggie?"

"Sarah will be nice," I told him.

"How far away is Maine?" he asked.

"You know how far. Far away, by the sea."

"Will Sarah bring some sea?" he asked.

"No, you cannot bring the sea."

The sheep ran in the field, and far off the cows moved slowly to the pond, like turtles.

"Will she like us?" asked Caleb very softly.

I watched a marsh hawk wheel down behind the barn.

He looked up at me.

"Of course she will like us." He answered his own question. "We are nice," he added, making me smile.

We waited and watched. I rocked on the porch and Caleb rolled a marble on the wood floor. Back and forth. Back and forth. The marble was blue.

We saw the dust from the wagon first, rising above the road, above the heads of Jack and Old Bess. Caleb climbed up onto the porch roof and shaded his eyes.

"A bonnet!" he cried. "I see a yellow bonnet!"

The dogs came out from under the porch, ears up, their eyes on the cloud of dust bringing Sarah. The wagon passed the fenced field, and the cows and sheep looked up, too. It rounded the windmill and the barn and the windbreak of Russian olive that Mama had planted long ago. Nick began to bark, then Lottie, and the wagon clattered into the yard and stopped by the steps.

"Hush," said Papa to the dogs.

And it was quiet.

Sarah stepped down from the wagon, a cloth bag in her hand. She reached up and took off her yellow bonnet, smoothing back her brown hair into a bun. She was plain and tall.

"Did you bring some sea?" cried Caleb beside me.

"Something from the sea," said Sarah, smiling. "And me." She turned and lifted a black case from the wagon. "And Seal, too."

Carefully she opened the case, and Seal, gray with white feet, stepped out. Lottie lay down, her head on her paws, staring. Nick leaned down to sniff. Then he lay down, too.

"The cat will be good in the barn," said Papa. "For mice."

Sarah smiled. "She will be good in the house, too."

Sarah took Caleb's hand, then mine. Her hands were large and rough. She gave Caleb a shell—a moon snail, she called it—that was curled and smelled of salt.

"The gulls fly high and drop the shells on the rocks below," she told Caleb. "When the shell is broken, they eat what is inside."

"That is very smart," said Caleb.

"For you, Anna," said Sarah, "a sea stone."

And she gave me the smoothest and whitest stone I had ever seen.

"The sea washes over and over and around the stone, rolling it until it is round and perfect."

"That is very smart, too," said Caleb. He looked up at Sarah. "We do not have the sea here."

Sarah turned and looked out over the plains.

"No," she said. "There is no sea here. But the land rolls a little like the sea."

My father did not see her look, but I did. And I knew that Caleb had seen it, too. Sarah was not smiling. Sarah was already lonely. In a month's time the preacher might come to marry Sarah and Papa. And a month was a long time. Time enough for her to change her mind and leave us.

Papa took Sarah's bags inside, where her room was ready with a quilt on the bed and blue flax dried in a vase on the night table.

Seal stretched and made a small cat sound. I watched her circle the dogs and sniff the air. Caleb came out and stood beside me.

"When will we sing?" he whispered.

I shook my head, turning the white stone over and over in my hand. I wished everything was as perfect as the stone. I wished that Papa and Caleb and I were perfect for Sarah. I wished we had a sea of our own.

The dogs loved Sarah first. Lottie slept beside her bed, curled in a soft circle, and Nick leaned his face on the covers in the morning, watching for the first sign that Sarah was awake. No one knew where Seal slept. Seal was a roamer.

Sarah's collection of shells sat on the windowsill.

"A scallop," she told us, picking up the shells one by one, "a sea clam, an oyster, a razor clam. And a conch shell. If you put it to your ear you can hear the sea." She put it to Caleb's ear, then mine. Papa listened, too. Then Sarah listened once more, with a look so sad and far away that Caleb leaned against me.

"At least Sarah can hear the sea," he whispered.

Papa was quiet and shy with Sarah, and so was I. But Caleb talked to Sarah from morning until the light left the sky.

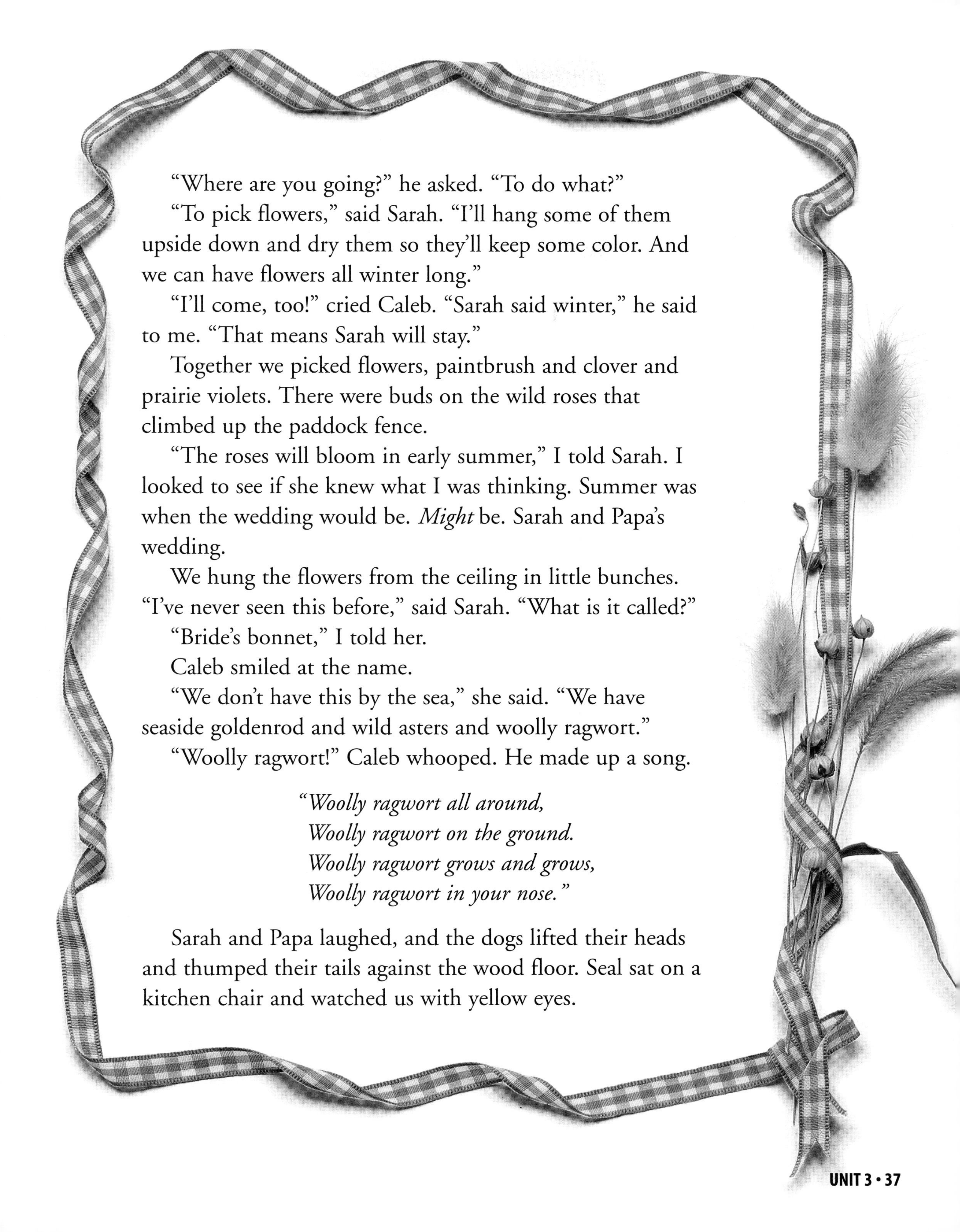

"Where are you going?" he asked. "To do what?"

"To pick flowers," said Sarah. "I'll hang some of them upside down and dry them so they'll keep some color. And we can have flowers all winter long."

"I'll come, too!" cried Caleb. "Sarah said winter," he said to me. "That means Sarah will stay."

Together we picked flowers, paintbrush and clover and prairie violets. There were buds on the wild roses that climbed up the paddock fence.

"The roses will bloom in early summer," I told Sarah. I looked to see if she knew what I was thinking. Summer was when the wedding would be. *Might* be. Sarah and Papa's wedding.

We hung the flowers from the ceiling in little bunches. "I've never seen this before," said Sarah. "What is it called?"

"Bride's bonnet," I told her.

Caleb smiled at the name.

"We don't have this by the sea," she said. "We have seaside goldenrod and wild asters and woolly ragwort."

"Woolly ragwort!" Caleb whooped. He made up a song.

"Woolly ragwort all around,
Woolly ragwort on the ground.
Woolly ragwort grows and grows,
Woolly ragwort in your nose."

Sarah and Papa laughed, and the dogs lifted their heads and thumped their tails against the wood floor. Seal sat on a kitchen chair and watched us with yellow eyes.

We ate Sarah's stew, the late light coming through the windows. Papa had baked bread that was still warm from the fire.

"The stew is fine," said Papa.

"Ayuh." Sarah nodded. "The bread, too."

"What does 'ayuh' mean?" asked Caleb.

"In Maine it means yes," said Sarah. "Do you want more stew?"

"Ayuh," said Caleb.

"Ayuh," echoed my father.

After dinner Sarah told us about William. "He has a gray-and-white boat named *Kittiwake.*" She looked out the window. "That is a small gull found way off the shore where William fishes. There are three aunts who live near us. They wear silk dresses and no shoes. You would love them."

"Ayuh," said Caleb.

"Does your brother look like you?" I asked.

"Yes," said Sarah. "He is plain and tall."

At dusk Sarah cut Caleb's hair on the front steps, gathering his curls and scattering them on the fence and ground. Seal batted some hair around the porch as the dogs watched.

"Why?" asked Caleb.

"For the birds," said Sarah. "They will use it for their nests. Later we can look for nests of curls."

"Sarah said 'later,'" Caleb whispered to me as we spread his hair about. "Sarah will stay."

Sarah cut Papa's hair, too. No one else saw, but I found him behind the barn, tossing the pieces of hair into the wind for the birds.

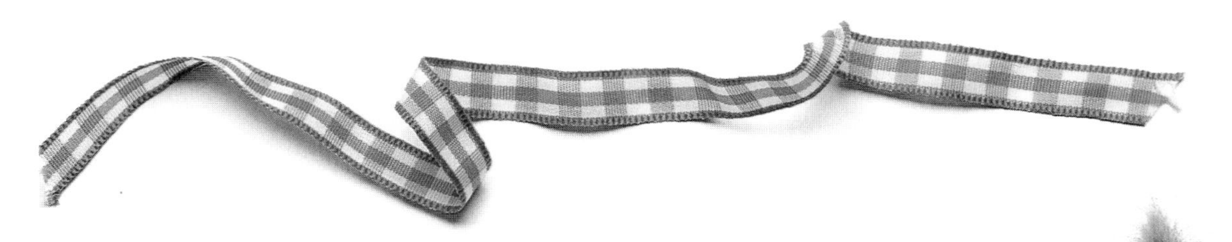

Sarah brushed my hair and tied it up in back with a rose velvet ribbon she had brought from Maine. She brushed hers long and free and tied it back, too, and we stood side by side looking into the mirror. I looked taller, like Sarah, and fair and thin. And with my hair pulled back I looked a little like her daughter. Sarah's daughter.

And then it was time for singing.

Sarah sang us a song we had never heard before as we sat on the porch, insects buzzing in the dark, the rustle of cows in the grasses. It was called "Sumer Is Icumen in," and she taught it to us all, even Papa, who sang as if he had never stopped singing.

"Sumer is icumen in,
Lhude sing cuccu!"

"What is sumer?" asked Caleb. He said it "soomer," the way Sarah had said it.

"Summer," said Papa and Sarah at the same time. Caleb and I looked at each other. Summer was coming.

"Tomorrow," said Sarah, "I want to see the sheep. You know, I've never touched one."

"Never?" Caleb sat up.

"Never," said Sarah. She smiled and leaned back in her chair. "But I've touched seals. Real seals. They are cool and slippery and they slide through the water like fish. They can cry and sing. And sometimes they bark, a little like dogs."

Sarah barked like a seal. And Lottie and Nick came running from the barn to jump up on Sarah and lick her face and make her laugh. Sarah stroked them and scratched their ears and it was quiet again.

"I wish I could touch a seal right now," said Caleb, his voice soft in the night.

"So do I," said Sarah. She sighed, then she began to sing the summer song again. Far off in a field, a meadowlark sang, too.

The sheep made Sarah smile. She sank her fingers into their thick, coarse wool. She talked to them, running with the lambs, letting them suck on her fingers. She named them after her favorite aunts, Harriet and Mattie and Lou. She lay down in the field beside them and sang, "Sumer Is Icumen in," her voice drifting over the meadow grasses, carried by the wind.

She cried when we found a lamb that had died, and she shouted and shook her fist at the turkey buzzards that came from nowhere to eat it. She would not let Caleb or me come near. And that night, Papa went with a shovel to bury the sheep and a lantern to bring Sarah back. She sat on the porch alone. Nick crept up to lean against her knees.

After dinner, Sarah drew pictures to send home to Maine. She began a charcoal drawing of the fields, rolling like the sea rolled. She drew a sheep whose ears were too big. And she drew a windmill.

"Windmill was my first word," said Caleb. "Papa told me so."

"Mine was flower," I said. "What was yours, Sarah?"

"Dune," said Sarah.

"Dune?" Caleb looked up.

"In Maine," said Sarah, "there are rock cliffs that rise up at the edge of the sea. And there are hills covered with pine and spruce trees, green with needles. But William and I found a sand dune all our own. It was soft and sparkling with bits of mica, and when we were little we would slide down the dune into the water."

Caleb looked out the window.

"We have no dunes here," he said.

Papa stood up.

"Yes we do," he said. He took the lantern and went out the door to the barn.

"We do?" Caleb called after him.

He ran ahead, Sarah and I following, the dogs close behind.

Next to the barn was Papa's mound of hay for bedding, nearly half as tall as the barn, covered with canvas to keep the rain from rotting it. Papa carried the wooden ladder from the barn and leaned it against the hay.

"There." He smiled at Sarah. "Our dune."

Sarah was very quiet. The dogs looked up at her, waiting. Seal brushed against her legs, her tail in the air. Caleb reached over and took her hand.

"It looks high up," he said. "Are you scared, Sarah?"

"Scared? Scared!" exclaimed Sarah. "You bet I'm not scared."

She climbed the ladder, and Nick began to bark. She climbed to the very top of the hay and sat, looking down at us. Above, the stars were coming out. Papa piled a bed of loose hay below with his pitchfork. The light of the lantern made his eyes shine when he smiled up at Sarah.

"Fine?" called Papa.

"Fine," said Sarah. She lifted her arms over her head and slid down, down, into the soft hay. She lay, laughing, as the dogs rolled beside her.

"Was it a good dune?" called Caleb.

"Yes," said Sarah. "It is a fine dune."

Caleb and I climbed up and slid down. And Sarah did it three more times. At last Papa slid down, too, as the sky grew darker and the stars blinked like fireflies. We were covered with hay and dust, and we sneezed.

In the kitchen, Caleb and I washed in the big wooden tub and Sarah drew more pictures to send to William. One was of Papa, his hair curly and full of hay. She drew Caleb, sliding down the hay, his arms like Sarah's over his head.

And she drew a picture of me in the tub, my hair long and straight and wet. She looked at her drawing of the fields for a long time.

"Something is missing," she told Caleb. "Something." And she put it away.

"'Dear William,'" Sarah read to us by lantern light that night. "'Sliding down our dune of hay is almost as fine as sliding down the sand dunes into the sea.'"

Caleb smiled at me across the table. He said nothing, but his mouth formed the words I had heard, too. *Our dune.*

The days grew longer. The cows moved close to the pond, where the water was cool and there were trees.

Papa taught Sarah how to plow the fields, guiding the plow behind Jack and Old Bess, the reins around her neck. When the chores were done we sat in the meadow with the sheep, Sarah beside us, watching Papa finish.

"Tell me about winter," said Sarah.

Old Bess nodded her head as she walked, but we could hear Papa speak sharply to Jack.

"Jack doesn't like work," said Caleb. "He wants to be here in the sweet grass with us."

"I don't blame him," said Sarah. She lay back in the grass with her arms under her head. "Tell me about winter," she said again.

"Winter is cold here," said Caleb, and Sarah and I laughed.

"Winter is cold everywhere," I said.

"We go to school in winter," said Caleb. "Sums and writing and books," he sang.

"I am good at sums and writing," said Sarah. "I love books. How do you get to school?"

"Papa drives us in the wagon. Or we walk the three miles when there is not too much snow."

Sarah sat up. "Do you have lots of snow?"

"Lots and lots and lots of snow," chanted Caleb, rolling around in the grass. "Sometimes we have to dig our way out to feed the animals."

"In Maine the barns are attached to the houses sometimes," said Sarah.

Caleb grinned. "So you could have a cow to Sunday supper?"

Sarah and I laughed.

"When there are bad storms, Papa ties a rope from the house to the barn so no one will get lost," said Caleb.

I frowned. I loved winter.

"There is ice on the windows on winter mornings," I told Sarah. "We can draw sparkling pictures and we can see our breath in the air. Papa builds a warm fire, and we bake hot biscuits and put on hundreds of sweaters. And if the snow is too high, we stay home from school and make snow people."

Sarah lay back in the tall grasses again, her face nearly hidden.

"And is there wind?" she asked.

"Do you like wind?" asked Caleb.

"There is wind by the sea," said Sarah.

"There is wind here," said Caleb happily. "It blows the snow and brings tumbleweeds and makes the sheep run. Wind and wind and wind!" Caleb stood up and ran like the wind, and the sheep ran after him. Sarah and I watched him jump over rock and gullies, the sheep behind him, stiff legged and fast. He circled the field, the sun making the top of his hair golden. He collapsed next to Sarah, and the lambs pushed their wet noses into us.

"Hello, Lou," said Sarah, smiling. "Hello, Mattie."

The sun rose higher, and Papa stopped to take off his hat and wipe his face with his sleeve.

"I'm hot," said Sarah. "I can't wait for winter wind. Let's swim."

"Swim where?" I asked her.

"I can't swim," said Caleb.

"Can't swim!" exclaimed Sarah. "I'll teach you in the cow pond."

"That's for cows!" I cried.

But Sarah had grabbed our hands and we were running through the fields, ducking under the fence to the far pond.

"Shoo, cows," said Sarah as the cows looked up, startled. She took off her dress and waded into the water in her petticoat. She dived suddenly and disappeared for a moment as Caleb and I watched. She came up, laughing, her hair streaming free. Water beads sat on her shoulders.

She tried to teach us how to float. I sank like a bucket filled with water and came up sputtering. But Caleb lay on his back and learned how to blow streams of water high in the air like a whale. The cows stood on the banks of the pond and stared and stopped their chewing. Water bugs circled us.

"Is this like the sea?" asked Caleb.

Sarah treaded water.

"The sea is salt," said Sarah. "It stretches out as far as you can see. It gleams like the sun on glass. There are waves."

"Like this?" asked Caleb, and he pushed a wave at Sarah, making her cough and laugh.

"Yes," she said. "Like that."

I held my breath and floated at last, looking up into the sky, afraid to speak. Crows flew over, three in a row. And I could hear a killdeer in the field.

We climbed the bank and dried ourselves and lay in the grass again. The cows watched, their eyes sad in their dinner-plate faces. And I slept, dreaming a perfect dream. The fields had turned to a sea that gleamed like sun on glass. And Sarah was happy.

WORKSHOP 1

How to
Make an Exploration Map

When explorers travel to far-off places, they are finding new routes and discovering geographical features that may not have been recorded before. Explorers often mark their routes on special exploration maps.

What is an exploration map? An exploration map shows an explorer's route through a certain area. It also includes the usual information shown on a map: natural features such as mountains, volcanoes, and rivers; and features created by people, such as roads and borders.

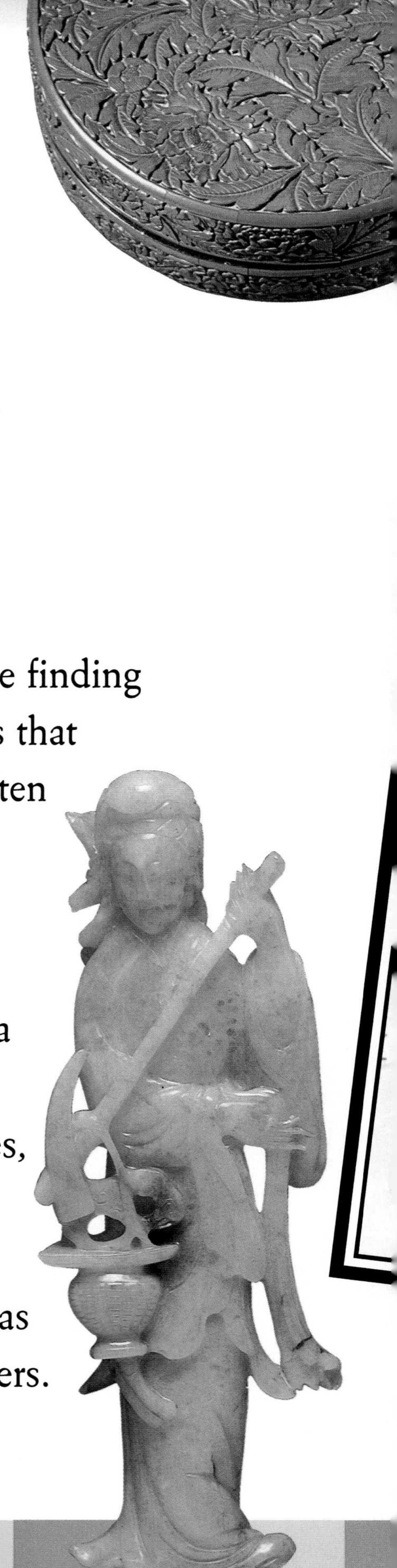

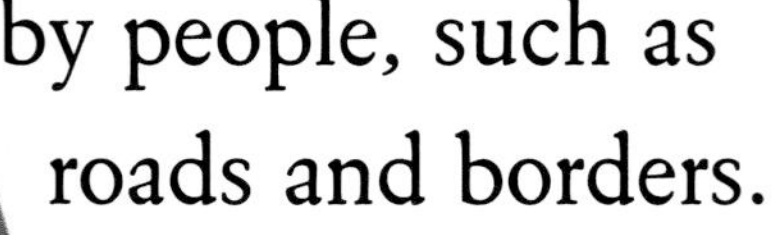

Many maps use symbols such as arrows and colored lines to stand for different routes.

Important places like oceans and mountains are included on the map.

The map legend tells what the symbols on the map represent.

The green line shows the routes traveled by the explorer Cheng Ho.

1 Brainstorm a Common Goal

Break into teams and brainstorm a list of ideas for your map. Think of interesting places you've been, places you've learned about through books or movies, or local places of interest. Each team member should make a suggestion. Take a team vote to find out which is the most popular idea.

TOOLS

- paper and pencil
- colored markers
- tracing paper
- ruler
- reference books and maps

2 Research Your Place

- Find maps or pictures of the place that your team selected. As a group, study the maps or pictures and decide what parts you want to include.
- Draw the outline of the map. Then sketch in some of the important features.
- Each team member can draw his or her own route on the map. Have each person use a different color.
- Add landmarks to help guide you on your way.

3 Create Map Symbols

With your group, create symbols that will show important features on your map. For example, you may wish to use blue lines for rivers and dotted lines for borders. Make the symbols look like the things they represent, such as trees to show a forest or ships to show a harbor. Add these symbols to your map's legend. A map legend is a list of the symbols that appear on the map. Next to each symbol is an explanation of what it stands for.

- Choose a place you all want to learn more about.
- Sketch the map in pencil first, in case you need to make changes.
- Research the place you want to make a map of. You never know what interesting facts you'll discover.

4 Finish and Display Your Map

When your team is satisfied with the map, use colored markers to draw the final outline, features, and routes. Working with your team, display the map. Explain to the class why you selected your route and what they would see if they took that route.

If You Are Using a Computer . . .

Create your map on the computer, using the Paint Tools. Use clip art, such as arrows, to create the symbols for your map.

THINK

Why is it important to bring maps on an expedition?

Dr. Mae Jemison
Astronaut

SECTION 2

Teams explore to gain knowledge.

Daring Destinations

Follow Matthew Henson and Robert Peary to the North Pole. Then read about a group of kids who travel to Antarctica.

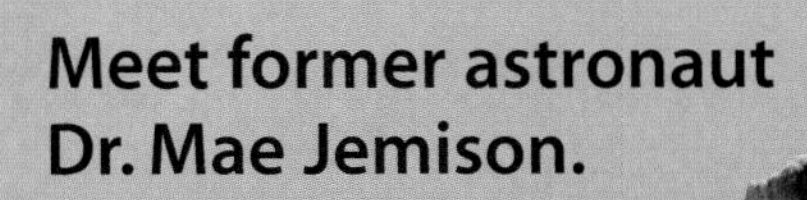

Meet former astronaut Dr. Mae Jemison.

Take a trip into the future and find out what it's like to visit Earth for the first time.

WORKSHOP 2

Decide on a place you want to explore, and then make a team profile.

MEET YOUR CREW

Each crew member aboard the ship is called a specialist. Here's what each specialist does:

ENVIRONMENTAL CONTROL: Keeps air breathable and comfortable; takes care of the fresh water supply.

METEOROLOGIST: Keeps track of weather.

SOURCE
JUNIOR • WORLD • BIOGRAPHIES
Matthew Henson
Arctic Explorer
SEAN DOLAN
Biography
PEARY & HENSON
ATLA

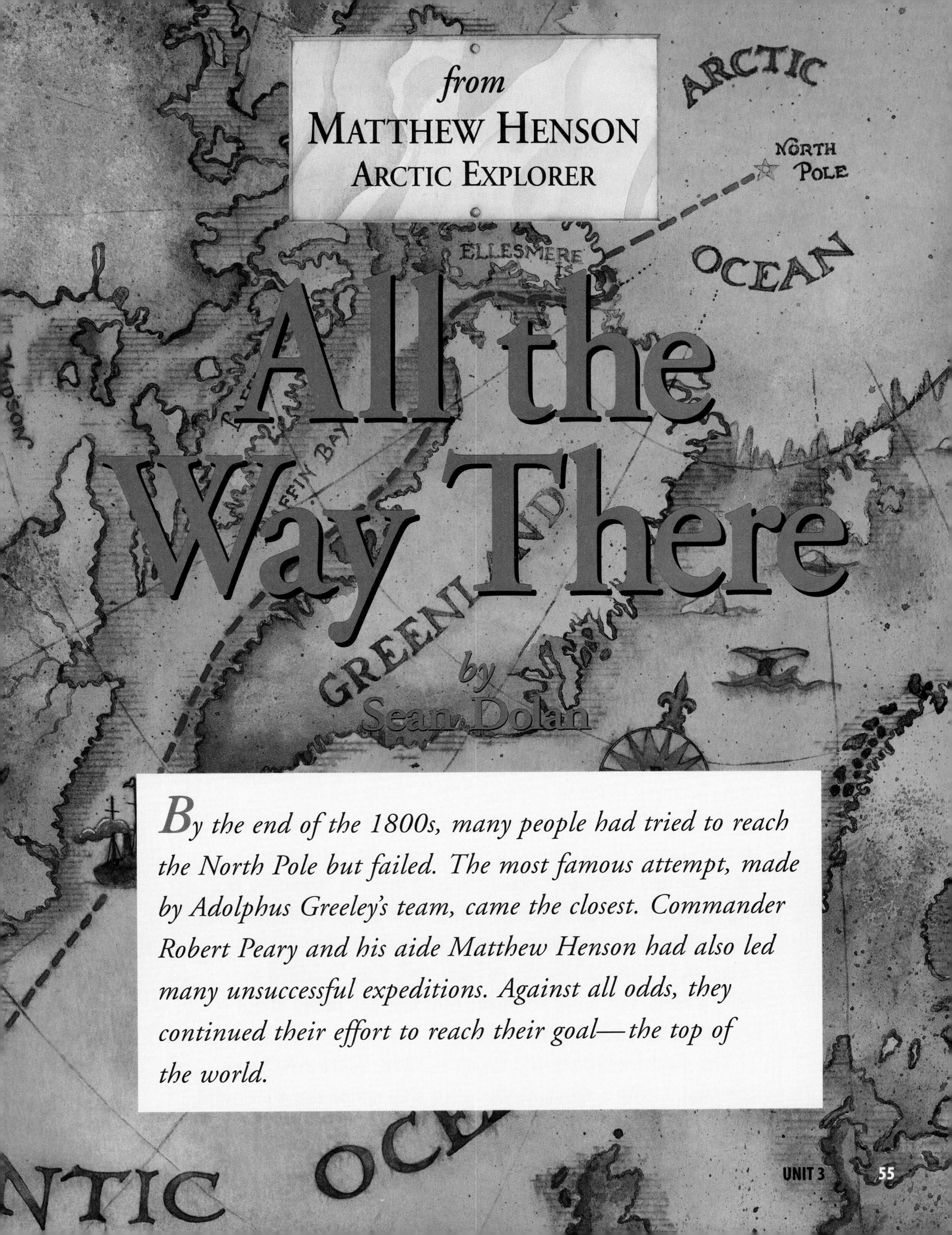

from

MATTHEW HENSON ARCTIC EXPLORER

All the Way There

by Sean Dolan

By the end of the 1800s, many people had tried to reach the North Pole but failed. The most famous attempt, made by Adolphus Greeley's team, came the closest. Commander Robert Peary and his aide Matthew Henson had also led many unsuccessful expeditions. Against all odds, they continued their effort to reach their goal—the top of the world.

Henson relaxes on top of one of the sleds he built for travel in the Arctic. In addition to his carpentry skills, Henson was an expert handler of a dog team.

Henson and Peary returned to the Arctic four times between 1896 and 1908, but they could not reach the North Pole. The first two trips, made in 1896 and 1897, were the most successful. Using the *Hope* and a gigantic crane, Peary and Henson managed to remove a huge meteorite, weighing 35 tons, that had fallen on Greenland long ago. (A meteorite is a large particle of matter, similar to rock or stone, from outer space.) The meteorite immediately went on display in the Museum of Natural History in New York City. It added to Peary's fame, but it did not make him feel any better about his failure to reach the North Pole.

The most frustrating trip began in 1898. Peary now had a new plan. Using a specially designed ship called the *Windward,*

Peary planned to sail much farther northward along Greenland's coast before landing. This way, his party would not have to travel so far over land to reach the Pole. The *Windward* was supposed to have engines so powerful that it could batter its way through the Arctic ice.

The plan did not work. In the fall of 1898, the ship became hopelessly stuck in ice off Ellesmere Island, which is just to the west of Greenland. Peary announced a new scheme. The men would abandon the *Windward* and march to Fort Conger. The fort was on the northern shore of Ellesmere Island. It was also the place where the men of the Greeley expedition had waited in vain to be rescued.

In temperatures of 60 degrees below zero, Henson cut a trail through the ice to Fort Conger. Although it was already winter, Peary insisted on starting out immediately. It was a bad mistake. This was a different sort of journey than any he and Henson had taken before. Beneath the ice this time was not land, as on Greenland, but the waters of the Arctic Ocean. At different spots huge and strangely shaped pressure ridges sprang up. These were created by the force of two bodies of ice crashing into each other, driven by the ocean currents beneath them. At night, Peary, Henson, and the four Eskimos who traveled with them could hear the ice groaning and creaking. Sometimes the explorers came upon huge open areas of water where the ice had opened up. They would then have to change direction to get around them.

Peary and Henson made it to Fort Conger, but at great cost. Peary's feet became badly frostbitten, and he was unable to walk. Henson strapped him to his sled and in only 11 days brought him the 250 miles back to the *Windward,* where the ship's doctor was forced to cut off all but the big toe on each of Peary's feet.

Several dog teams and sleds travel across the Arctic ice. Notice how the dogs fan out to pull their loads rather than work side by side in pairs of two along a tight column. This makes pulling easier, but it is possible only in landscapes where there are no trees or other obstacles.

Despite this setback, Peary was determined to stay in the Arctic. He and Henson remained for four more years. During that time, they made three separate attempts at the Pole. All fell short. On April 21, 1902, Peary wrote in his journal, "The game is off. My dream of 16 years is ended. . . . I cannot accomplish the impossible." The discouraged explorers returned home.

Henson also thought that the quest had come to an end. Even before the last expedition, he had begun to tell friends that he was through with Arctic exploration, but his friend George Gardner had convinced him to continue by telling him how important it was for black Americans to have Henson as a role model. Blacks are proud of you and all that you have achieved, Gardner told his friend. Think how proud they will be if a black man reaches the North Pole. Still, Henson was glad to have a break from his polar labors. After he returned to the United States, he took a job on the Pennsylvania Railroad, which enabled him to see much of the country. He also asked his sweetheart, Lucy Ross, to marry him.

But Peary could not abandon his dream forever, and neither could Henson. In 1905, Peary set off on a new expedition, and Henson was with him. This time, a new ship, the *Roosevelt,* succeeded in smashing its way through the Arctic ice. Sledding over extremely treacherous ice, Henson and Peary came within 175 miles of the Pole. This was the closest that anyone had ever come. They returned to the United States both frustrated and certain that next time they would make it.

Peary and Henson's sixth polar expedition departed from Long Island, New York, on July 6, 1908. With the two men this time were four other adventurers. All of them were younger than the 42-year-old Henson, but Henson knew that his vast experience would more than make up for the youthful high spirits of his comrades.

This time the expedition had good luck right from the beginning. The weather was just cold enough to keep the surface frozen with a minimum of breaks in the ice, but not too cold to work and travel in. Henson wrote in his diary that he had never seen such smooth sea ice, and the group made rapid progress. After every five days, Peary sent one of the members of his party back to the ship. The final assault on the Pole would be made by just Peary, one other member of his expedition, and a couple of Eskimos. In this way, only a small load of supplies would have to be carried the entire length of the journey. But who Peary would ask to join him at the Pole remained a mystery.

The explorers continued on, averaging a very fast 16 miles a day. On March 28, 1909, they passed the farthest point north they had ever reached. Two days later, Peary asked the third remaining member of the expedition to return to the ship. Matthew Henson would go with him to the North Pole.

The next day, April 1, Peary, Henson, and four Eskimos, Seegloo, Ootah, Eginwah, and Ooqueah, began their final dash for the Pole, which was now 130 miles away. Because of his crippled feet Peary was traveling slowly, but Henson drove his lead team at a furious pace. On the morning of April 6, Henson woke up Seegloo and Ootah. "Ahdoolo! . . . Ahdoolo!" he called, a little more urgently than usual. They were just 35 miles from the Pole.

At Peary's orders, Henson and the two Eskimos forged ahead. They were supposed to stop just short of the Pole to let Peary catch up. That afternoon, when Henson stopped for a rest, he realized that he had made a mistake. If his calculation was correct, he had not only reached the Pole, but gone beyond it! He backtracked a little bit and waited for Peary. The commander of the expedition took out his instruments, took his readings, and announced in a matter-of-fact voice that at last, after so many years of hardship, they had reached their destination. Henson explained to Ootah, "We have found what we hunt." The Eskimo shrugged his shoulders, still unable to fully understand these strange outsiders from another part of the world. "There is nothing here," Ootah said. "Only ice."

An Eskimo family in Greenland converses and plays outside its tent, which is made from the skins of seals. During the summer, Eskimos often lived in tents instead of in igloos.

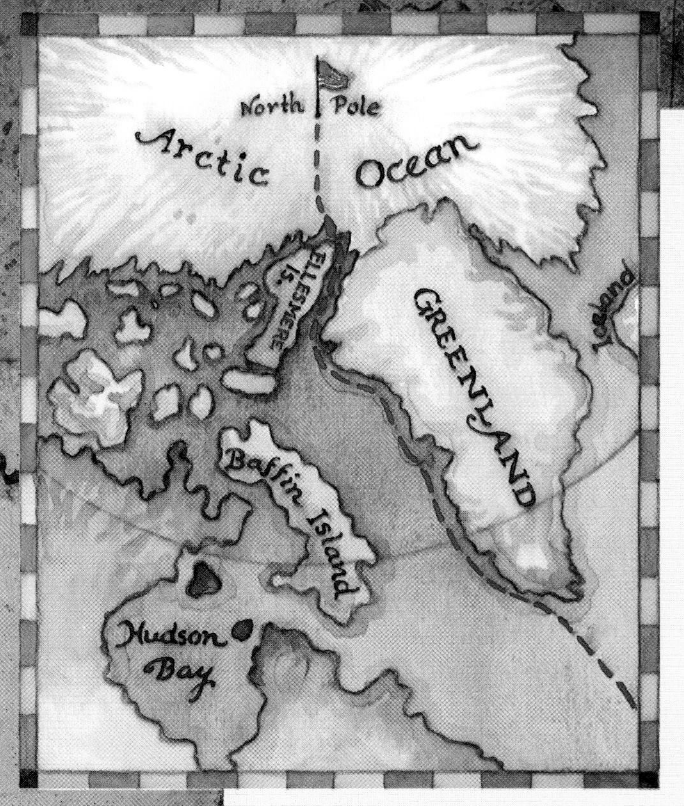

Henson and Peary's successful route to the North Pole.

With an American flag in his hand, Henson climbed to the top of a nearby pressure ridge. Peary snapped his picture. Then Henson helped set up camp. After a long night's sleep, the expedition headed home. Henson's exploring days were over.

The rest of Matthew Henson's life was frustrating in many ways. Peary was treated as a national hero, but Henson was slighted. Racist reporters asked Peary why he had allowed a Negro to accompany him to the North Pole. Peary, who was unwilling to share the credit for his achievement, made things worse with his answer. He had been forced to take Henson with him all the way, he said, because Henson was too ignorant to make it back to the ship on his own. This was completely unfair, of course, for many times it had been only Henson's courage and intelligence that saved the expedition from disaster. While Peary received large fees for giving lectures and was granted a rich pension from the government, Henson was forced to park cars in a Brooklyn garage to earn his living.

But Matthew Henson was not the kind of man to let bitterness ruin his life. He later got a good job with the U.S. Customs Bureau, and he lived a long, rich, full life until he died in 1955, at the age of 88. During his final years he took satisfaction in his own knowledge of all that he had achieved. If any doubted him, there was always the picture Peary had taken at the North Pole.

That photograph showed Matthew Henson, a black American, with the flag of his country in his hand at the top of the world. And anyone who doubted his achievements could always ask the Eskimos, who for years afterward told legends about a very great man named Miy Paluk. The Eskimos even added a new word to their language: The word *ahdoolo* came to stand for a very special kind of courage. It was used not only to mean bravery and endurance, but to mean the ability to face even the hardest work and the greatest challenge with hope and good spirits. It is a fitting word with which to remember Matthew Henson.

Triumph at the Pole: Atop an icy hill near the North Pole, Henson and his Eskimo friends hoist the American flag and several other banners.

AWARD WINNING Magazine

Standing Up for ANTARCTICA

YOUNG EXPLORERS wave their expedition flags in Antarctica with Jacques-Yves Cousteau (in the red cap). They are, from the left, Elise Otzenberger, 12, Europe; Oko Joseph Shio, 12, Africa; Kelly Jean Matheson, 12, Australia; Cory Gillmer, 13, North America; Fumiko Matsumoto, 13, Asia; and Jeronimo Brunner, 12, South America.

Six students from six continents visited Antarctica last year with explorer Jacques-Yves Cousteau. The purpose of the expedition was to point out the need to protect Antarctica for future generations.

As they approached the continent by ship, the students saw icebergs glittering in the sun. Seals and whales bobbed in the icy waters.

Once ashore the explorers visited a penguin rookery, or nesting ground, and met scientists at research stations of Brazil, Poland, and the Soviet Union. They also saw the wreck of a ship that had spilled fuel in 1989, killing wildlife.

The students, each representing a continent, will never forget their journey or the sights and sounds of Antarctica. Kelly Matheson, 12, of Australia, remembers icebergs breaking off into the sea. "All night long, we could hear the ice cracking like thunder and falling into the water," she says.

Will Antarctica remain largely unspoiled in the future? These young people will do all they can to make sure it does.

IN A PENGUIN ROOKERY, or nesting site, a snow-coated, Adélie chick waits for a meal. Parent penguins feed their young partly digested krill, which they bring back from the icy waters surrounding the continent of Antarctica.

Dr. Mae Jemison

Astronaut

An *astronaut* reaches for the stars.

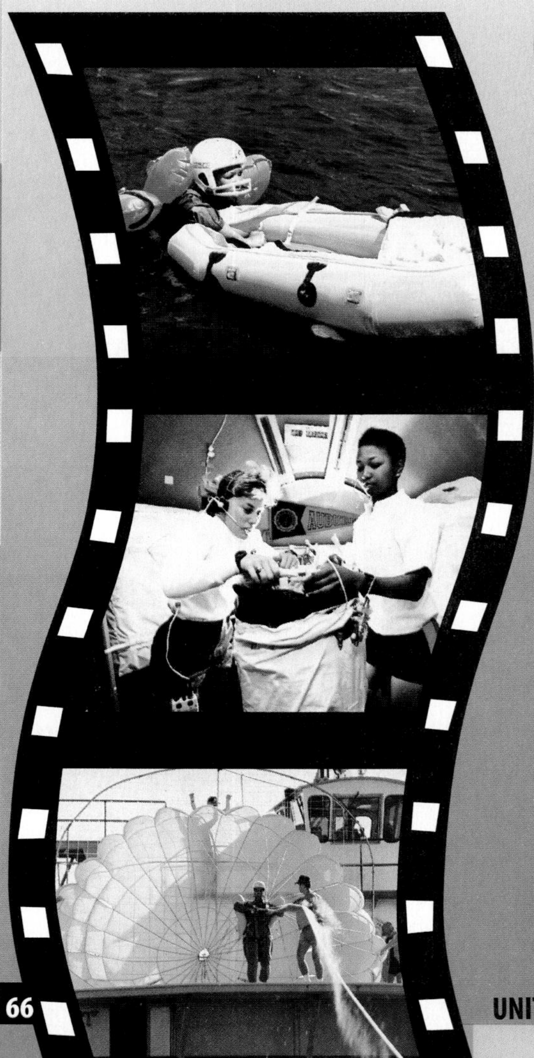

On September 12, 1992, a team of astronauts boarded the space shuttle *Endeavor*. Mission Control gave the final ten-second countdown: 3...2...1... Then the rockets ignited, and the shuttle zoomed into outer space. On board was Dr. Mae Jemison—physician, chemical engineer, and astronaut.

PROFILE

Name: Dr. Mae Jemison

Occupation: doctor, chemical engineer, astronaut, entrepreneur

Languages: English, Russian, Japanese, and Swahili

Hobbies: dance, weight training, reading history, photography

Childhood dream: to travel through outer space

QUESTIONS
for Dr. Mae Jemison

Find out why Dr. Jemison *became* an astronaut.

Q **A space mission involves a lot of people working together. Would you say that teamwork is an important part of the process?**

A I think teamwork is important in anything that you do. To be an astronaut means working with a team. Each astronaut has a job to do while in space, and those jobs can be complicated. But the bulk of the work is done by the people who stay on the ground—the scientists and engineers who get the shuttle ready. We're all part of the same team.

Q **What was your job during the space shuttle flight?**

A I was the science mission specialist. My job was to be the representative of the scientists on the ground who had designed the experiments. I was their eyes, ears, and hands. I did experiments to find out how the human body adapts to weightlessness.

Q **When did you decide that you wanted to become an astronaut?**

A As a child, I watched the Gemini and Apollo launches on television in the 1960s. When I watched the astronauts walk on the moon, I knew that I would go into space one day.

Q When did you start working toward your goal of joining the space program?

A I started working toward my goal when I was still in school. I got my degree in chemical engineering and then went on to become a doctor. In 1985 I decided to apply to NASA's astronaut program. I was accepted in 1987.

Q What advice would you give to kids who want to become astronauts?

A There are not enough spaces for everyone to become an astronaut. But all kinds of people are involved in making space exploration work, so remember you can always be involved. My advice is to find something that you like to do. Don't be limited by others who have a limited imagination.

Dr. Mae Jemison's Tips for Working Together as a Team

1. Share your ideas with the others on your team.
2. Remember that everyone is a part of the team.
3. Be willing to compromise.

SOURCE

Science Fiction

THE BEST NEW THING

by Isaac Asimov

illustrated by Tom Leonard

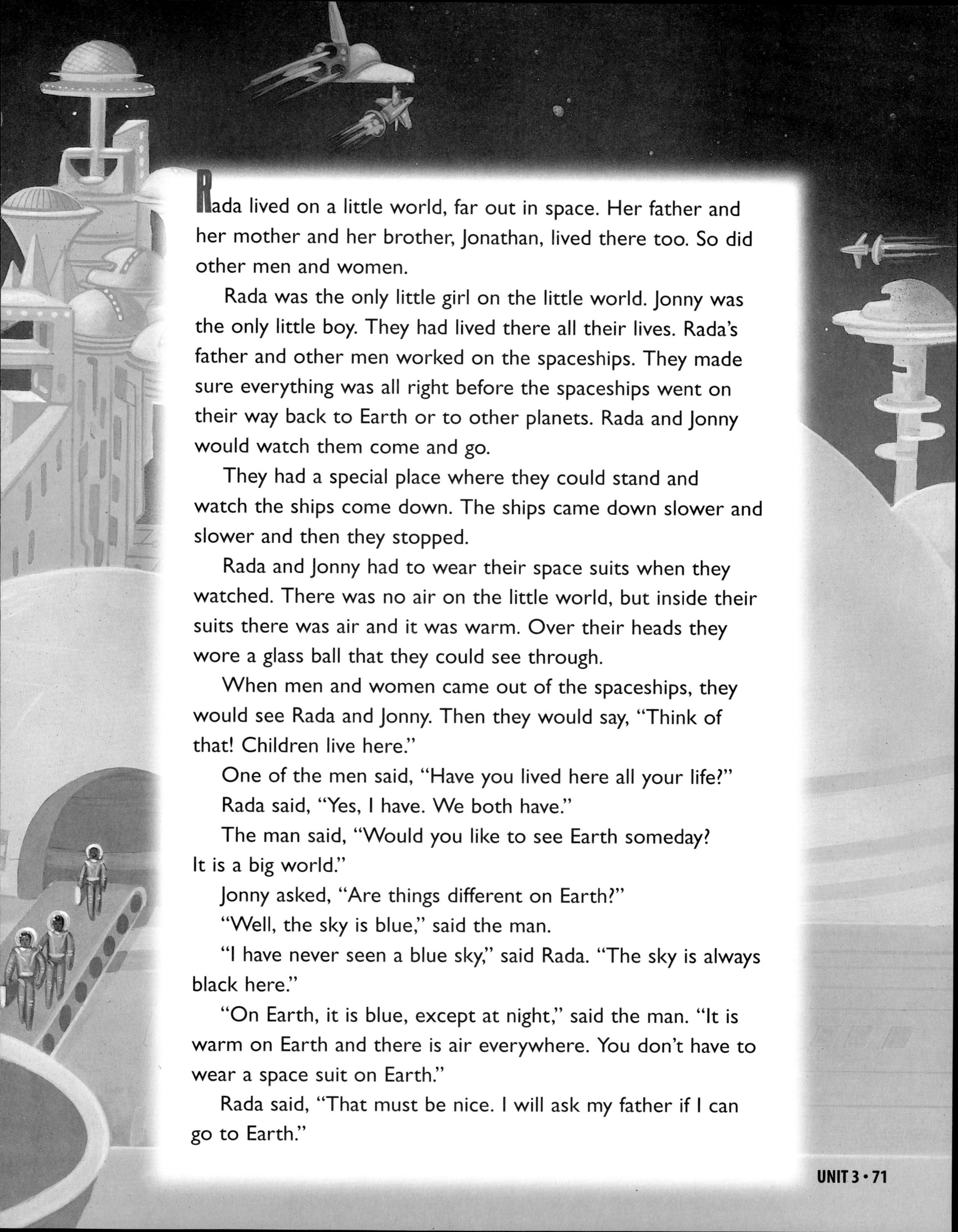

Rada lived on a little world, far out in space. Her father and her mother and her brother, Jonathan, lived there too. So did other men and women.

Rada was the only little girl on the little world. Jonny was the only little boy. They had lived there all their lives. Rada's father and other men worked on the spaceships. They made sure everything was all right before the spaceships went on their way back to Earth or to other planets. Rada and Jonny would watch them come and go.

They had a special place where they could stand and watch the ships come down. The ships came down slower and slower and then they stopped.

Rada and Jonny had to wear their space suits when they watched. There was no air on the little world, but inside their suits there was air and it was warm. Over their heads they wore a glass ball that they could see through.

When men and women came out of the spaceships, they would see Rada and Jonny. Then they would say, "Think of that! Children live here."

One of the men said, "Have you lived here all your life?"

Rada said, "Yes, I have. We both have."

The man said, "Would you like to see Earth someday? It is a big world."

Jonny asked, "Are things different on Earth?"

"Well, the sky is blue," said the man.

"I have never seen a blue sky," said Rada. "The sky is always black here."

"On Earth, it is blue, except at night," said the man. "It is warm on Earth and there is air everywhere. You don't have to wear a space suit on Earth."

Rada said, "That must be nice. I will ask my father if I can go to Earth."

She jumped high to see where her father was. She jumped very high, higher than the man—much higher than the man. When she was that high, she could see all around the spaceship. She did not see her father, so she knew he must be inside the spaceship.

She pushed a little button on her suit. Some air came out fast. It went *s-s-s-s*. That made her go down again. She came down very near the man.

The man said, "You do that very well."

Jonny said, "I can do it, too. See?"

He jumped high—and then made himself come down headfirst. He landed very softly.

The man laughed and said, "That is well done, too, but you could not do that on Earth."

Rada said, "Why not?"

"On Earth," said the man, "you can only jump a little way. Earth is so big, it holds you down. If you jump up, Earth pulls you down right away. And you could roll down any slanting place."

Then the man had to go into the spaceship again. Rada and Jonny waited for their father.

When their father came, Rada and Jonny went underground with him. Rada and Jonny and their father and mother lived inside the little world, in large, comfortable rooms.

It was warm and nice inside their home. There were books and toys and good things to eat. And there was air for them to breathe, so they could take off their big, clumsy space suits. Jonny and Rada liked to run around with not many clothes on. Of course, even indoors they couldn't run without bouncing high into the air, because the little world was too little to pull them down.

Jonny said, "Daddy, is it true that you don't have to wear a space suit on Earth?"

His father said, "Yes, it is. There is air on Earth, just like the air that we have to manufacture here so we can breathe in these rooms."

Jonny said, "And is the sky really blue there?"

"That's right," his father answered. "And there are white things in the sky called clouds. Sometimes drops of water come from the sky. That is rain."

Rada thought about this for a minute, and then she said, "If the ground has water on it, doesn't that make it slippery?"

Her father laughed, and then he said, "The rain doesn't stay on top of the ground. It sinks into the ground and helps to make the grass grow."

Rada knew about grass, because her father and mother had told her about it. But she liked to hear about it over and over again. So she said, "Tell me about grass again, Daddy."

"Grass is like a green carpet that grows on the ground. It is soft and very beautiful," he said.

"I would like to see it," said Rada. "And I would like to feel it too. Will we go to Earth someday, Daddy?"

"Oh yes, Rada," her father said. "Perhaps we can go soon."

Rada was so happy to hear this that she wanted to put her arms about her father. She walked up the wall to be near his head.

Rada could do that on her little world, because that world was too little to pull her down. She could walk on the wall or anywhere because her shoes were made to stick to everything.

When she walked on the wall, the wall was under her feet just like a floor. Her head was near her father's head now and she put her arms around him.

"Thank you, Daddy," she said.

Her father hugged her and said, "You know, if you were on Earth, you could not walk on the wall. Earth would pull you down."

Rada's mother came into the room. She pushed down on the floor with her feet. That made her move up. She came to a stop near the top of the room by pushing the air with her hand.

She held two containers. She said, "Rada! Jonny! Here is your milk."

When she let go of the containers, they stayed in the air.

"Oh good, I'm thirsty," Rada said. She pushed the wall with her feet and moved to the container. She opened the container and put a straw into the opening.

Jonny moved up into the air and came near the other container. He said, "I don't want to use a straw, Mommy. May I roll the milk into a ball?"

"All right, but be careful not to get any on your clothes," his mother said.

Jonny opened the container and shook it. The milk floated out and made a soft white ball. Some of it made little tiny balls. Jonny pushed the tiny balls with his finger and they all went back into the big white ball.

He pushed the air with his hands and moved his head very near the ball. He put his lips to it and sucked it in. It was fun to drink milk that way.

His father said "If you drank milk that way on Earth, it would get all over your clothes. You will have to remember many things like that when you are on Earth."

"Have I ever been there, Daddy?" asked Rada.

"Oh yes," said her father, "but you can't remember it because you were only a baby when you came here with Mommy and me. And Jonny wasn't even born. Now it will soon be time to go back to Earth. We will take you with us."

Rada moved to her father and put her head on top of his. Her feet were in the air. Jonny had finished his milk and he was moving around and around his father, pushing the air to make himself go.

"Can you see the stars on Earth, Daddy?" asked Rada. On their little world, they could always see the stars because the sky was always dark.

"Yes, you can," said her father. "Part of the time."

Rada and Jonny talked a long time about Earth. They could hardly sleep that night. They kept thinking about Earth.

There were so many new things on Earth to think about. There was air that was everywhere. There were the blue sky and the rain, the wind and the flowers. And there were birds and animals.

The next day their father showed them pictures of some of the new things. They saw that the ground could be flat in some places and hilly in others. Soon they would see and feel all these things for themselves.

There would be other boys and girls to play with on Earth. There would be so many new things to see and do.

But there was one new thing Rada especially wanted to do. She told Jonny about it and he wanted to do it too. They didn't tell their father or mother. It was something they had never done in all their lives. On Earth, they were going to find out what it felt like.

Rada and Jonny had to make themselves strong for living on Earth.

Her mother said, "Now, Rada, Earth is a big world. It will pull at you hard. You must be strong so that you can walk in spite of all that pull."

Jonny said, "Yes, Rada, you have to be as strong as I am."

But Mother said, "You will have to be stronger than you are now, too, Jonny."

There were springs on the wall in the exercise room. Rada and Jonny had to pull on them. They stood on the wall and

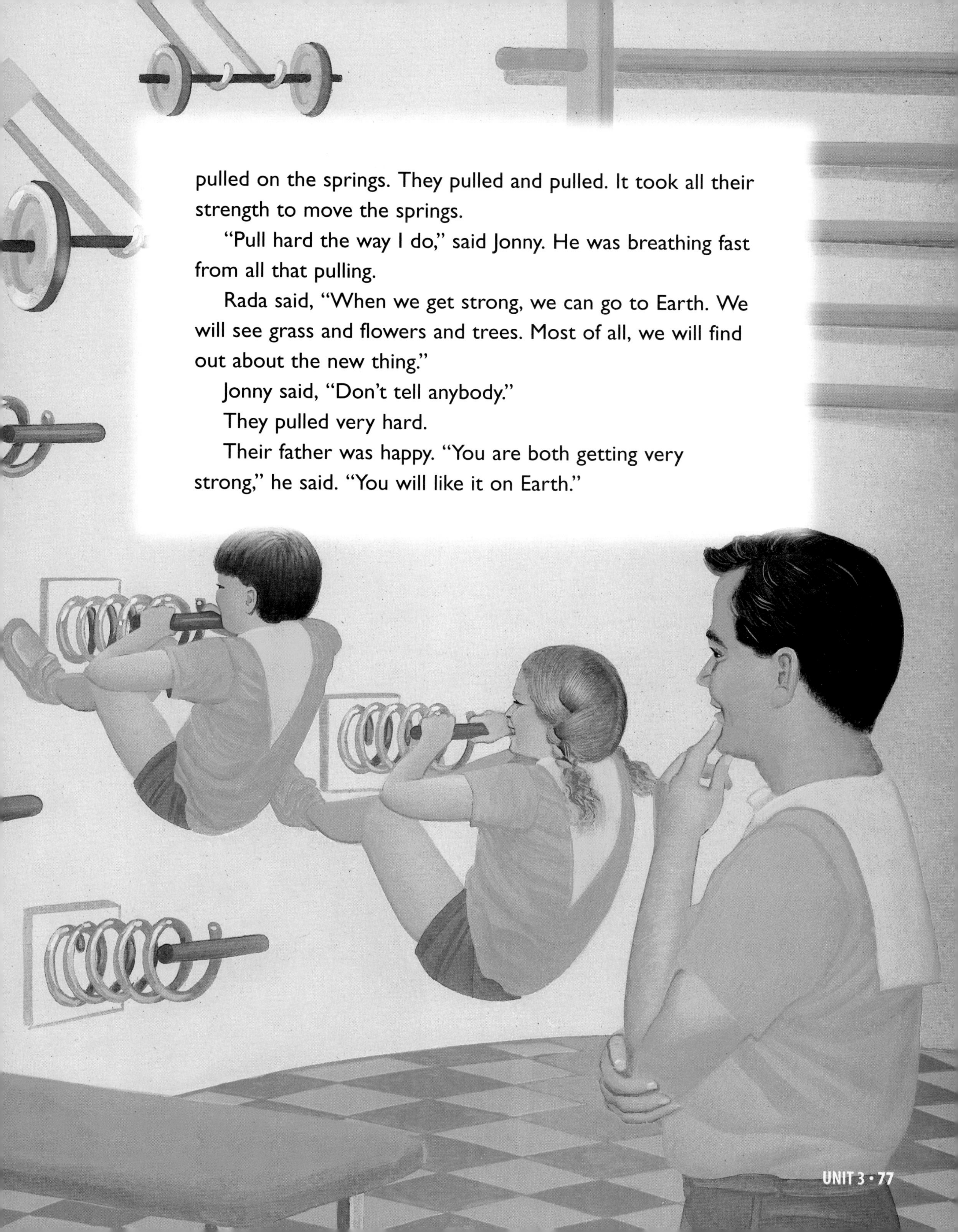

pulled on the springs. They pulled and pulled. It took all their strength to move the springs.

"Pull hard the way I do," said Jonny. He was breathing fast from all that pulling.

Rada said, "When we get strong, we can go to Earth. We will see grass and flowers and trees. Most of all, we will find out about the new thing."

Jonny said, "Don't tell anybody."

They pulled very hard.

Their father was happy. "You are both getting very strong," he said. "You will like it on Earth."

One day a spaceship came and their father said, "This is the ship that will take us to Earth."

They all put on their space suits. Their father was ready to go. So was their mother. But Rada and Jonny were ready first.

Rada felt a little bit sorry. She would miss her little world. When they were getting into the spaceship, she turned and said, "Goodbye, little world. Maybe I will see you again someday." Then she jumped very high so she could see almost all of their side of the little world.

"Good-bye," she said again. "It is time for me to go to Earth now."

Jonny called her from the spaceship. "Come on, slowpoke. We're all waiting for you."

On the spaceship they went to their little room. It had chairs with seatbelts.

Their father said, "Let me put the seatbelts around you, children. They must hold you when the spaceship starts to move."

He fastened their seatbelts so they couldn't move. Then their father and mother sat in their own chairs and fastened their own seatbelts. The chairs were very soft.

Then the spaceship started to move. There was a big noise all through the ship and Rada and Jonny were pushed against the soft, soft chair. They were pushed harder and harder but the seatbelts kept everything all right.

"I'm not frightened," said Jonny. "Are you frightened, Rada?"

"Just a little bit," said Rada. She could see the little world as the ship moved away from it. The little world was smaller than ever. Soon it was just a dot and then all Rada could see were the stars.

"Can we see Earth, Daddy?" Jonny asked.

"It looks like a star from here. It's that bright one there," said his father.

"Look at Earth, Rada," said Jonny. He was very excited.

Rada looked at the bright star and was happy. Soon she would be on Earth and would know about the new thing. She knew Jonny was thinking about it, too.

"Wake up, Rada," said her father. "We are coming down to Earth. Jonny is awake already."

Rada opened her eyes. "Can we get out of the ship now, Daddy?"

"Soon, Rada," said her father. "You must wait a little while."

Rada looked out the window. Down below she could see a big, big world. She had never seen anything so very, very big. It was green and brown and lots of other colors too. She could see water, too, and that was blue.

Above all the green and brown and blue and other colors of the Earth was the sky.

Jonny said, "How big everything is!"

And Rada said, "How pretty everything is!"

They could hardly wait.

When the ship stopped, Rada took off her belt. She was the first one to get out of the chair. Jonny was second.

Jonny tried to walk. "The floor is holding my foot," he said.

"Pull harder," said his father.

Jonny did and at last he succeeded in lifting his foot from the floor.

"Aren't we going to put on our space suits?" asked Rada.

"Don't forget, we don't have to put on space suits on Earth," said her father.

"Oh, yes," said Rada. "That's one of the new things." She and Jonny were waiting for another new thing, too. They squeezed each other's hands but they didn't say anything.

They went down and down and down inside the ship to get to a little door that would let them out on the Earth. It was hard to walk, but they were beginning to get used to it.

The door opened and they all walked out. There was flat paving all around the spaceship, as there had been on the little world. But at the edge of the paving there was grass. There had been no grass on the little world.

"My," said Mother, "doesn't the air smell sweet?"

"Oh, yes," said Rada. She could feel the air moving. That was the wind. It blew her dress and her hair.

It was warm and the sun was very big and yellow.

Jonny said, "Look how big the sun is." The sun had looked much smaller from their little world.

"Don't look right at the sun," his father said quickly. "That would hurt your eyes."

"What is that sound?" asked Rada.

"It is a bird singing," said her mother.

Rada had never heard a bird singing. She had never felt the wind. She had never seen such a big sun and such bright sunlight.

These were all new things.

Now it was time for the best new thing of all. Now she would find out what it was really like.

She said, "Come on, Jonny."

Jonny said, "Look at the grass. And there's a little hill just like the one in the pictures. Let's try it."

Rada said, "Look, Mother. See how I can run."

It was hard to run because Earth pulled at her legs. She ran with all her might to the grassy hill. Jonny was running, too.

Jonny said, "I can run faster than you." But they reached the grass together. Both were breathing hard from running.

Then they came to the little hill and they climbed to the top. That was even harder than walking, but they made it. They looked at each other and laughed, and then they both lay down on the grass and rolled down the hill. When they reached the bottom, they stood up, laughing and breathing hard.

Their father and mother came to them.

"Are you hurt, children?" their father asked.

"You should not run like that till you are used to Earth's pull," said their mother.

"Oh, but we wanted to," said Rada. "We are so happy because we know, now, about the new thing. It is something we had never done before."

"What new thing?" asked her father.

"We rolled down the hill," said Rada. "We could never do that before, because our own little world never pulled us. But it was really fun. I think it's the best new thing of all."

"Yes," said Jonny, "that is the best new thing of all."

And they ran up to the top of the hill to try it again.

Workshop 2

How to

Create a Team Profile

If you were going on an expedition, would you go all by yourself? Probably not. Depending on where you were going, you would want people along who have specific skills. You would want to create a team profile.

What is a team profile? A team profile is a list of job titles and the skills that are needed for each job. Different expeditions require different skills. For an archaeological expedition, a team profile might include an archaeologist, a medical doctor, and a photographer.

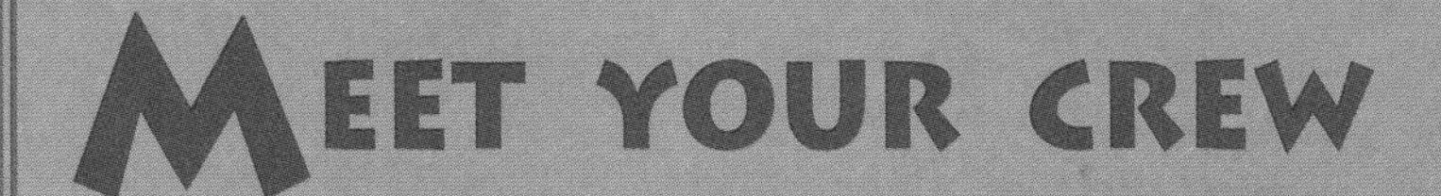

MEET YOUR CREW

Each crew member aboard the ship is called a specialist. Here's what each specialist does:

The team's work is divided among professionals.

ENVIRONMENTAL CONTROL:
Keeps air breathable and comfortable; takes care of the fresh water supply.

Each team member has a job title.

METEOROLOGIST:
Keeps track of weather.

COMMUNICATIONS:
Maintains radio contact between crew members, ship, and command center.

Each job has important responsibilities.

BIOLOGIST:
Looks for life forms.

ENGINEER:
Keeps ship's engines and electronics working.

MEDICAL OFFICER:
Tends to the health and well-being of all crew members.

A doctor is an important member of any team.

1 Choose an Adventure

Choose an adventure that interests your team. It could be a space mission, an underwater expedition, or an exciting idea of your own. Once your team has agreed on the goal of your expedition, decide where it will take place. Look at an atlas for ideas.

TOOLS

- atlas or globe
- reference books
- magazines and newspapers
- paper and pencil
- posterboard and markers

2 Make a Checklist

Once you've chosen an adventure, make a checklist of important skills your team will need. Think about the place you are going. How will you get there? What will the environment be like? Use reference books, magazines, and newspapers to research the place and the skills needed to survive there. This research will help you write your skills checklist.

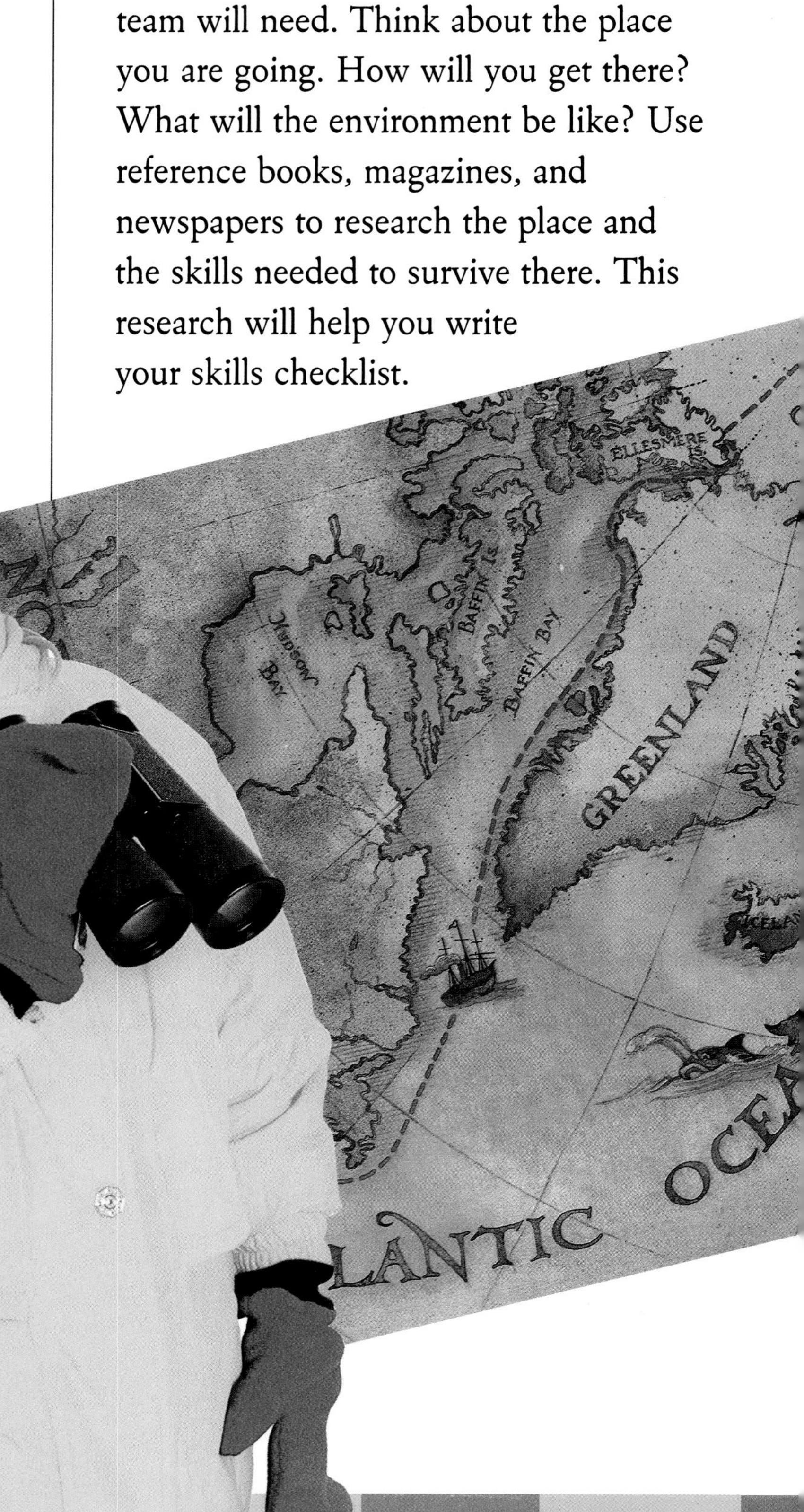

3 Choose a Job Title

After your team decides what skills will be needed on the expedition, make a list of job titles. Next to each job title, describe the skills and responsibilities of that job. Then, have each team member pick a job title from the list. Discuss why the role of each team member is important to the success of the expedition.

Tips

- Use maps, reference books, and magazines to help you think of adventure possibilities.
- Do some research! Read about people who have already been on your adventure. What kind of specialists were on the team? What problems and challenges did they face?

4 Present Your Team Profile

Create a team poster. Make a poster with drawings or photos of each crew member. Underneath each picture put the team member's job title and a description of duties. Draw a picture or a map of the place your expedition is going to. Be sure to include interesting facts that your team discovered while doing research. Present your team poster to the rest of your class.

If You Are Using a Computer . . .

Write the job title and a description of each team member's skills on the computer. Print it out and use it on your poster. Be creative with the font sizes and styles. You may also want to use the Record Tools to describe your job on the team.

Dr. Mae Jemison
Astronaut

SECTION 3

Scientific teams search for new knowledge about the environment.

Science Search

Learn how one tree in the rain forest provides food and shelter for many animals.

Investigate the world beneath the sea with marine biologist Eugenie Clark.

Find out how you can become a member of the Jason Project.

PROJECT

Research an interesting place, and give a multimedia show about it.

TAKE A TRIP THAT'S OUT OF THIS WORLD.

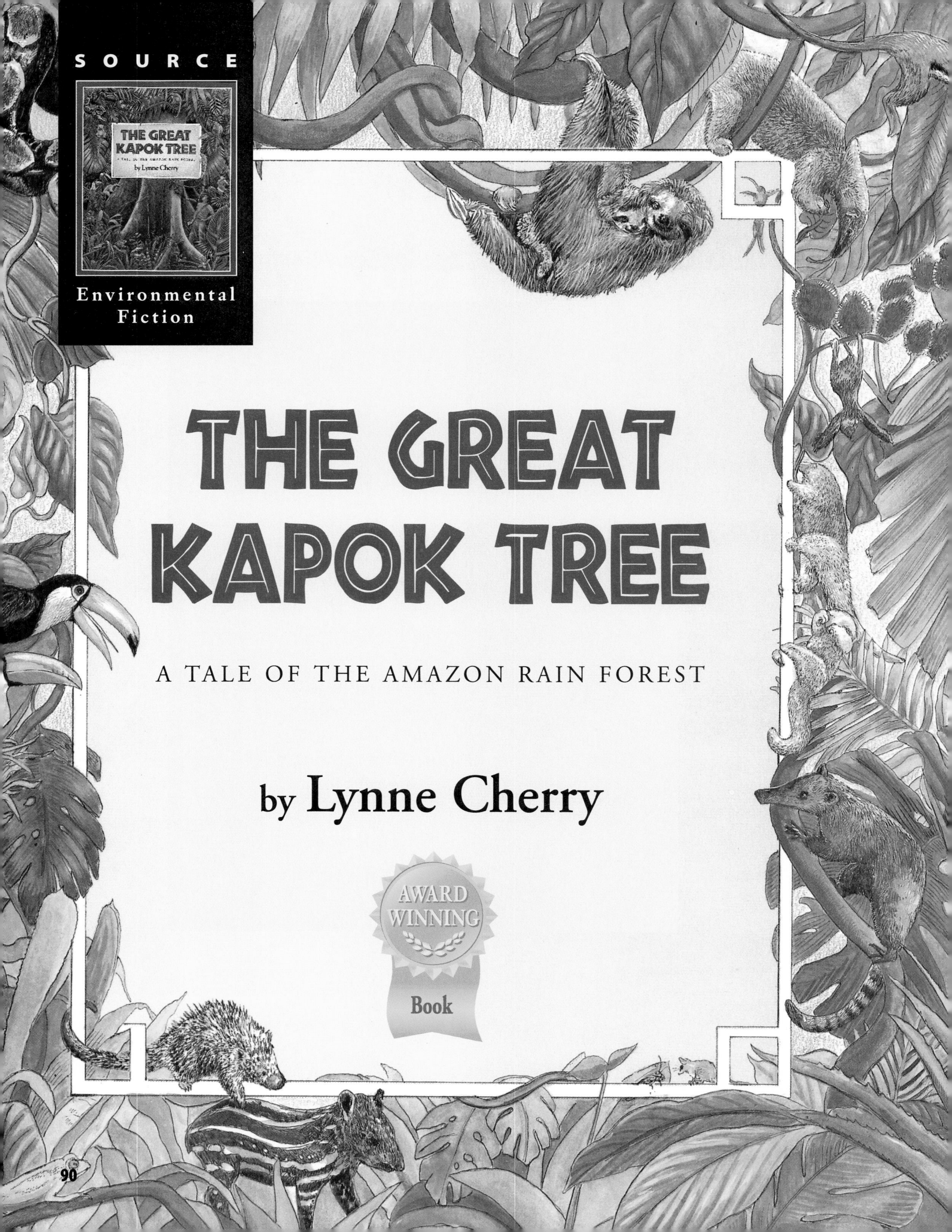

THE GREAT KAPOK TREE

A TALE OF THE AMAZON RAIN FOREST

by **Lynne Cherry**

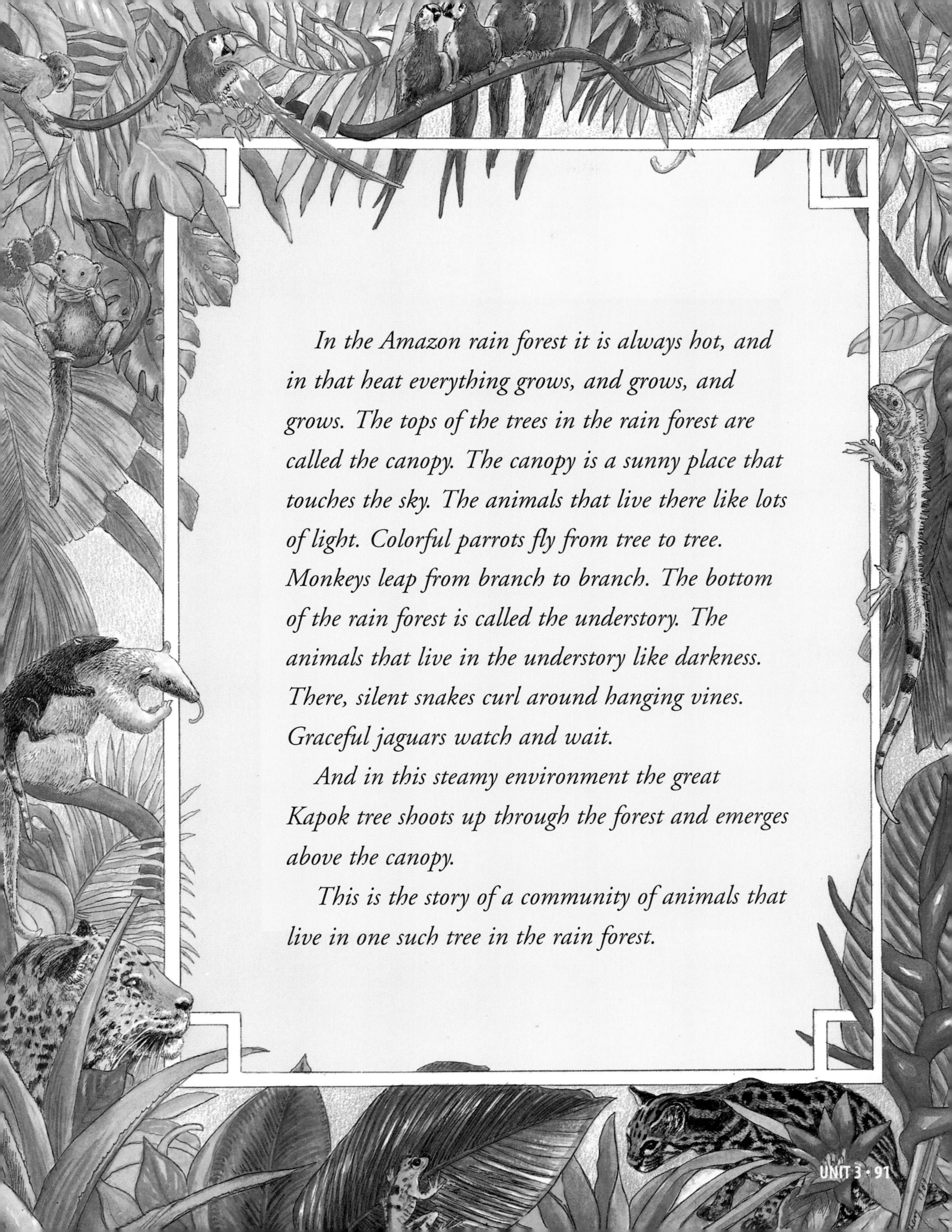

In the Amazon rain forest it is always hot, and in that heat everything grows, and grows, and grows. The tops of the trees in the rain forest are called the canopy. The canopy is a sunny place that touches the sky. The animals that live there like lots of light. Colorful parrots fly from tree to tree. Monkeys leap from branch to branch. The bottom of the rain forest is called the understory. The animals that live in the understory like darkness. There, silent snakes curl around hanging vines. Graceful jaguars watch and wait.

And in this steamy environment the great Kapok tree shoots up through the forest and emerges above the canopy.

This is the story of a community of animals that live in one such tree in the rain forest.

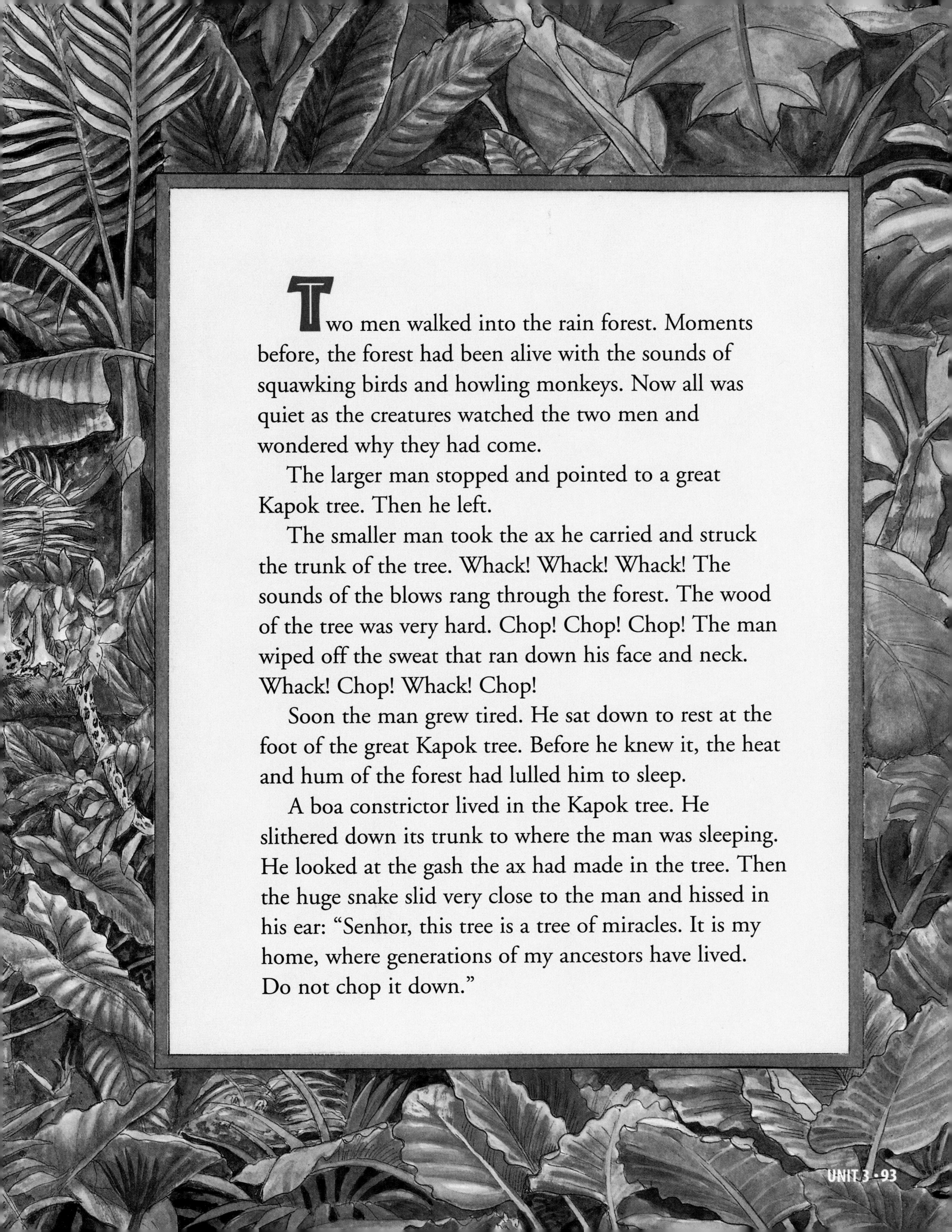

Two men walked into the rain forest. Moments before, the forest had been alive with the sounds of squawking birds and howling monkeys. Now all was quiet as the creatures watched the two men and wondered why they had come.

The larger man stopped and pointed to a great Kapok tree. Then he left.

The smaller man took the ax he carried and struck the trunk of the tree. Whack! Whack! Whack! The sounds of the blows rang through the forest. The wood of the tree was very hard. Chop! Chop! Chop! The man wiped off the sweat that ran down his face and neck. Whack! Chop! Whack! Chop!

Soon the man grew tired. He sat down to rest at the foot of the great Kapok tree. Before he knew it, the heat and hum of the forest had lulled him to sleep.

A boa constrictor lived in the Kapok tree. He slithered down its trunk to where the man was sleeping. He looked at the gash the ax had made in the tree. Then the huge snake slid very close to the man and hissed in his ear: "Senhor, this tree is a tree of miracles. It is my home, where generations of my ancestors have lived. Do not chop it down."

A bee buzzed in the sleeping man's ear: "Senhor, my hive is in this Kapok tree, and I fly from tree to tree and flower to flower collecting pollen. In this way I pollinate the trees and flowers throughout the rain forest. You see, all living things depend on one another."

A troupe of monkeys scampered down from the canopy of the Kapok tree. They chattered to the sleeping man: "Senhor, we have seen the ways of man. You chop down one tree, then come back for another and another. The roots of these great trees will wither and die, and there will be nothing left to hold the earth in place. When the heavy rains come, the soil will be washed away and the forest will become a desert."

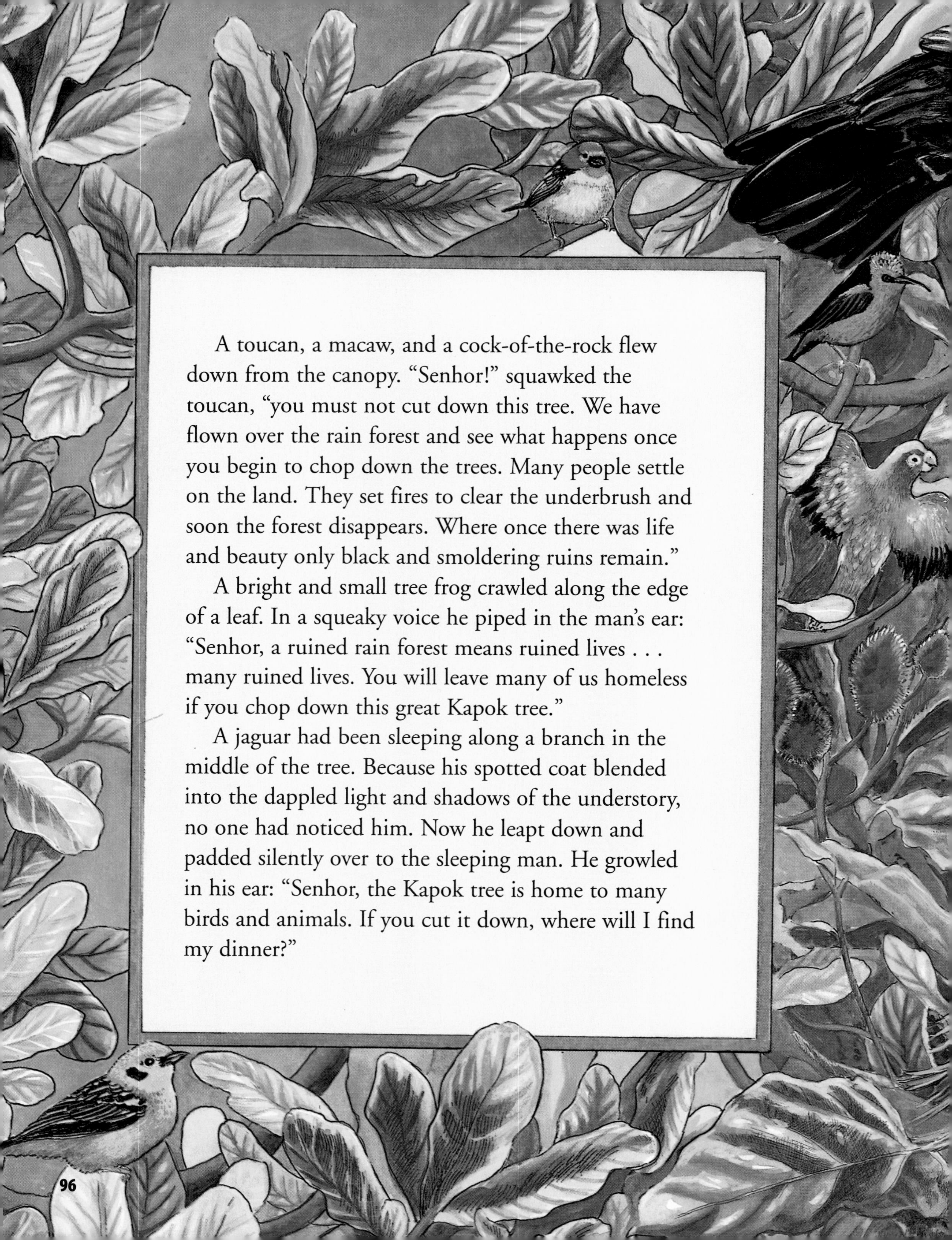

A toucan, a macaw, and a cock-of-the-rock flew down from the canopy. "Senhor!" squawked the toucan, "you must not cut down this tree. We have flown over the rain forest and see what happens once you begin to chop down the trees. Many people settle on the land. They set fires to clear the underbrush and soon the forest disappears. Where once there was life and beauty only black and smoldering ruins remain."

A bright and small tree frog crawled along the edge of a leaf. In a squeaky voice he piped in the man's ear: "Senhor, a ruined rain forest means ruined lives . . . many ruined lives. You will leave many of us homeless if you chop down this great Kapok tree."

A jaguar had been sleeping along a branch in the middle of the tree. Because his spotted coat blended into the dappled light and shadows of the understory, no one had noticed him. Now he leapt down and padded silently over to the sleeping man. He growled in his ear: "Senhor, the Kapok tree is home to many birds and animals. If you cut it down, where will I find my dinner?"

Four tree porcupines swung down from branch to branch and whispered to the man: "Senhor, do you know what we animals and humans need in order to live? Oxygen. And, Senhor, do you know what trees produce? Oxygen! If you cut down the forests you will destroy that which gives us all life."

Several anteaters climbed down the Kapok tree with their young clinging to their backs. The unstriped anteater said to the sleeping man: "Senhor, you are chopping down this tree with no thought for the future. And surely you know that what happens tomorrow depends upon what you do today. The big man tells you to chop down a beautiful tree. He does not think of his own children, who tomorrow must live in a world without trees."

A three-toed sloth had begun climbing down from the canopy when the men first appeared. Only now did she reach the ground. Plodding ever so slowly over to the sleeping man, she spoke in her deep and lazy voice: "Senhor, how much is beauty worth? Can you live without it? If you destroy the beauty of the rain forest, on what would you feast your eyes?"

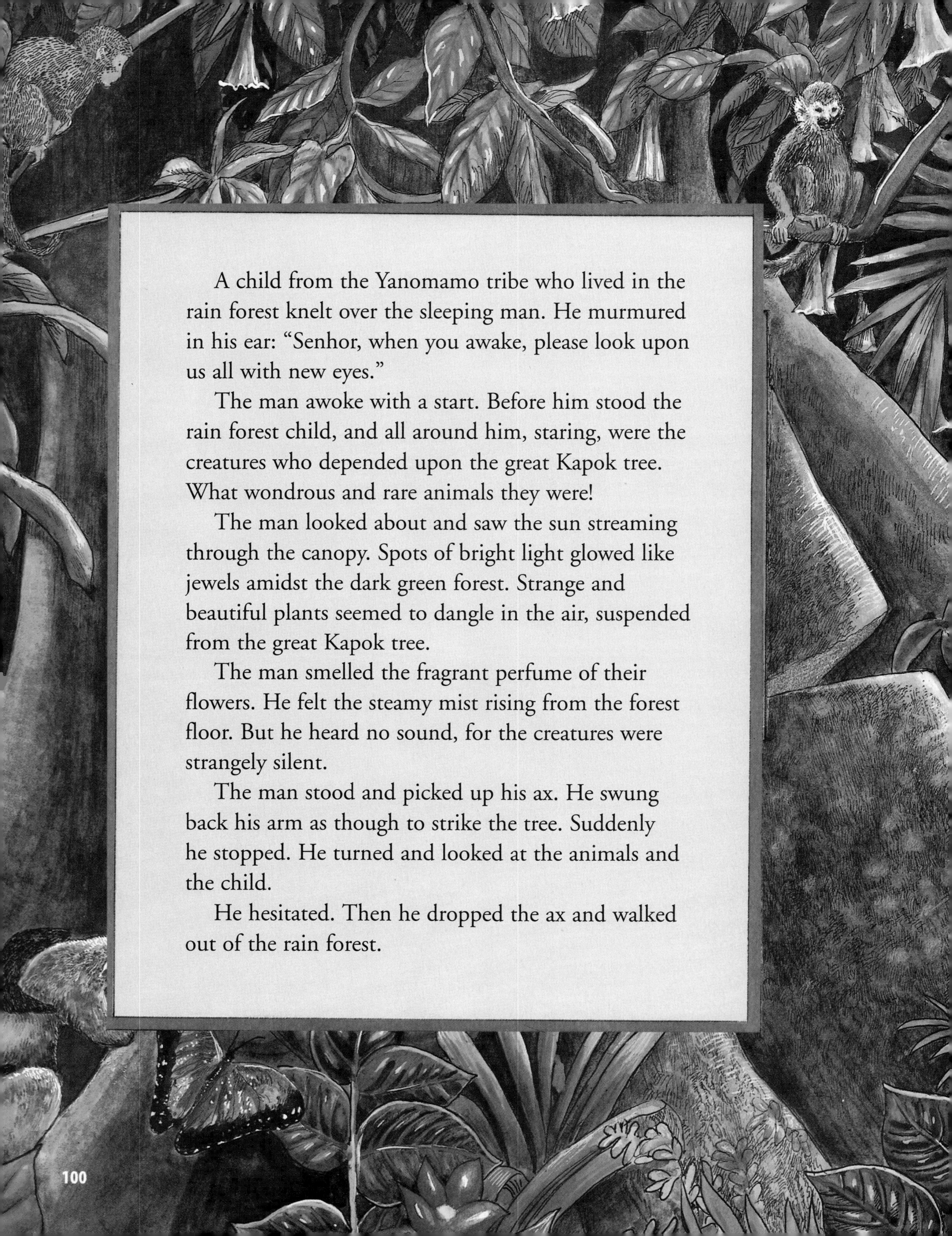

A child from the Yanomamo tribe who lived in the rain forest knelt over the sleeping man. He murmured in his ear: "Senhor, when you awake, please look upon us all with new eyes."

The man awoke with a start. Before him stood the rain forest child, and all around him, staring, were the creatures who depended upon the great Kapok tree. What wondrous and rare animals they were!

The man looked about and saw the sun streaming through the canopy. Spots of bright light glowed like jewels amidst the dark green forest. Strange and beautiful plants seemed to dangle in the air, suspended from the great Kapok tree.

The man smelled the fragrant perfume of their flowers. He felt the steamy mist rising from the forest floor. But he heard no sound, for the creatures were strangely silent.

The man stood and picked up his ax. He swung back his arm as though to strike the tree. Suddenly he stopped. He turned and looked at the animals and the child.

He hesitated. Then he dropped the ax and walked out of the rain forest.

scarlet macaw
toucan
Brazilian tree frog
coati
scamander
red-necked tanager
emerald tree boa
tree frog
three-toed sloth
urania butterfly
cock-of-the-rock
tree porcupine
mother & baby tapir
mother & baby giant anteater
Vindula arsinoë butterfly
baby hoatzin
Amazonian katydid
poison arrow frog
ARCTIC OCEAN
GREENLAND
EUROPE
NORTH AMERICA
ATLANTIC OCEAN
AFRICA
Central America
CARIBBEAN SEA
THE AMAZON RAIN FOREST
Rio Negro
Manaus
AMAZON RIVER
Equator
Brazil
SOUTH AMERICA
PACIFIC OCEAN
today's rain forests
original extent of rain forests
Tropical Rain Forests

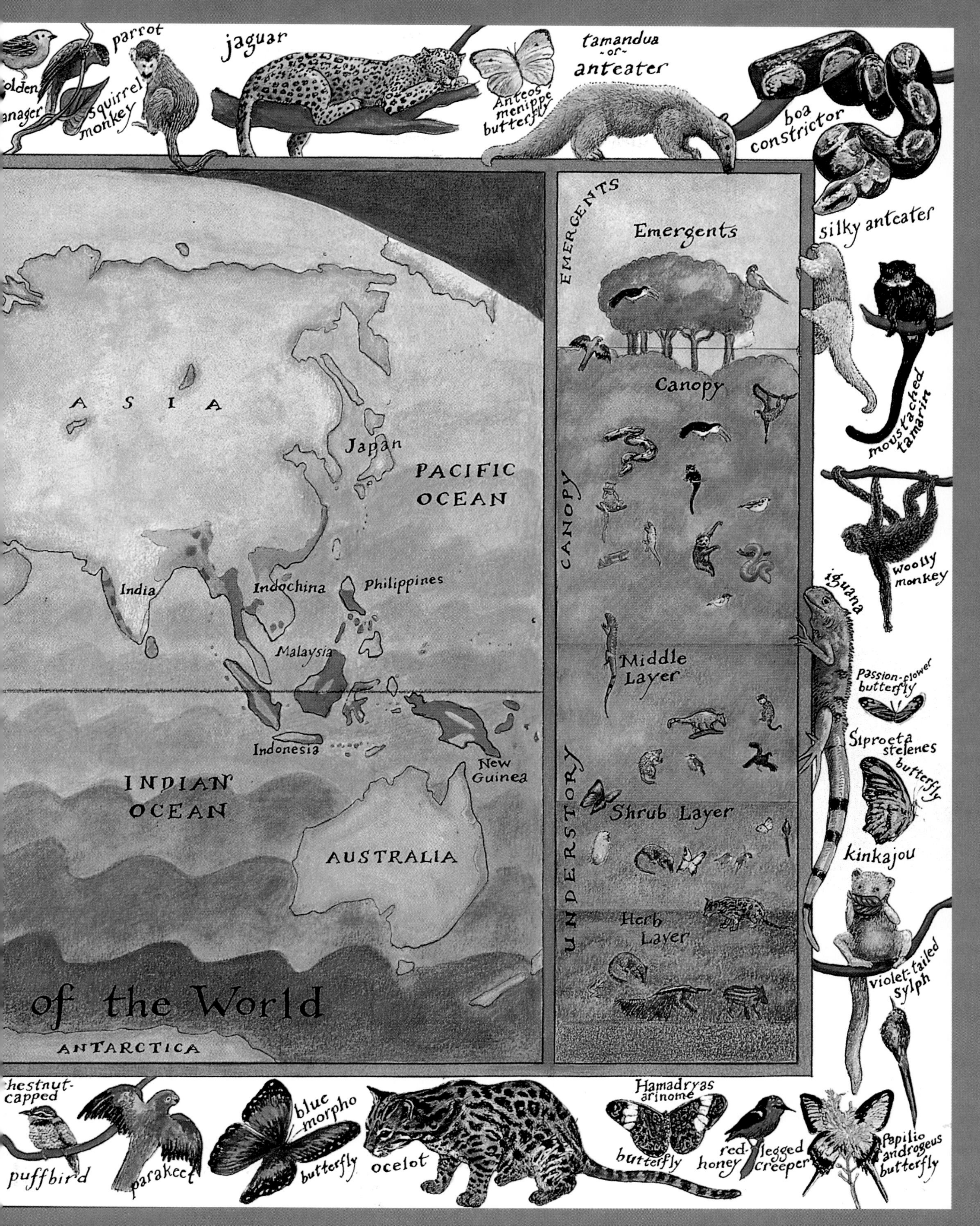

olden
anager
parrot
squirrel monkey
jaguar
Anteos menippe butterfly
tamandua -or- anteater
boa constrictor
silky anteater
moustached tamarin
woolly monkey
iguana
Passion-flower butterfly
Siproeta stelenes butterfly
kinkajou
violet-tailed Sylph
ASIA
Japan
PACIFIC OCEAN
India
Indochina
Philippines
Malaysia
Indonesia
New Guinea
INDIAN OCEAN
AUSTRALIA
of the World
ANTARCTICA
EMERGENTS
Emergents
Canopy
CANOPY
Middle Layer
UNDERSTORY
Shrub Layer
Herb Layer
hestnut-capped puffbird
parakeet
blue morpho butterfly
ocelot
Hamadryas arinome butterfly
red-legged honey creeper
Papilio androgeus butterfly

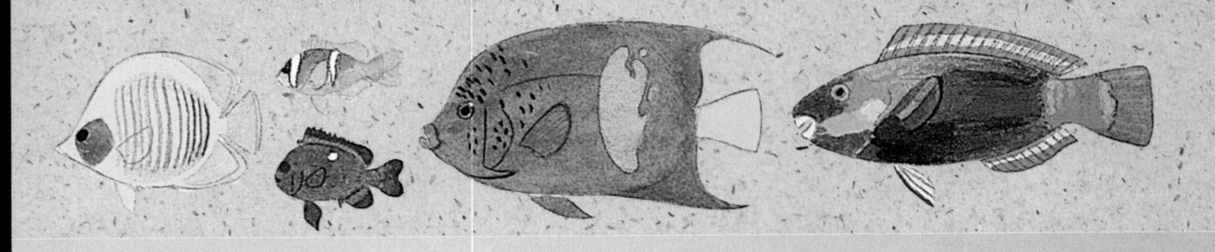

FROM

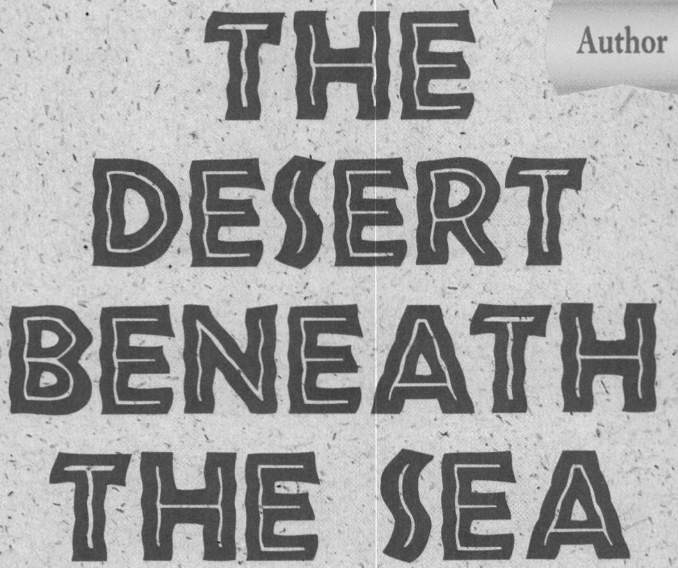

By
Ann McGovern
and Eugenie Clark

Illustrated by
Craig Phillips

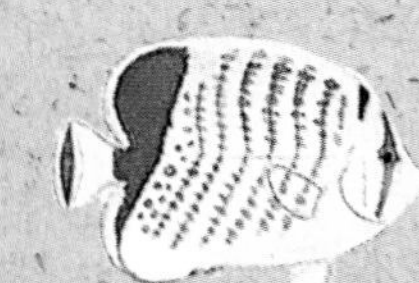

How Marine Biologists Study the Undersea Desert

Marine biologist Eugenie Clark is known as the Shark Lady. She studies sharks all over the world. But she is also interested in the tiny creatures who live in the desert beneath the sea.

A scientist like Eugenie Clark studies fish in many different ways. As a young girl, she studied fish in an aquarium at home. Now she goes on expeditions to observe the creatures in their homes in the sea. She goes scuba diving to study their behavior firsthand. Many people enjoy diving with her—students, her grown children, other scientists and diving friends, including author Ann McGovern.

Eugenie and Ann have a lot of fun on these expeditions. But they work hard, too.

They learn to lie quietly on the sea bottom, careful not to disturb the creatures they are studying.

Ann takes notes for her books and Eugenie records her findings. They write with a pencil tied to a plastic slate or on special underwater paper held to a clipboard with two rubber bands.

Eugenie and her scuba-diving friends watch how the creatures behave . . . how they act alone and with other sand dwellers . . . how they fight, feed, and mate . . . how the seasons and the sun and moon and currents affect them. They study the creatures at sunrise, at dusk, and in the dark of night.

Eugenie also studies the kind of water and sand in which the creatures live. She spends many hours in libraries and museums all over the world. She reads information by other scientists.

Back in her lab at the University of Maryland where she is a professor of Zoology, Eugenie does further study. She examines fish preserved in alcohol by *dissecting*, or cutting them open. She studies tiny parts of them under microscopes.

She counts the rays in each fin and the scales on their bodies. She measures many parts of the fish.

She examines what remains in the fishes' stomachs to find out what they eat. Sometimes she has to play detective. From only a few fish scales or bones, she tries to figure out the kind of food that was eaten.

In a notebook, she records all her information, called *data.* This data can also be put into a computer, revealing other fish facts. As she writes her findings, she analyzes and studies the computer images.

Her data is published in scientific magazines and books for other scientists to read. Sometimes she writes for popular magazines, like *National Geographic.* Her stories are illustrated with beautiful photographs.

If You Joined an Underwater Expedition

Suppose you were a scuba diver and were invited to take part in an underwater study. You would be one of fourteen people—including Ann McGovern—who volunteered to live on a dive boat for a week to study the sand tilefish of the Caribbean Sea.

The leaders of the expedition—Eugenie Clark and Joan Rabin—would give you jobs to do. You would help them try to find answers to many questions about the sand tilefish.

How deep down do these fish build their burrows? What are they made of? Does each fish build its burrow alone or with other tilefishes? Why are the tops of burrows built so big? Is it to show off? Is it to build an artificial reef to attract their food?

Coral reefs around the world are being damaged in shallow waters where people drop their trash—sometimes right in the tilefish's territory. How does the tilefish react to this?

Your first job would be to scuba dive to locate the sand tilefish. Its pale color makes it hard to spot when it hovers above the sandy bottom. You would learn to tell males from females. Males are larger and develop streamers on their tails. They behave differently from females.

Tilefish homes, called *burrows*, are easy to locate because of the mountains of coral rubble piled on top. Some of them are over eight feet across. Juvenile tilefish build small burrows. Once you find a burrow, you mark it with a plastic marker with your initials and a number. All week, you would study that area and the tilefish that live there. You would see that only one tilefish lives in each burrow.

You would measure the size of the roof mounds and the distances between them. You use a compass and a cotton string that is knotted in measured lengths. After each scuba dive, you give your information to Eugenie or Joan. They record your observations in a scientific way. They make detailed drawings and maps of the whole area. Your observations would be part of a scientific study.

Another job would be to help Joan *excavate*, or take apart, a large roof mound. These are made mostly of pieces of broken coral. A tilefish can easily build its burrow and roof mound again.

First Joan divides the large mound into four parts with her diving knife, the way you might divide a pie. One quarter, or *quadrant*, would be studied. You pick up the coral pieces carefully and put them into your collecting bag. When the bag is filled, a lift bag is inflated to bring the heavy rubble up to the boat.

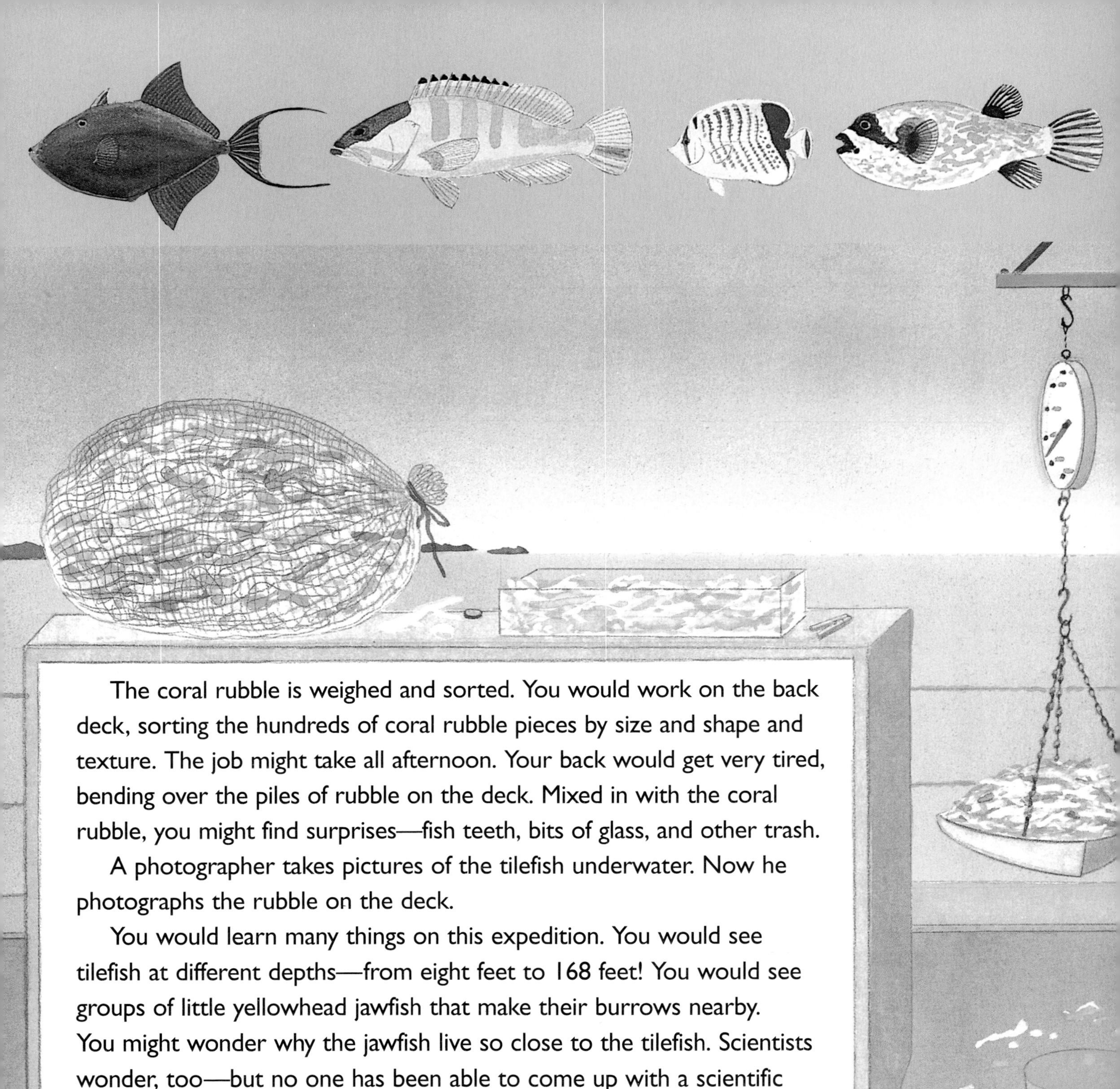

The coral rubble is weighed and sorted. You would work on the back deck, sorting the hundreds of coral rubble pieces by size and shape and texture. The job might take all afternoon. Your back would get very tired, bending over the piles of rubble on the deck. Mixed in with the coral rubble, you might find surprises—fish teeth, bits of glass, and other trash.

A photographer takes pictures of the tilefish underwater. Now he photographs the rubble on the deck.

You would learn many things on this expedition. You would see tilefish at different depths—from eight feet to 168 feet! You would see groups of little yellowhead jawfish that make their burrows nearby. You might wonder why the jawfish live so close to the tilefish. Scientists wonder, too—but no one has been able to come up with a scientific reason, so far.

On many dives, you would see a tilefish pick up a piece of coral in its mouth. It would swim up to a big mound. Yet the tilefish makes its mound even bigger by adding another piece of coral on top! Scientists are still investigating the reasons why tilefish keep building.

Divers check up on the fish at night, too. When the sun sets, the tilefish cover the openings to their burrows by fanning the sand with their tails. Then they dive through the soft, new sand that closes over them. Here they sleep until morning, protected from danger.

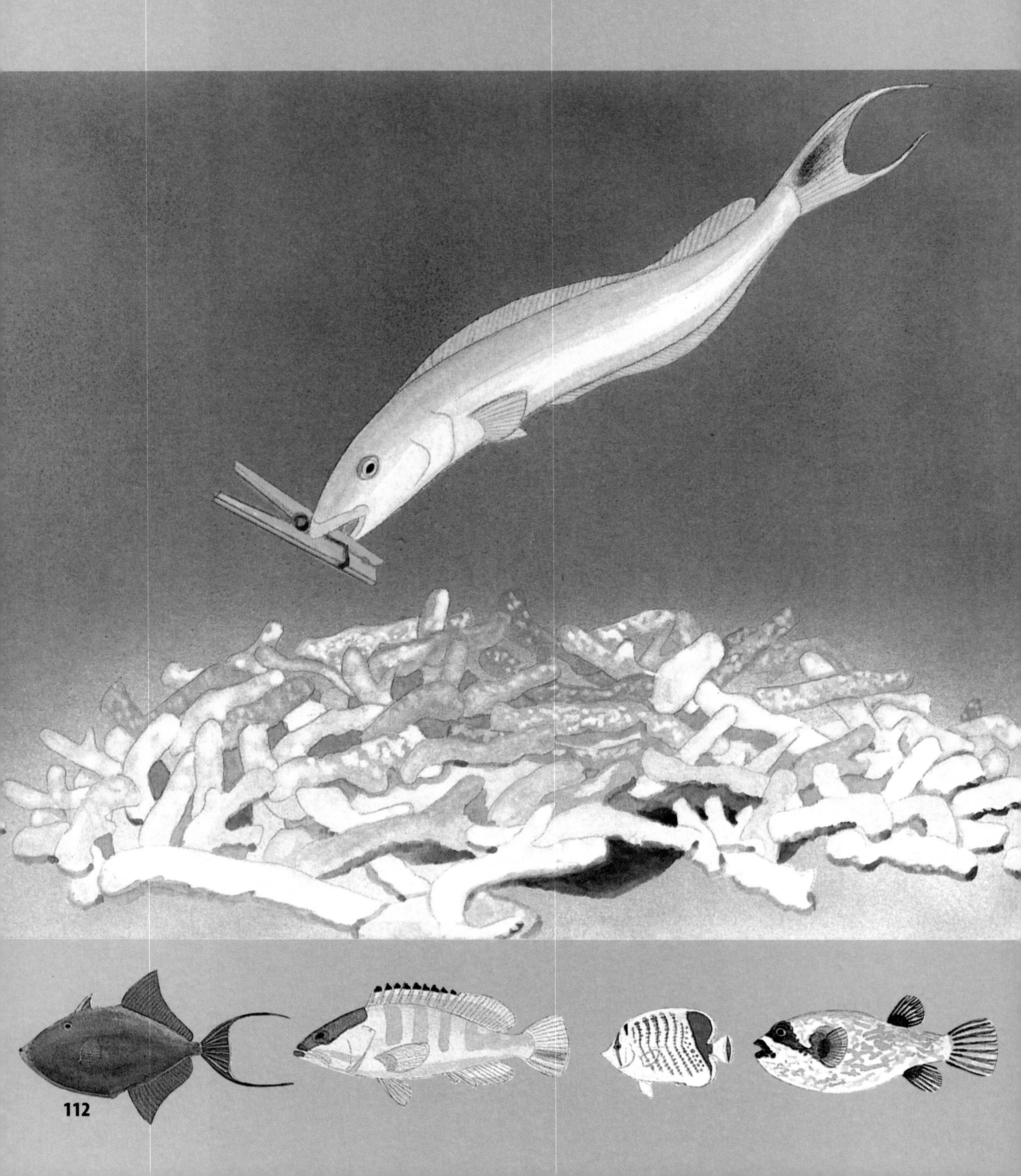

Joan and Eugenie want to see what happens if a burrow entrance is blocked. They ask you to help. Tilefish move objects by carrying them or dragging them with their mouths. At the entrance of one burrow, you place a red plastic checker. At the second, you block the entrance with a golf ball. You put a clothespin in front of the last burrow.

You watch to see if the tilefish moves them. The red checker doesn't completely block the entrance so the tilefish simply ignores it and slips in and out of the burrow.

The golf ball is too round and smooth for the tilefish to get hold of in its mouth, so it does not use that burrow opening again.

And the clothespin? The tilefish can pick it up easily and move it to the top of its burrow.

Probably the most important fact you would learn is that sand tilefish can make a home out of almost anything. If there is no coral around, they use pieces of a light bulb, parts of shipwrecks, bits of glass, a fishnet or a clothespin—even little pieces of diving equipment. They seem to use anything that might have dropped into the sea.

Sometimes sand tilefish make their home in plastic pipes or under wooden boards that are lying on the sandy bottom. It seems they can live in almost any kind of shelter.

A Mystery Fish

One day, Eugenie and her friend David Shen were diving in the Red Sea. They were studying razorfish when David noticed a strange fish swimming by. David had never seen such a fish before.

It looked like a tiny jawfish with a big head and four dark patches on its back. It was a female with her belly bulging with eggs. He took many pictures of the fish.

David motioned to Eugenie. She swam over to the mystery fish. She, too, had never seen anything like it. They collected it in a plastic bag and brought it to the surface. They kept it alive in a bucket of seawater and brought it to David Fridman at the aquarium. Surely he would be able to identify the fish.

But David Fridman didn't know what it was, either. By chance, a scientist from a museum in Germany happened to be visiting the Red Sea. He got very excited when he saw the strange little fish and asked to take it back to his museum.

It turned out to be a new species. He preserved the fish by pickling it in a jar with special chemicals. He described it in a scientific paper and named it *Stalix davidsheni,* after David Shen.

David Shen says today, "I often wonder what that little fish was doing, swimming over the sand. It was not the usual jawfish behavior. Jawfish usually build their burrows in sand and rubble. They almost never wander far from their homes. Was this rare fish looking for its mate?"

Since that day in 1984, no other *Stalix davidsheni* has been seen, but Eugenie and David keep looking.

David Shen joined Eugenie and Ann McGovern on a Red Sea trip in 1980 because he wanted to learn about fish. It was his first expedition. Since then he has become an expert underwater photographer, and some of his pictures have been on magazine covers.

David has also become an expert on many kinds of fish. He became fascinated with the desert beneath the sea and produced a movie about it. He helped Eugenie map the largest colony of garden eels in the world. He knows fish by their scientific names.

If you help scientists, like David does, perhaps some day, you, too, will have a fish named after you!

The Jason Project

Passport to Adventure

The Jason Project is named after a character in Greek mythology. In Greek myths, Jason was the first great explorer to sail the seas. His ship was called the Argo, so the sea-going members of the Jason Project are called "argonauts."

Picture this. You are at the controls of a deep-sea submersible. Your robot-like vehicle has dived down more than a mile under the ocean's surface. All around you, the sea is pitch black, except where your vehicle's floodlights pierce the darkness. You can see tiny, brightly colored sea animals dancing through the light beams.

Cautiously, you steer your way into a deep undersea canyon. You enter what seems to be a mysterious new planet. All around you, giant tube worms sway. Huge crabs crawl by in slow motion. You are at the bottom of the ocean, seeing what few humans have ever seen.

Finally, it's time for you to leave. You turn over the controls to another pilot. Then you turn around. Watching you are your classmates, teachers, and a big audience. You are not underwater at all. You have just been on an electronic field trip as a member of the Jason Project team!

The Jason Project gives students all over the world a chance to be part of an underwater discovery team. The project is the brainchild of Dr. Robert Ballard, an oceanographer and deep-sea explorer, who discovered and visited the wreck of the *Titanic.* After making his famous discovery in a manned submersible, Ballard got thousands of letters from students. "I realized that we could put this incredible robot technology to work to excite students about the thrills of scientific discovery," he says.

Ballard has set up a team of scientists, computer experts, and explorers to work with young people interested in underwater exploration. A complex communications network allows students to become part of Ballard's discovery team.

This is how it works. Scientists aboard a research ship send a remote-operated robot vehicle named *Jason* down into the ocean depths. Pictures from the robot are transmitted from the research ship to a satellite. From there, they are beamed to auditoriums across the United States.

Lucky students in the audience become "pilots" and sit at control panels where they can talk to the scientists and drive the robot vehicle. The audiences can watch on huge screens set up in the auditoriums. A few young people are even luckier! For each expedition of the Jason Project, several student "argonauts" are chosen. They accompany the scientists on board the research ship and become members of the exploration team.

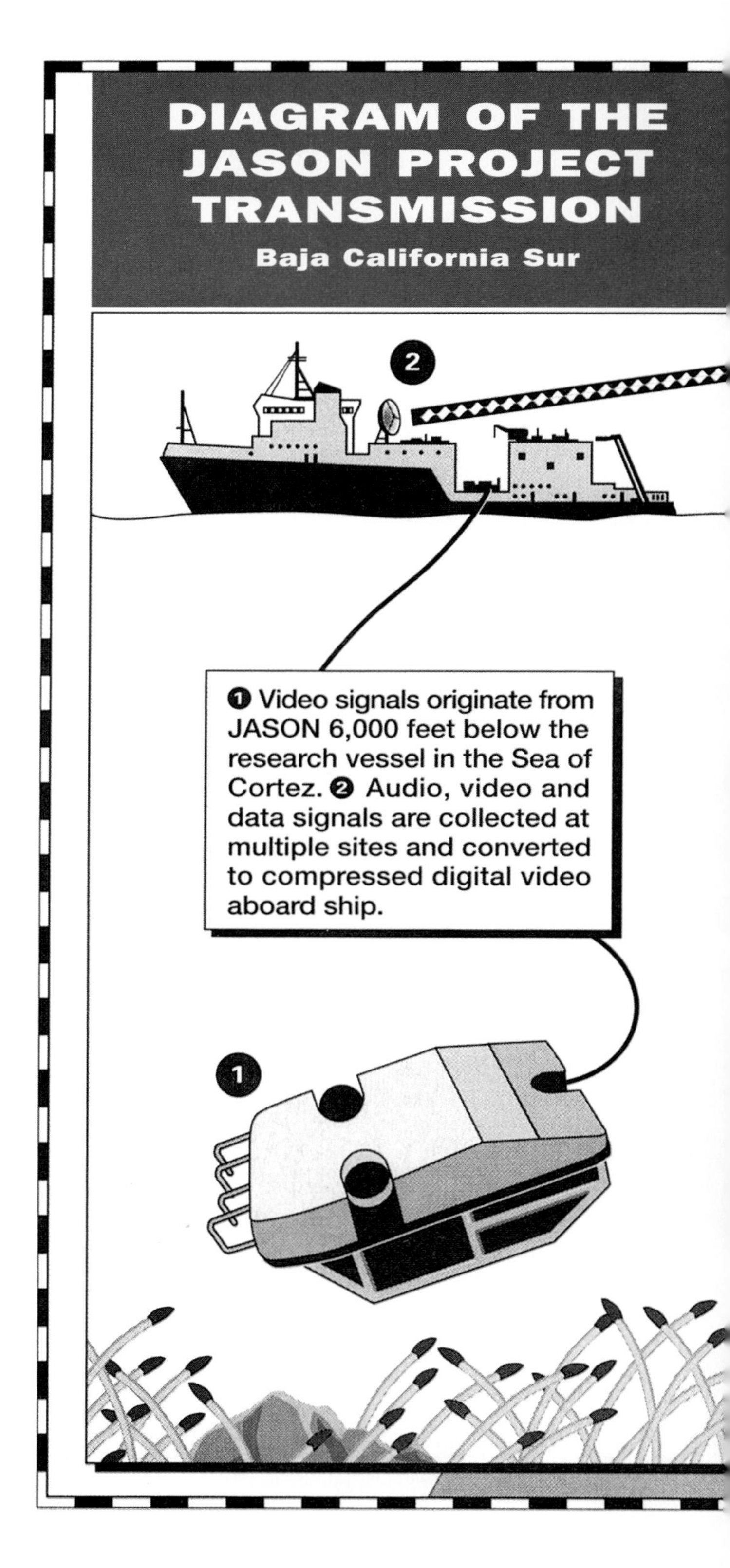

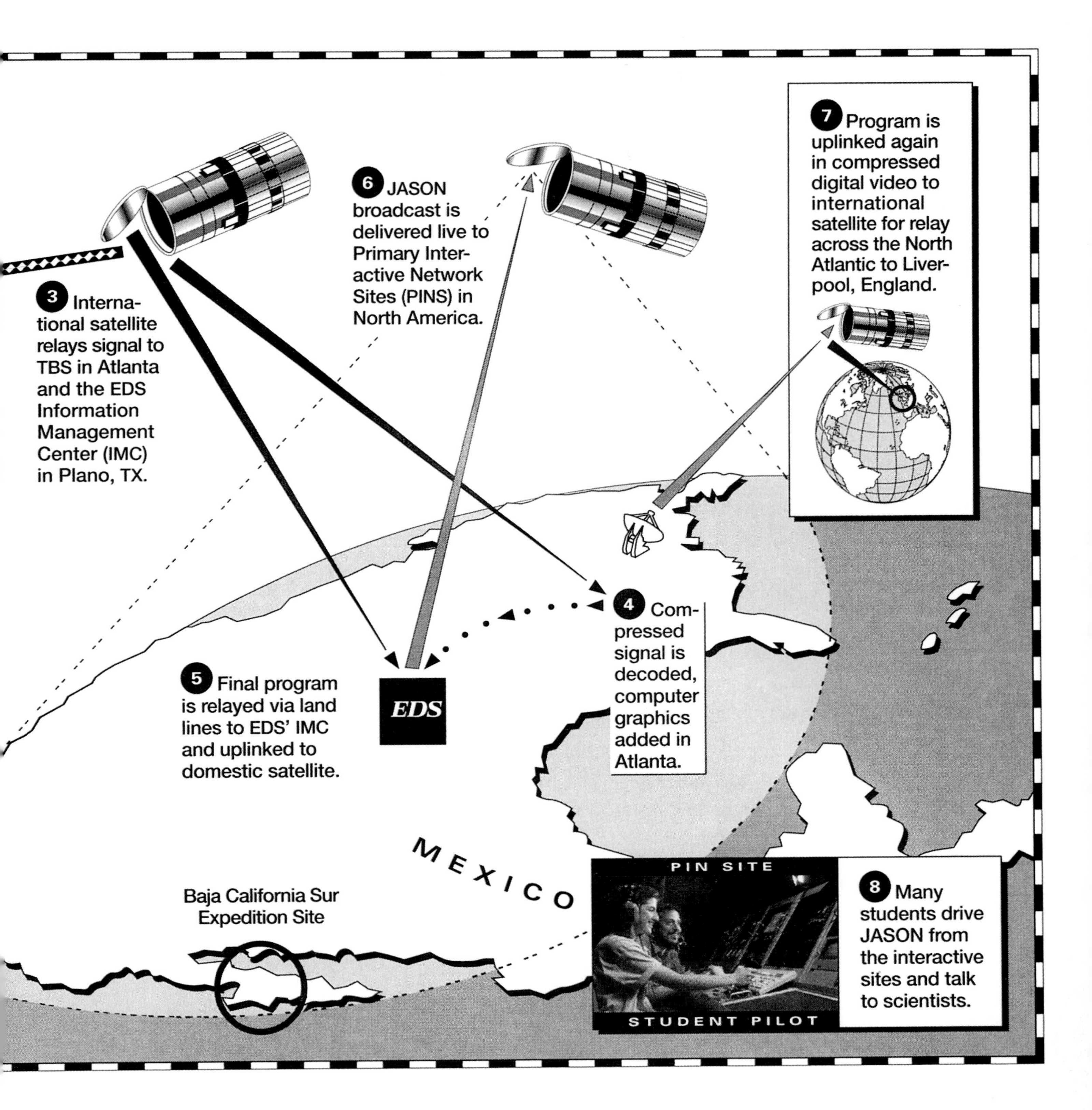
7 Program is uplinked again in compressed digital video to international satellite for relay across the North Atlantic to Liverpool, England.
6 JASON broadcast is delivered live to Primary Interactive Network Sites (PINS) in North America.
3 International satellite relays signal to TBS in Atlanta and the EDS Information Management Center (IMC) in Plano, TX.
4 Compressed signal is decoded, computer graphics added in Atlanta.
5 Final program is relayed via land lines to EDS' IMC and uplinked to domestic satellite.
EDS
MEXICO
Baja California Sur Expedition Site
PIN SITE
STUDENT PILOT
8 Many students drive JASON from the interactive sites and talk to scientists.

TEAMWORK TIPS

It definitely takes teamwork to make the Jason Project work. Two team members, Ernie Radowick and Christina Torruella give these tips for successful teamwork:

 HAVE A MISSION EVERYONE BELIEVES IN. **The mission of the Jason Project is to excite students about science and technology and get them involved in scientific discovery. "The feedback we get from students is my biggest satisfaction," says Radowick.**

 KEEP FOCUSED. **"Everyone should have a specific task," says Torruella. "The danger is spreading yourself too thin," she warns. "Ask yourself, what do I have to do to accomplish my job. Then do it."**

 MAKE THE SUCCESS OF THE PROJECT YOUR GOAL. **"The key is dedicated people who are willing to do whatever it takes for the project to succeed," says Radowick.**

 ENJOY WHAT YOU DO. **Torruella gives this advice: "If you enjoy what you are doing, you will always succeed."**

The Jason Project has taken fantastic voyages all over the globe. Almost 1.5 million students have joined the project scientists on these journeys of discovery.

VOYAGE I — MAY 1989

The destination was the Mediterranean Sea. A robot vehicle photographed the wreck of a Roman ship that sank over 1,600 years ago.

VOYAGE II — MAY 1990

The Jason Project traveled to Lake Ontario. It sent down a robot to view the wrecks of two ships that sank during the War of 1812, a conflict between the United States and Great Britain.

VOYAGE III — DECEMBER 1991

The team journeyed to the Galápagos Islands in the Pacific Ocean, where scientists studied wildlife on the islands and below the sea.

VOYAGE IV — MARCH 1993

In the Sea of Cortez, scientists photographed tube worms and watched migrating whales. The three-person submarine, the *Turtle,* was used for underwater exploration.

VOYAGE V — MARCH 1994

Scientists explored the rain forest of Belize while a robot vehicle explored sea life in the second largest barrier reef in the Western Hemisphere.

PROJECT

How to Create a

Multimedia Presentation

Bring your *team's* journey to *life* with *words* and pictures.

If you rocketed into space, how could you share the excitement of the journey? One way is through a multimedia presentation. A multimedia presentation uses words, pictures, sound effects, and music to make an experience come alive. The idea for a presentation can start with a script. Then pictures, sound effects, lighting, models, and anything else can be added.

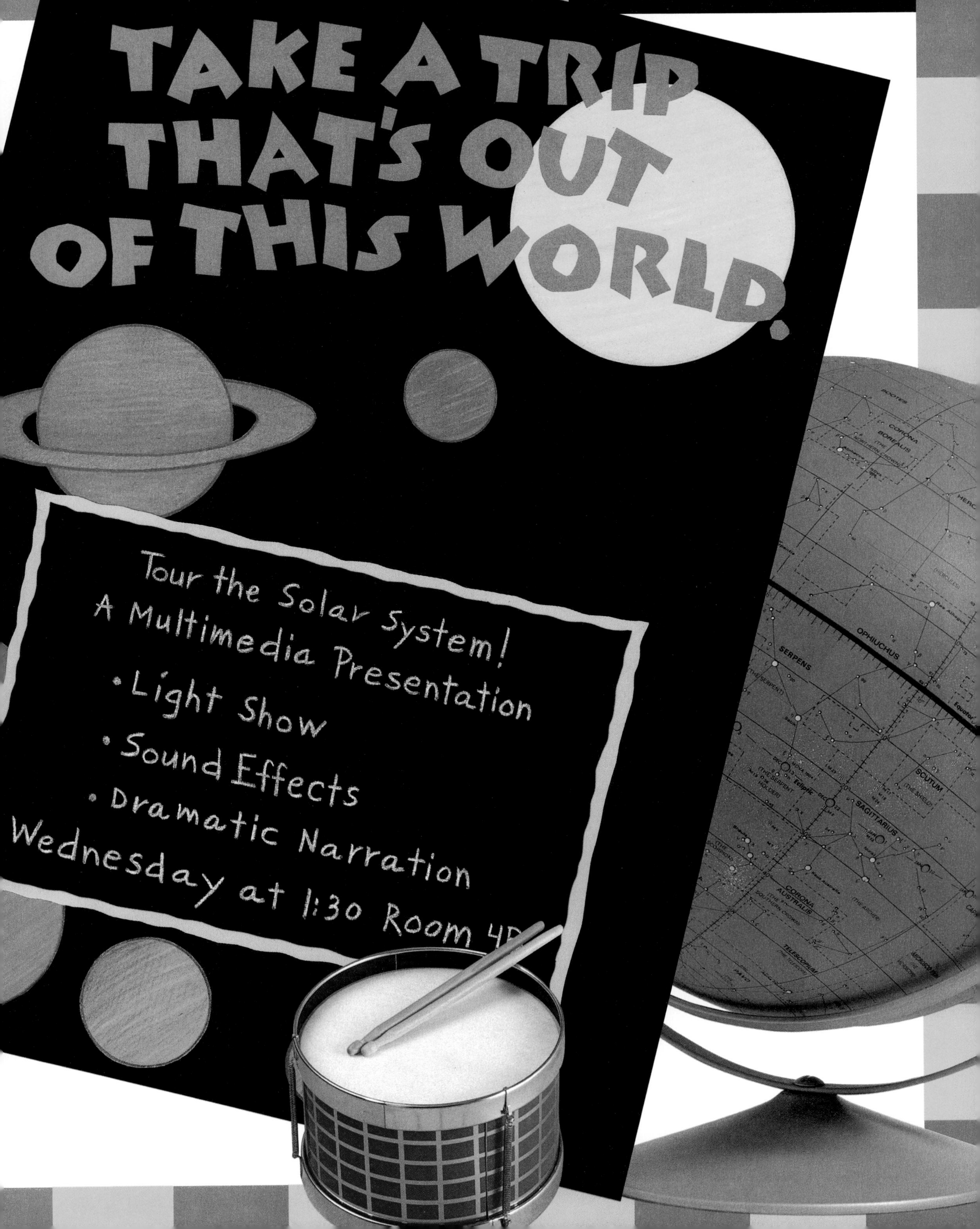

TAKE A TRIP THAT'S OUT OF THIS WORLD.

Tour the Solar System!
A Multimedia Presentation

- Light Show
- Sound Effects
- Dramatic Narration

Wednesday at 1:30 Room 4D

1 Explore Your Options

Your multimedia presentation will tell about an exciting place. So, first your team needs to choose a location. Pick a place that you want to learn more about. It can be as far away as Mars or as near as a location you can visit. Once you've chosen the place, it's time to gather facts and pictures for your show. Have each team member check a different source. Use atlases, travel books, magazines, encyclopedias, and newspapers. Team members can share their findings with the group.

TOOLS

- paper and pencil
- glue or tape
- colored markers
- magazine and newspaper pictures
- reference books and travel magazines
- tape recorder (optional)

Tips

- Use several different kinds of pictures and props in your show, such as original drawings, photographs, maps, and a globe.
- If you want to use a picture or map from a reference book, someone in the group can make a drawing or trace the original.
- If your pictures are small, mount them onto a posterboard. This will help them stand out.

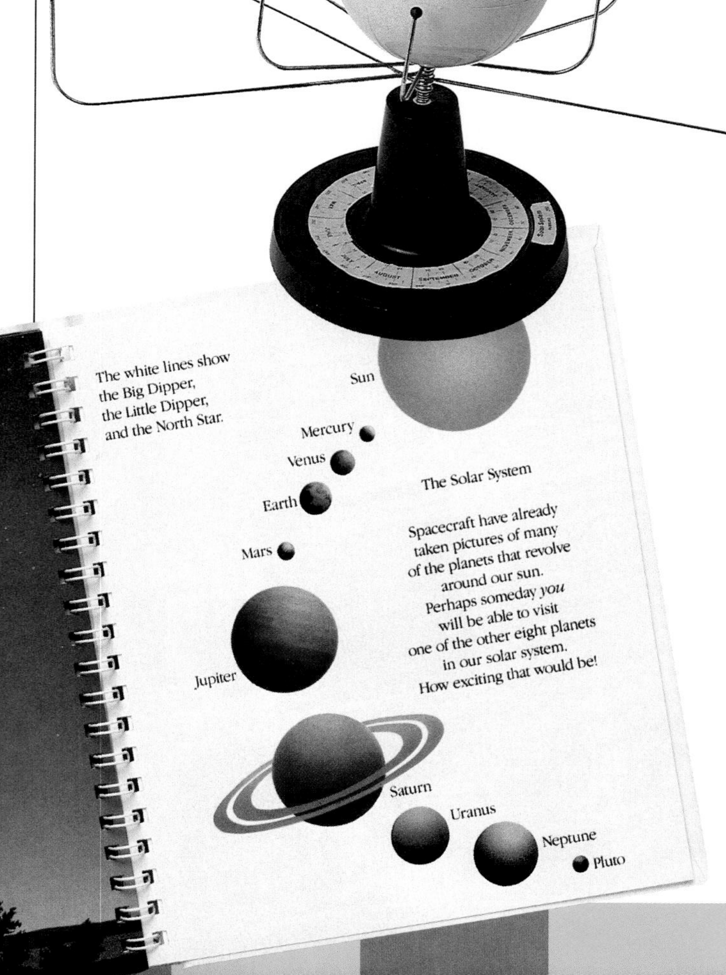

2 Organize Your Material

Gather the materials you'll need for your show. Here are some things you may want to include.

- Captions: Write captions under all the pictures. Decide as a group what the captions will say.
- A Script: If you want, write a script and include stage directions.
- Music and Sound Effects: If you can borrow a tape recorder, some members of your team can record music or sound effects.
- A Model: Create a model to use in your presentation.

Before you put your presentation together, take a few minutes to answer these questions with your group.

- **Did we pick exciting, colorful pictures?**
- **Have we found interesting facts to go with our pictures?**
- **Did we decide how to organize our presentation?**
- **Do we need a script to go with our presentation?**

3 Put It All Together

As a team, decide how to present your show. Here are some ideas. Tape your pictures together on a long sheet of paper. Two team members can unroll the paper while another team member reads the captions or the script. Mount several pictures onto pieces of posterboard. Narrate your trip while playing your music or a sound effects tape, if you made one. If you want a spotlight, try using a flashlight and dimming the lights. Think of different ways to perform your show, and then choose one.

4 Present Your Multimedia Show

Before you perform your show in front of the class, you may want to rehearse it a few times. Every team member should take part in the performance. While you are rehearsing, you may think of other things to add to your performance. Remember to discuss any changes with the rest of the team.

When it's time to perform, speak up so your classmates will hear you. At the end of your performance, don't forget to have your team take a bow.

If You Are Using a Computer . . .

Create your multimedia presentation on the computer. Choose photographs and clip art to show each stage of your team's journey. Use the Record Tools to narrate your presentation. Have fun adding music and sound effects. Then present your journey on the computer, using the Slide Show Tools.

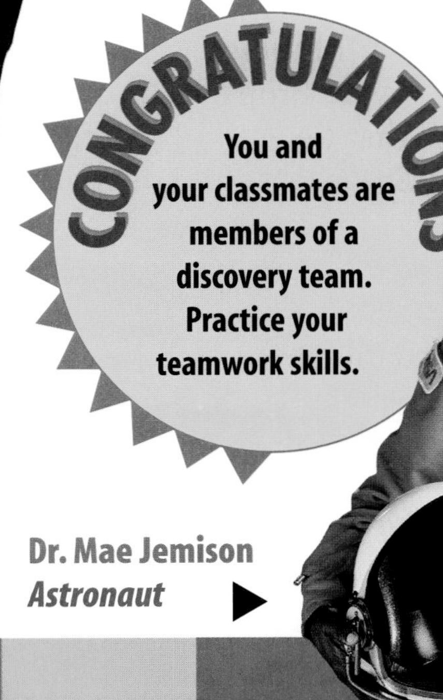

Dr. Mae Jemison
Astronaut ▶

Glossary

Arc•tic (ärk′tik) *noun* The region lying north of the Arctic Circle.

as•tro•naut (as′trə nôt′) *noun* A person who is trained to fly in a spacecraft.

Word History

Astronaut is a compound of two Greek words: *astron,* which means "star," and *nautes*, which means "sailor." So an astronaut is a sailor among the stars.

bon•net (bon′it) *noun* A hat with a wide brim and ribbons that tie under the chin.

buz•zards (buz′ərdz) *noun* Large birds with dark feathers, broad wings, and heads without feathers. ▲ **buzzard**

ca•noe•ing (kə nōō′ing) *verb* Paddling or traveling in a light narrow boat called a canoe. ▲ **canoe**

can•o•py (kan′ə pē) *noun* The tops of the trees in the rain forest.

com•pass (kum′pəs) *noun* An instrument that shows directions, such as north, south, east, and west. The hiker carried a *compass*.

cor•al reefs (kôr′əl rēfs′) *noun* Lines or strips of coral lying at or near the surface of the ocean. Many kinds of fish live among the *coral reefs*. ▲ **coral reef**

deep-sea (dēp sē′) *adjective* Having to do with the deeper parts of the sea.

ex•ca•vate (eks′kə vāt′) *verb* To dig a hole; to take apart. She helped the scientist *excavate* the pottery.

find•ings (fīn′dingz) *noun* Conclusions reached after observation and research. When the experiment was over, she analyzed her *findings*. ▲ **finding**

astronaut

flax (flaks) *noun*
A kind of plant that has blue flowers, the seeds of which are used to make linseed oil.

freeze-dried
(frēz′drīd′) *verb*
Processed a substance, such as food, by drying it in a frozen state under a high vacuum, so that it will keep for a long time.
▲ **freeze-dry**

frost•bit•ten
(frôst′bit′n) *adjective*
Injured by exposure to extreme cold. The mountain climber's *frostbitten* fingers were numb.

huge (hyo͞oj) *adjective*
Of a very great size; enormous.

jag•uar (jag′ wär) *noun*
A large wild cat with brownish-yellow fur and black spots, similar to a leopard.

ka•pok tree
(kā′pok trē′) *noun*
A kind of silk-cotton tree that grows in the Amazon rain forest.

launch•es
(lônch′ iz) *noun*
The act of sending off space shuttles or rockets into outer space. She watched two space shuttle *launches* on TV.
▲ **launch**

jaguar

ma•rine bi•ol•o•gist
(mə rēn′ bī ol′ə jist) *noun*
Scientist who studies living things that make their home in the sea.

mead•ow•lark
(med′ō lärk′) *noun*
A songbird with a yellow breast marked with a black V.

out•doors•men
(out dôrz′ mən) *noun*
People who spend a lot of time outdoors, doing activities such as camping and hiking.
▲ **outdoorsman**

a	add	o͝o	took	ə =
ā	ace	o͞o	pool	a in *above*
â	care	u	up	e in *sicken*
ä	palm	û	burn	i in *possible*
e	end	yo͞o	fuse	o in *melon*
ē	equal	oi	oil	u in *circus*
i	it	ou	pout	
ī	ice	ng	ring	
o	odd	th	thin	
ō	open	t͟h	this	
ô	order	zh	vision	

Glossary

pad•dock (pad′ ək) *noun* A fenced area where horses exercise or graze. He fed an apple to the horse in the *paddock*.

pet•ti•coat (pet′ē kōt′) *noun* A kind of slip worn under a skirt or dress.

plan•et (plan′it) *noun* Any of the nine large bodies in the solar system that revolve around the sun. Mars is a *planet*.

Word History

The word **planet** comes from the Greek word *planetai.* Ancient astronomers observed that while most stars stayed fixed in one place, a few of them would change position. They called these moving stars *planetai*, which means "wanderers."

po•lar (pō′lər) *adjective* Of or near the South or North Pole.

prai•rie (prâr′ē) *noun* A large area of flat or slightly rolling grasslands.

pres•sure ridges (presh′ər rijəs) *noun* Raised strips of ice and snow formed by the force of two bodies of ice crashing together.
▲ **pressure ridge**

quest (kwest) *noun* An adventurous expedition. The prospector was on a *quest* for gold.

rain for•est (rān′fôr′ist) *noun* A tropical forest, usually in an area that has a high annual rainfall.

Fact File

The temperature in a **rain forest** stays at about 80° F all year long. An average of 100 to 200 inches of rain falls throughout the year. The ground or floor of the rain forest is in almost total shade.

sci•en•tist (sī′ən tist) *noun* A person who is a specialist in science, especially the natural sciences.

sloth (slôth) *noun* A slow-moving, tree-dwelling mammal with claws like hooks that inhabits the tropical forests of South and Central America.

Fact File

The **sloth** moves so slowly on the ground that it only covers about 6.5 feet every minute. In the trees, the sloth moves a little faster, sometimes covering as much as 10 feet in a minute.

sloth

space mis•sion
(spās′ mish′ən) *noun*
A project that a group of specialists is sent to do in space.

space shut•tle
(spās′ shut′l) *noun*
An airplane-like spacecraft designed to transport people and cargo between Earth and space.

space suit
(spās′ so͞ot′) *noun*
A pressurized suit worn by astronauts that controls temperature and supplies them with oxygen.

space•ships
(spās′ ships) *noun*
Vehicles used for space travel.

sub•mers•i•ble
(səb mûr′sə bəl) *noun*
A vessel built to operate under water, usually a submarine.

tile•fish (tīl′fish′) *noun*
A large fish with yellow spots on its body found in the deep waters of the Atlantic.

tou•can (to͞o′kan) *noun*
A brightly colored tropical bird with a large beak.

toucan

tum•ble•weeds
(tum′bəl wēds′) *noun*
Plants that break away from their roots in the autumn and are blown by the wind.
▲ **tumbleweed**

un•der•sto•ry
(un′dər stôr′ē) *noun*
A layer of shrubs and trees that only grow from 10 to 50 feet above the floor of a rain forest.

weight•less•ness
(wāt′lis′nes) *noun*
The state of having little or no weight because of the lack of gravity.

white wa•ter
(hwīt′ wô′tər) *noun*
Foaming, frothy water as in whitecaps and rapids.

wil•der•ness
(wil′dər nis) *noun*
A wild place or region that is uninhabited.

a	add	o͝o	took	ə =
ā	ace	o͞o	pool	a in *above*
â	care	u	up	e in *sicken*
ä	palm	û	burn	i in *possible*
e	end	yo͞o	fuse	o in *melon*
ē	equal	oi	oil	u in *circus*
i	it	ou	pout	
ī	ice	ng	ring	
o	odd	th	thin	
ō	open	t͟h	this	
ô	order	zh	vision	

Authors & Illustrators

Isaac Asimov *pages 70–83*

This author has written more science and science-fiction books than any other writer. Now, even fifty years after some of his books were first published, they are still considered the best of their kind. His nonfiction work was also popular because he could write clear explanations of difficult subjects. He once said, "I'm on fire to explain, and happiest when it's something reasonably intricate, which I can make clear step by step." Isaac Asimov died in 1992.

Lynne Cherry *pages 90–103*

To research the illustrations and the text for *The Great Kapok Tree,* Lynne Cherry traveled to the Amazon rain forest in Brazil. As she sat by a jungle stream, a group of monkeys swung through the trees and a hummingbird hovered only a foot away! By writing the book, she hoped to give her readers a glimpse into a beautiful and marvelous world, one that is being destroyed at an alarming rate.

Eugenie Clark *pages 104–115*

When Eugenie Clark was a little girl, living in New York City, she became interested in sharks. Every weekend, she spent hours at the city's aquarium. She never doubted she'd grow up to become a scientist. Today, many people call her "The Shark Lady" because she has made so many important discoveries about these fish.

"When I drive along in my car, I have conversations with my characters. People think I'm singing along with the radio."

Patricia MacLachlan *pages 30–47*

This author was an avid reader as a child. She often read a whole book on the way home from the library—with her mother guiding her across streets and down curbs! Her father would act out parts in books she was reading, making them come to life. Family stories about an ancestor who was a mail-order bride from Maine helped give Patricia MacLachlan the idea for the now famous character of Sarah from *Sarah, Plain and Tall.*

Allen Say *pages 10–23*

Like Luke in *The Lost Lake,* Allen Say's daughter Yuriko spends part of her time living with her mother and part of her time with her father. Yuriko says that her earliest memories of her father are the wonderful stories he told her when she was very small. He made up the stories himself, and drew pictures to accompany his words as he spoke.

Books &

Author/Illustrator Study

More by Allen Say

Bicycle Man
This book is set in Japan shortly after World War II and is based on one of Allen Say's childhood memories.

El Chino
This biography uses beautiful pictures to help tell the story of a Chinese-American man who discovers his life's work on a visit to Spain.

Grandfather's Journey
This Caldecott-winning book tells the story of Allen Say's grandfather.

Allen Say

Fiction

Just My Luck
by Emily Moore
Olivia and Jeffrey set out to discover why Mrs. Dingle's poodle is missing.

To Find the Way
by Susan Nunes
illustrated by Cissy Greg
Long ago, the ancient Polynesians sailed from Tahiti to Hawaii. This book tells how a great navigator used his knowledge of astronomy to guide his people across thousands of miles of ocean.

Wingman
by Daniel Pinkwater
A boy who loves comic books invents his own Chinese-American superhero—Wingman. Together they fly over ancient China, and the boy learns to take pride in his heritage and its traditions.

Nonfiction

Discover Dinosaur Babies
by Miriam Schlein
Paleontologists describe their new discoveries about how dinosaur babies were cared for by their parents.

Night Dive
by Ann McGovern
photographs by Marin Scheiner and James Scheiner
A twelve-year-old girl describes the excitement of taking part in a scuba diving expedition at night.

One Giant Leap
by Mary Ann Fraser
Through art and text, the author recreates the drama of the first time humans walked on the moon.

xMedia

Videos

For All Mankind
Columbia Tristar
This documentary describes the Apollo mission to the moon, and how the astronauts prepared for the historical flight. (80 minutes)

Maricela
Public Media
Maricela and her mother have just come from El Salvador and are trying to adjust to life in the United States. With the help of some American friends, they discover many things about their homeland and about themselves. (55 minutes)

Sarah, Plain and Tall
Republic Home Video
This video, based on Patricia MacLachlan's beloved book, tells the story of how Anna and Caleb discover what it means to be a family. (98 minutes)

Software

Eagle Eye Mysteries: London
EA Kids
Join Jake and Jennifer Eagle in London as they solve 50 cases in historical locations.

Oceans Below
Software Toolworks
(Macintosh, IBM, MPC)
Video clips, music, photos, and a dramatic narrative help make this almost as exciting as a real diving adventure.

Where in Space Is Carmen Sandiego?
Broderbund
(Apple, Macintosh, IBM)
No longer content with stealing from folks on Earth, Carmen and her crew are loose in outer space! Track her across the universe in this exciting game.

Magazines

National Geographic World
National Geographic Society
This magazine has articles about outdoor adventure, new science discoveries, and unusual careers. The photographs create a you-are-there feeling.

Odyssey
Kalbach Publishing
This is the magazine to read if you want to keep up with the latest information on space exploration and astronomy.

A Place to Write

Kennedy Space Center,
Spaceport USA
Mail Code TWRS
Kennedy Space Center, FL 32899

Write for information about how the center operates, and what there is to see when you visit the center.

Acknowledgments

Grateful acknowledgment is made to the following sources for permission to reprint from previously published material. The publisher has made diligent efforts to trace the ownership of all copyrighted material in this volume and believes that all necessary permissions have been secured. If any errors or omissions have inadvertently been made, proper corrections will gladly be made in future editions.

Front cover: Illustration from FAMILY PICTURES by Carmen Lomas Garza. Copyright © 1990 by Carmen Lomas Garza. Reprinted by permission of Children's Book Press.

Back cover: Top: Illustration from FAMILY PICTURES by Carmen Lomas Garza. Copyright © 1990 by Carmen Lomas Garza. Reprinted by permission of Children's Book Press. Border by Vicki Wehrman. Middle: Cover by Elwood Smith. Top: © NASA.

Acknowledgments

Grateful acknowledgment is made to the following sources for permission to reprint from previously published material. The publisher has made diligent efforts to trace the ownership of all copyrighted material in this volume and believes that all necessary permissions have been secured. If any errors or omissions have inadvertently been made, proper corrections will gladly be made in future editions.

Unit Opener: Illustration from FAMILY PICTURES by Carmen Lomas Garza. Copyright © 1990 by Carmen Lomas Garza. Reprinted by permission of Children's Book Press. Border by Vicki Wehrman.

Interior: "Class-Picture-Taking Day" and cover from STAYING NINE by Pam Conrad. Text copyright © 1988 by Pam Conrad. Cover illustration copyright © 1988 by Mike Wimmer. Reprinted by permission of HarperCollins Publishers.

Selections from BIG SCIENCE: BONES AND MUSCLES. Copyright © 1990 by Scholastic Inc. Reprinted by permission.

Selections from the Table of Contents of BOY by Roald Dahl. Copyright © 1984 by Roald Dahl. Reprinted by permission of Farrar, Straus & Giroux, Inc. By permission also of Murray Pollinger, London.

"The Rag Coat" from THE RAG COAT by Lauren Mills. Copyright © 1991 by Lauren A. Mills. Reprinted by permission of Little, Brown and Company.

Selections and cover from THE POOL PARTY by Gary Soto. Text copyright © 1993 by Gary Soto. Cover illustration copyright © 1993 by Robert Casilla. Used by permission of Delacorte Press, a division of Bantam Doubleday Dell Publishing Group, Inc.

Selections and cover from PENNY POLLARD'S GUIDE TO MODERN MANNERS by Robin Klein, illustrated by Ann James. Text copyright © 1989 by Robin Klein. Illustrations copyright © 1989 by Ann James. Published by Oxford University Press. OXFORD is a trademark of Oxford University Press. Used by permission.

Cover from WHEN I WAS NINE by James Stevenson. Copyright © 1986 by James Stevenson. By permission of Greenwillow Books, a division of William Morrow & Company, Inc.

"The President's Wife" and cover from FRONT PORCH STORIES AT THE ONE-ROOM SCHOOL by Eleanora E. Tate. Text copyright © 1992 by Eleanora E. Tate. Used by permission of Bantam Books, a division of Bantam Doubleday Dell Publishing Group, Inc. Cover illustration by Eric Velasquez. Used by permission of the illustrator.

"Barbara Bush" from *Scholastic News*, April 14, 1989. Copyright © 1989 by Scholastic Inc. Reprinted by permission.

"Under the Back Porch" by Virginia Hamilton, illustrated by Pat Cummings. Text copyright © 1992 by Virginia Hamilton, illustration copyright © 1992 by Pat Cummings. All selections from HOME edited by Michael J. Rosen. Copyright © 1992 by HarperCollins Publishers. Jacket illustration by Leo and Diane Dillon. Jacket illustration copyright © 1992 by Leo and Diane Dillon. Reprinted by permission.

"Cherokee Summer" adapted from CHEROKEE SUMMER by Diane Hoyt-Goldsmith, with photographs by Lawrence Migdale. Text copyright © 1993 by Diane Hoyt-Goldsmith. Photographs copyright © 1993 by Lawrence Migdale. Text illustrations copyright © 1993 by Murv Jacob. Maps copyright © by Square Moon Productions. The new version of the Cherokee syllabary is used courtesy of Durbin Feeling of the Tsa-La-Gi Library, Tahlequah, OK 74465. Reprinted by permission of Holiday House.

Selections and cover from FAMILY PICTURES by Carmen Lomas Garza. Copyright © 1990 by Carmen Lomas Garza. Reprinted by permission of Children's Book Press.

Cover from FOURTH GRADE RATS by Jerry Spinelli, illustrated by Paul Casale. Illustration copyright © 1991 by Paul Casale. Published by Scholastic Inc.

Cover from THE LAST PRINCESS: THE STORY OF PRINCESS KA'IULANI OF HAWAI'I by Fay Stanley, illustrated by Diane Stanley. Illustration copyright © 1991 by Diane Stanley Vennema. Published by Simon & Schuster Books for Young Readers, Simon & Schuster Children's Publishing Division.

Cover from MY NAME IS MARÍA ISABEL by Alma Flor Ada, illustrated by K. Dyble Thompson. Illustration copyright © 1993 by K. Dyble Thompson. Published by Atheneum Books for Young Readers, Simon & Schuster Children's Publishing Division.

Cover from STEALING HOME by Mary Stolz, illustrated by Pat Cummings. Illustration copyright © 1992 by Pat Cummings. Published by HarperCollins Children's Books, a division of HarperCollins Publishers.

Photography and Illustration Credits

Photos: © John Lei for Scholastic Inc., all Tool Box items unless otherwise noted. p. 2 cl, tl, bl: © John Bessler for Scholastic Inc. pp. 2-3 background: © John Lei for Scholastic Inc. p. 3 bc: © John Lei for Scholastic Inc.; tc: © Ana Esperanza Nance for Scholastic Inc. p. 4 tc: © Ana Esperanza Nance for Scholastic Inc.; cl: Susi Dugaw for Scholastic Inc.; c: © Ana Esperanza Nance for Scholastic Inc.; baby: © The Stock Market; bc: © Ken Karp for Scholastic Inc.; cr: © Scott Harvey for Scholastic Inc.; tr: © Focus on Sports p. 5: © Ana Esperanza Nance for Scholastic Inc. p. 6: © Ana Esperanza Nance for Scholastic Inc. pp. 8-9 © Buckley School Collection/Superstock. pp. 12, 16, 18, 21: © Susi Dugaw for Scholastic Inc. pp. 22-23 cl: © Don Mason/The Stock Market; all others: © Ken Karp for Scholastic Inc. p. 24 bl: © M. Elaine Adams/Little Brown. p. 25 cr: courtesy of Jerry Spinelli. p. 26: © Focus on Sports. p. 27 tr: © Ken Karp for Scholastic Inc.; br: courtesy of Jerry Spinelli; bl: © Richard Megna/Fundamental Photographs for Scholastic Inc. p. 28 tr: © I. Bernard/Animals Animals; cl: © Zig Leszczynski/Animals Animals; br: © Comstock. p. 29 cl: courtesy of Jerry Spinelli. p. 30 cl: © Scott Harvey for Scholastic Inc.; tr: © John Bessler for Scholastic Inc.; tl, bl: © John Lei for Scholastic Inc.; c: © Ana Esperanza Nance for Scholastic Inc. p. 31 c: © Scott Harvey for Scholastic Inc.; cr: © John Bessler for Scholastic Inc. p. 32 bl: © John Bessler for Scholastic Inc.; br: © Scott Harvey for Scholastic Inc. p. 33 cr: © Scott Harvey for Scholastic Inc.; bl: © John Bessler for Scholastic Inc. p. 36 bl: © Richard Kaylin/Tony Stone Images, Inc.; tr: © Robert P. Carr/Bruce Coleman Inc.; br: © Rainer Grosskopf/Tony Stone Images Inc. p. 37 bl: © Stanley Bach for Scholastic Inc.; tr: © Spencer Jones/FPG International Corp.; br: © Scott Harvey for Scholastic Inc. pp. 38-39 © Private Collection/Superstock. pp. 64-65 border: © Paul Halagan; c: © John Lei for Scholastic Inc. p. 66 br: © Stanley Bach for Scholastic Inc; cl: © Bob Torrez/Tony Stone Images, Inc. p. 67 br: © Scott Harvey for Scholastic Inc. pp. 68-69 © Private Collection/A.K.G., Berlin/Superstock. p. 82 cl: © Cynthia Johnson/The Gamma Liaison. p. 83 br: © Brad Markel/The Gamma Liaison. pp. 86-87 © Lawrence Migdale. p. 89 tr: © Lawrence Migdale; bl: © Tony Stone Images. p. 96 bl: © Lawrence Migdale. pp. 97-99: © Lawrence Migdale. pp. 106-107: © John Lei for Scholastic Inc. p. 107 br: © Craig Tuttle/The Stock Market. p. 108 bl, cr: © John Lei for Scholastic Inc.; br: © Stanley Bach for Scholastic Inc.; cl: © David Young-Wolf/Photo Edit. p. 109 cl, br: © John Lei for Scholastic Inc.; bc: © David Madison; tr: © Stanley Bach for Scholastic Inc. p. 110 c: © Stanley Bach for Scholastic Inc.; bl: © John Lei for Scholastic Inc.; tr: © Don Mason/The Stock Market tr, bl: (leaves): © Don Mason/The Stock Market. pp. 110-111 c: © Stanley Bach for Scholastic Inc. p. 111 bc: © Don Mason/The Stock Market; tr: © Don Mason/The Stock Market; br: © Scott Harvey for Scholastic Inc. p. 112 bl: Comstock, Inc. p. 113 cr: © Jeff Isaac Greenberg/ Photo Researchers, Inc. p. 114 cl: © Bill Longcore/ Photo Researchers, Inc. pp. 114-115 tc: © "The Greenhouse Effect" by Sally A. Sellers. p. 116 Virginia Hamilton: © Carlo Ontal; Diane Hoyt-Goldsmith: © Holiday House; Pam Conrad: © Sarah Conrad. p. 117 Eleanora Tate: © Zack E. Hamlett, III; Gary Soto: © courtesy of Scholastic Trade Department; Lauren Mills: © Little Brown & Company. p. 119 bl: © Schomburg Center for Research in Black Culture; br: © Stephen Ogilvy for Scholastic Inc.

Illustrations: pp. 11-21: Joel Spector; pp. 40, 42, 44-47, 49-50, 53: Hugh Harrison; pp. 54-61: Tony De Luz; pp. 70-81: Eric Velasquez; p. 86-99 border: © Lawrence Migdale; p. 101: Jessica Wolk-Stanley,

Acknowledgments

Grateful acknowledgment is made to the following sources for permission to reprint from previously published material. The publisher has made diligent efforts to trace the ownership of all copyrighted material in this volume and believes that all necessary permissions have been secured. If any errors or omissions have inadvertently been made, proper corrections will gladly be made in future editions.

Unit Opener: Elwood Smith.

Interior: "A Piece of String Is a Wonderful Thing" from A PIECE OF STRING IS A WONDERFUL THING by Judy Hindley, illustrated by Margaret Chamberlain. Text copyright © 1993 by Judy Hindley. Illustrations copyright © 1993 by Margaret Chamberlain. Printed in the U.S. by Candlewick Press. Reprinted by permission.

"The Invention of Sneakers" and cover from STEVEN CANEY'S INVENTION BOOK. Copyright © 1985 by Steven Caney. Reprinted by permission of Workman Publishing Company, Inc. All rights reserved.

Sample letter from PUTTING IT IN WRITING by Steve Otfinoski. Copyright © 1993 by Scholastic Inc. All rights reserved. Published by Scholastic Inc. Used by permission.

"The Doughnuts" and cover from HOMER PRICE by Robert McCloskey. Copyright © 1943, renewed © 1971 by Robert McCloskey. Used by permission of Viking Penguin, a division of Penguin Books USA Inc.

Selection and cover from MISTAKES THAT WORKED by Charlotte Foltz Jones, illustrated by John O'Brien. Text copyright © 1991 by Charlotte Foltz Jones. Illustrations copyright © 1991 by John O'Brien. Used by permission of Doubleday, a division of Bantam Doubleday Dell Publishing Group, Inc.

"The Inventor Thinks Up Helicopters" and cover from THE TIGERS BROUGHT PINK LEMONADE by Patricia Hubbell, illustrations by Ju-Hong Chen. Text copyright © 1988 by Patricia Hubbell. Jacket art and illustration copyright © 1988 by Ju-Hong Chen. Reprinted with the permission of Atheneum Books for Young Readers, an imprint of Simon & Schuster Children's Publishing Division.

Diagrams from "Invent America," from January/February 1993 issue of *3-2-1 Contact America*. Copyright © 1993 by Children's Television Workshop (New York, NY). All rights reserved.

"The Star Ship" and cover from THE COMPUTER NUT by Betsy Byars, cover illustration by Scott Gladden. Text copyright © 1984 by Betsy Byars. Used by permission of Puffin Books, a division of Penguin Books USA Inc. Cover illustration copyright © 1991 by Scott Gladden. Reprinted by permission of Scholastic Inc.

"The First Computers: A History Play" by Richard Chevat, from *Scholastic News*, January 13, 1989. Copyright © 1989 by Scholastic Inc. Reprinted by permission.

"LAFFF" and cover from WITHIN REACH, edited by Donald R. Gallo. "LAFFF" by Lensey Namioka, copyright © 1993. All rights reserved by Lensey Namioka. Cover illustration copyright © 1993 by HarperCollins Publishers. Used by permission of HarperCollins Publishers.

"Things to Come" from *3-2-1 Contact Magazine*, May 1991. Copyright © 1991 by Children's Television Workshop (New York, NY). All rights reserved.

Cover from DANNY DUNN AND THE HOMEWORK MACHINE by Jay Williams and Raymond Abrashkin, illustrated by Ezra Jack Keats. Illustration copyright © 1958 by Ezra Jack Keats. Published by McGraw-Hill Inc.

Cover from EUREKA! IT'S AN AIRPLANE! by Jeanne Bendick, illustrated by Sal Murdocca. Illustration copyright © 1992 by Sal Murdocca. Published by The Millbrook Press.

Cover from ON THE BANKS OF PLUM CREEK by Laura Ingalls Wilder, illustrated by Garth Williams. Illustration copyright © 1953, renewed 1981 by Garth Williams. Published by HarperCollins Publishers.

Cover from THE REAL McCOY: THE LIFE OF AN AFRICAN-AMERICAN INVENTOR by Wendy Towle, illustrated by Wil Clay. Illustration copyright © 1993 by Wil Clay. Published by Scholastic Inc.

Photography and Illustration Credits

Photos: © John Lei for Scholastic Inc, all Tool Box items unless otherwise noted. pp. 2-3 c: © Greg Nikas/The Picture Cube. p. 2 tl, bl: © Louis Bencze for Scholastic Inc.; cl: © DEJA SHOE. p. 3 bc: © Louis Bencze for Scholastic Inc.; tc: Ana Esperanza Nance for Scholastic Inc. p. 4-6: © Ana Esperanza Nance for Scholastic Inc. p. 10 br: © Mary Evans Picture Library. pp. 10-11 tc: © Ana Esperanza Nance for Scholastic Inc.; p. 10 cl: © Dumbarton Oaks Research Library and Collections, Washington D.C.; p. 10 bl: © Science and Society Picture Library. p.11 thermometer: © Michael Holford/British Museum; cl: © The Science Museum/Science & Society Picture Library. pp. 12-13 tc: © Ana Esperanza Nance for Scholastic Inc.; p. 12 tl: © The Science Museum/Science & Society Picture Library; cr: © Michael Holford/British Museum; cl (Anna Wessels): © College of Physicians of Philadelphia; br (radio): © The Marconi Company Limited; bl (Marie Curie): © Mary Evans Picture Library. p. 13 cl (computer): © UPI/Bettman Newsphotos; bl (Walkman): © Sony Electronics; tr: © Richard Megna/Fundamental Photographs; br (games): Kermani/Gamma Liaison. p. 32 bl: © Richard Megna/ Fundamental Photographs for Scholastic Inc. p. 33 br: © courtesy Shell Chemical Company. p. 34 br, p. 35 bc: © Richard Megna/Fundamental Photographs for Scholastic Inc. p. 36 tl: © The Bettmann Archive/Goodyear Tire Co. p. 37 tr: © Richard Megna/Fundamental Graphics for Scholastic Inc.; br: © Mary Evans Picture Library. p. 38 bl: Culver Pictures; cr: © courtesy Spalding; pp. 38-39 br: © Richard Megna/Fundamental Photographs for Scholastic Inc. p. 40 c (Lewis w/plastic bottles): © Barbara Gundle/Small Planet Photography; c (Lewis w/female co-worker and w/shoes): © Louis Bencze for Scholastic Inc.; bl: © Louis Bencze for Scholastic Inc.; tc (tire): © Laine Whitcomb for Scholastic Inc.; tc (nuts & bolts): Ana Esperanza Nance for Scholastic Inc. pp. 40-41 c: © Louis Bencze for Scholastic Inc. p. 41 cr: © DEJA SHOE. p. 42 cr: © Barbara Gundle/Small Planet Photography; bl: © DEJA SHOE. p. 43 cr, bl: © Louis Bencze for Scholastic Inc. pp. 44-45: © John Lei for Scholastic Inc. p. 46 bc: © Stanley Bach for Scholastic Inc.; all others: © John Lei for Scholastic Inc. p. 47 br: © Louis Bencze for Scholastic Inc. p. 51 tl: © Richard Megna/ Fundamental Photographs for Scholastic Inc. pp. 78-79 c: © John Lei for Scholastic Inc. p. 80 br: © Stanley Bach for Scholastic Inc. p. 81 bl, tr: © Stanley Bach for Scholastic Inc.; br: © Louis Bencze for Scholastic Inc. p. 123 © John Lei for Scholastic Inc. p. 125 bl: © John Lei for Scholastic Inc. p. 126 bc: © Stanley Bach for Scholastic Inc. p. 127 bl, cr: © John Lei for Scholastic Inc.; br: © Louis Bencze for Scholastic Inc. p. 129 tc: © Steve Dunwell/The Image Bank. p. 130 bc: © John Henley/The Stock Market. p. 131 cr: © Chris Hackett/The Image Bank; bc: © Comstock, Inc. p. 132 tl: courtesy of Scholastic Trade Department; cl: courtesy of Workman Publishers; bl: © Andrew Hindley. p. 133 tr: courtesy of Charlotte Foltz Jones; br: © Don Perkins; cr: © Elaine S. Martens. p. 135 br: © Stephen Ogilvy for Scholastic Inc. p. 134 bl: © Schomburg Center for Research in Black Culture; tr: Gregory Heisler/The Image Bank.

Illustrations: pp. 8-9: Elwood Smith; pp: 10-11, 13: Tomo Narashima; pp. 48-49: Elwood Smith; pp. 68-75: John O'Brien; p. 80: Diane Blasius; pp. 82-83: Elwood Smith; pp. 84-93: Lisa Adams; pp. 94-97, 99: Dan Picasso; pp. 124-125: Diane Blasius.

Acknowledgments

Grateful acknowledgment is made to the following sources for permission to reprint from previously published material. The publisher has made diligent efforts to trace the ownership of all copyrighted material in this volume and believes that all necessary permissions have been secured. If any errors or omissions have inadvertently been made, proper corrections will gladly be made in future editions.

Unit Opener: © NASA.

Interior: "The Lost Lake" from THE LOST LAKE by Allen Say. Copyright © 1989 by Allen Say. Reprinted by permission of Houghton Mifflin Co. All rights reserved.

"Pushing the Limits" copyright © June 1992 by National Geographic Society. Reprinted with permission of *National Geographic* WORLD. WORLD is the official magazine for Junior Members of the National Geographic Society.

Text and book cover from SARAH, PLAIN AND TALL by Patricia MacLachlan. Text copyright © 1985 by Patricia MacLachlan. Cover illustration © 1987 by HarperCollins Publishers. Reprinted by permission of HarperCollins Publishers.

Selection from SCHOLASTIC ATLAS OF EXPLORATION by Dinah Starkey. Text and illustrations copyright © 1993 by HarperCollins Publishers Ltd. Used by permission.

"All the Way There" and cover from MATTHEW HENSON: ARCTIC EXPLORER by Sean Dolan, cover illustration by Bradford Brown. Copyright © 1992 by Chelsea House Publishers. Published by Chelsea House Publishers, a division of Main Line Book Co. Used by permission.

"Standing Up for Antarctica" reprinted by permission, *National Geographic* WORLD. Copyright © February 1991 by National Geographic Society.

"The Best New Thing" from THE BEST NEW THING by Isaac Asimov. Text copyright © 1971 by Isaac Asimov. Illustrations copyright © 1971 by the World Publishing Company. Reprinted by permission of HarperCollins Publishers.

Selection from U*S*KIDS, a *Weekly Reader* magazine, copyright © 1992 by Children's Better Health Institute, Benjamin Franklin Literary & Medical Society, Inc., Indianapolis, Indiana. Used by permission.

"The Great Kapok Tree" from THE GREAT KAPOK TREE: A TALE OF THE AMAZON RAIN FOREST by Lynne Cherry. Copyright © 1990 by Lynne Cherry. Reprinted by permission of Harcourt Brace & Company.

Selections and cover from THE DESERT BENEATH THE SEA by Ann McGovern and Eugenie Clark, illustrated by Craig Phillips. Text copyright © 1991 by Ann McGovern and Eugenie Clark. Illustrations copyright © 1991 by Craig Phillips. Reprinted by permission of Scholastic Inc.

Cover from DIGGING UP TYRANNOSAURUS REX by John R. Horner and Don Lessem. Illustration copyright © 1992 by Douglas Henderson. Photo credits: bottom photo Bruce Selyem/Museum of the Rockies; all others Greg Erickson/Museum of the Rockies. Published by Crown Publishers, Inc., a Random House Company.

Cover from JEM'S ISLAND by Kathryn Lasky, illustrated by Ronald Himler. Illustration copyright © 1982 by Ronald Himler. Published by Atheneum Books for Young Readers, Simon & Schuster Children's Publishing Division.

Cover from JUSTIN AND THE BEST BISCUITS IN THE WORLD by Mildred Pitts Walter, illustrated by Paul Tankersley. Illustration copyright © 1991 by Paul Tankersley. Published by Alfred A. Knopf, Inc.

Cover from WHO STOLE *THE WIZARD OF OZ?* by Avi, illustrated by Derek James. Cover illustration by Doron Ben-Ami. Cover art copyright © 1995 by Scholastic Inc. Originally published by Alfred A. Knopf, Inc.

Photography and Illustration Credits

Photos: © John Lei for Scholastic Inc., all Tool Box items unless otherwise noted. p. 2 cl: © Linda Drish for Scholastic Inc.; bl, tl: © John Bessler for Scholastic Inc.; p. 3 tc: © Telegraph Colour Library/FPG International Corp. pp. 2-3 background: NASA. p. 3 bc: NASA. p. 4 c: NASA/Peter Arnold, Inc.; tc: © Telegraph Colour Library/FPG International Corp. p. 5 c: © Ana Esperanza Nance for Scholastic Inc.; tc: © Telegraph Colour Library/FPG International Corp. p. 6 c: © David Jeffrey/The Image Bank; tc: © Telegraph Colour Library/FPG International Corp. pp. 8-9: © Team Russell/Adventure Photo & Film. pp. 24-29: © National Geographic Society. pp. 30-47: © Richard Megna/Fundamental Photographs. p. 48 tr: © Scala/Art Resource, NY; bl: © Barry Rosenthal/FPG International Corp.; br: © Sotheby Parke-Bernett/Art Resource, NY. p. 49 cr: © Sotheby Parke-Bernett/Art Resource, NY; tr: © J. Coolidge/The Image Bank. p. 50 br: © Stanley Bach for Scholastic Inc.; bc: © David Ball/The Stock Market; bl: © Travelpix/FPG International Corp. p. 51 bl: © W. & D. McIntyre/Photo Researchers, Inc.; br: NASA. pp. 52-53: © Al Grotell 1985. p. 54: © The Bettmann Archive. p. 56 tc: © Culver Pictures. pp. 58-59 tc: © The Bettmann Archive. p. 61 bc: © The Bettmann Archive; p. 63bc: © American Museum of Natural History. pp. 64-65 ghost back: © John Beatty/Tony Stone Worldwide. p.64 c: © The Cousteau Society; p. 65 br: © Peter Arnold Inc. br: © Peter Arnold Inc. p. 66 cl, tl, bl: © NASA; tr: NASA/JPL/TSADO/Tom Stack & Associates; tc: © Telegraph Colour Library/FPG International. p. 67 bl, c: NASA; br: © John Bessler for Scholastic Inc. p. 68: NASA. p. 69 c: © NASA/TSADO/Tom Stack & Associates; all others: NASA. pp. 84-85: © David Vaughn/Photo Researchers, Inc. p. 86 bl: © Stanley Bach for Scholastic Inc. p. 87 bl: © Stanley Bach for Scholastic Inc.; br: NASA. pp. 88-89: © J. Guichard/Sygma Scientific. pp. 116-117: © Todd Gipstein/Jason Foundation for Education. pp. 120-121 tc: © Todd Gipstein/Jason Foundation for Education; coral: © Herbert Schwartz/FPG International Corp. p. 122 br: © James Byron/The Stock Market. p. 123 bc: © Tony Freeman/Photo Edit; br: © John Lei for Scholastic Inc. p. 124 cr, bc: © John Lei for Scholastic Inc. p. 125 bl, bc, br: NASA; tr, cl: © Stanley Bach for Scholastic Inc. pp. 126-127 bc: © Stanley Bach for Scholastic Inc.; c: © John Lei for Scholastic Inc.; bc: © Tom Van Sant/Geosphere Project/The Stock Market; p. 127 tr: © WideWorld Photos Inc.; br: Courtesy NASA. p. 129 tc: NASA; bl: © Renee Lynn/Tony Stone Images. p. 131 tl: © Bud Lenhausen/Photo Researchers, Inc.; bl: © Tim Davis/Tony Stone Images. p. 132 cl: © Alex Gotfryd; bl: © Katie P. McManus; p. 133 br: © Richard Allen. p. 133 cr: © John MacLachlan. p. 133 tr: © Eugenie Clark. p. 134 br: © NASA/Peter Arnold, Inc. p. 135 br: © Stephen Ogilvy for Scholastic Inc.

Illustrations: pp. 48-49: Dinah Starkey; pp. 30, 33, 36, 40, 43, 47: Marni Backer; pp. 70-83: Tom Leonard.